Problems in
Applied Thermodynamics

Problems in Applied Thermodynamics

C. Bodsworth

Professor and Head of Department of Metallurgy designate, Brunel College

and

A. S. Appleton

Head of Department of Metallurgy designate, South Australia Institute of Technology, Adelaide

LONGMANS

LONGMANS, GREEN AND CO LTD
48 Grosvenor Street, London W.1

*Associated companies, branches and representatives
throughout the world*

© *C. Bodsworth and A. S. Appleton 1965*

First Published 1965

*Printed in Great Britain by
Spottiswoode, Ballantyne and Co Ltd
London and Colchester*

Preface

The student reading thermodynamics may choose from amongst many textbooks presenting detailed expositions of the derivation and inter-relation of thermodynamic quantities. However, it is often found that students have difficulty in applying the basic concepts of thermo-dynamics to practical problems. Frequently too, the more advanced worker in research is unaware that thermodynamic techniques are relevant to his particular problem and often can be applied using only the available data without recourse to experimentation. These de-ficiencies of training can be avoided or corrected if the formal study of thermodynamic theory is supplemented by a detailed examination of problems covering a wide range of applications. If these problems require the evaluation of quantities or conditions of practical applica-tion, the student will obtain a deeper appreciation of the value of thermodynamics as a useful discipline and will be more ready to strive towards mastery of more complex relations. This book is intended to assist and stimulate students and research workers in these ways. Although many of the examples have been drawn from metallurgical applications, the principles demonstrated apply to a wide range of situa-tions and any student or research worker concerned with a field amenable to the application of chemical thermodynamics should find the methods of use to him.

The basic thermodynamic relations are presented in chapter 1. It is assumed that the reader is, or has been, familiar with most of these, either from lecture course notes or from one of the available textbooks. They are presented only in sufficient detail to facilitate cross-reference with the worked examples. The treatments of dilute solutions, in terms of alternative standard states, and of dilute multicomponent solutions are presented in more detail, as these concepts are covered adequately in very few textbooks. Each of the six chapters following contain worked examples which illustrate the application of a particular thermodynamic concept or group of concepts, and are designed as a progressive course for students taking either University or Technical College courses in thermodynamics. Most of the examples are numerical and their evalua-tion demonstrates the application of thermodynamics to a practical situation or the derivation of additional thermodynamic quantities either from experimental results or from standard tabulated data. Generally, the examples in each chapter are of increasing complexity, and the arrangement of chapters follows the sequence in which thermodynamic concepts are most commonly introduced in a textbook or lecture course. Unworked exercises are given at the end of each chapter and the answers, together where necessary with guidance in their solution, are given in an appendix.

The worked examples begin with a statement of the problem, but in only a very few cases are the data required for obtaining the answer given in this statement. This practice, also used in the unworked exercises, differs from that usually followed in examinations where, from necessity, all the information required is given on the question paper. However, it is more realistic of the situation which is encountered in the practical application of thermodynamics for, in the latter, it is necessary first to decide on the method of solution and then to determine the availability of the data required for this solution. Finally, having obtained these data, the numerical calculation can be performed. This style of presentation of exercises is designed to develop a more analytical approach to the application of thermodynamics than that required when the necessary data are presented in the statement of the problem.

The application of the Gibbs–Duhem relation to data for components of a binary solution is widely practised, and various ways in which such application can be made are demonstrated in chapter 5. In recent years, a number of procedures have been outlined for extension of this application to ternary systems, but the detailed derivation and method of application of these procedures are available only in the original papers. In view of the wide potential application of these treatments, three of these procedures are outlined in chapter 8 and used to evaluate the activity of a component in a ternary solution. From these examples, the research worker should be able to decide on the most useful procedure for application to a particular set of data or, alternatively, the most suitable ternary compositions to examine experimentally for ease of treatment of the data.

A number of compilations of standard thermodynamic quantities are available, and some of these are referred to in the text. However, all the data used in the worked examples and required for the unworked exercises are tabulated in an appendix, most of these data being taken from *Metallurgical Thermochemistry* by Kubaschewski and Evans. Acknowledgement is made to these writers and their publisher, Pergamon Press, for permission to reproduce the data.

For the greater part of the text a knowledge of mathematics to an understanding of elementary differential and integral calculus is required. A few of the mathematical procedures used in the examples and necessary for some of the exercises are not so frequently encountered by many science and engineering students. Treatments of these (adequate for the the purposes of this book) are given in an appendix.

The uncertainty of thermochemical data is often large and precise calculations are not warranted. Consequently the use of a good ten-inch slide rule is entirely satisfactory (and indeed recommended) for calculation of most of the solutions to the worked examples and the exercises in this book. Where calculations require a higher precision, the necessity of using five-figure log tables has been noted. In general, the answers to the worked examples and to the exercises have been rounded off to the nearest 100 cal for quantities up to 10^5 cal, and to 1 kcal for larger quantities. In all cases, this practice is more than justified by the un-certainties in the available data.

The authors are indebted to their colleagues for comments on, and criticism of, the contents and presentation of the manuscript.

Contents

Notation

The notation selected for the various quantities are those in most common use and are largely based upon the recommendations of the International Union of Pure and Applied Physics (1955) and the International Union of Pure and Applied Chemistry (1955). Some changes have been made, however, to avoid confusion where a symbol has been commonly used to represent more than one quantity.

Symbol	Meaning	Common Units
A	Helmholtz function	cal mole^{-1}
a	Activity	
C	Molar heat capacity	cal deg^{-1} mole^{-1}
E	Electromotive force	volt
F	Faraday's constant	cal volt^{-1} g-equiv^{-1} (coulomb g-equiv^{-1})
f	Fugacity	atm
f	Activity coefficient (Henrian)	
f_Y^X	Interaction coefficient; the effect of element X on the Henrian activity coefficient of element Y	
G	Gibbs free energy	cal mole^{-1}
H	Enthalpy or Heat content	cal mole^{-1}
K	Equilibrium constant	
ln	Natural logarithm; $\log_e$	
log	Common logarithm; $\log_{10}$	
$L_{f, t}$	Latent heat of fusion, transformation	cal mole^{-1}
M	Molecular weight	gram
N	Mole fraction	
n	Number of moles	
P	Pressure	atm
p	Partial pressure	atm
Q	Heat absorbed	cal
R	Gas constant	cal deg^{-1}
S	Entropy	cal deg^{-1} mole^{-1}
T	Temperature	degree Kelvin
U	Internal Energy	cal mole^{-1}
V	Volume	cm^3 or litre
W	Work done by a system	cal
z	Electrochemical Valency	
X_A^0	Standard thermodynamic property of a component A	
$\bar{X}_A$	Partial molar thermodynamic property of a component A	

xi

Symbol	Meaning	Common Units
X^M	Integral molar thermodynamic property of mixing	
$\bar{X}^M_A$	Partial molar thermodynamic property of mixing (relative partial molar thermodynamic property) of a component A	
$\bar{X}^E_A$	Excess partial molar thermodynamic property of a component A	
γ	Activity coefficient (Raoultian)	
γ^0	Activity coefficient (Raoultian) at infinite dilution	
ϵ^Y_X	Interaction parameter $\dfrac{\partial \ln f_X}{\partial N_Y}$	
e^Y_X	Interaction parameter $\dfrac{\partial \log f_X}{\partial \mathrm{wt}\% Y}$	
μ	Chemical potential	cal mole^{-1}
(g)	Gas	
(l)	Liquid	
(s)	Solid	

CHAPTER 1

Basic Thermodynamic Relations

The **internal energy** (U) of a system is defined through the First Law of Thermodynamics:

$$U = Q - W \qquad 1.1$$

in terms of Q the heat transferred into the system and W the work done by the system. For an infinitesimally small change:

$$dU = \delta Q - \delta W, \qquad 1.2$$

or, when only mechanical work is done against an external pressure P:

$$dU = \delta Q - P\,dV \qquad 1.3$$

where $(+)\ dV$ is the volume increase of the system.

The **enthalpy** (H) of a system is defined as:

$$H = U + PV. \qquad 1.4$$

For an infinitesimally small change:

$$dH = dU + P\,dV + V\,dP \qquad 1.5$$

which, on addition of *1.3*, gives:

$$dH = \delta Q \qquad 1.6$$

at constant pressure. That is, the enthalpy change in any reaction at constant pressure equals the heat of reaction. Thus for the reaction:

$$m\mathrm{A} + n\mathrm{B} = p\mathrm{C} + q\mathrm{D}$$

the enthalpy change is:

$$\Delta H = \Delta Q_p = \sum H\,(\text{Products}) - \sum H\,(\text{Reactants}) \qquad 1.7$$

$$= pH_{\mathrm{C}} + qH_{\mathrm{D}} - mH_{\mathrm{A}} - nH_{\mathrm{B}}$$

where H_{C}, H_{D}, etc., are the enthalpies per mole of components C, D, etc.

Conventionally, the enthalpies of pure elements are zero at 298°K and the heats of reactions in which compounds are formed from their component elements at 298°K are the Standard Heats of Formation of the compounds. Values of these are listed, for example, by K. K. Kelley [1] and Kubaschewski and Evans [2].

Heats of reaction have additive properties. Thus, if two successive reactions A and B, with heats of reaction (or enthalpy changes) ΔH_A and ΔH_B, are equivalent to an overall reaction C, then the heat of reaction is given by:

$$\Delta H_C = \Delta H_A + \Delta H_B. \qquad 1.8$$

This relation is called **Hess's law.**

The **heat capacity** (C) of a system is defined as:

$$C = \frac{\delta Q}{dT} \qquad 1.9$$

where δQ is the quantity of heat absorbed when a system increases in temperature by an infinitesimally small amount dT. Hence, from *1.3*, the heat capacity at constant volume is given by:

$$C_v = \left(\frac{\partial U}{\partial T}\right)_V \qquad 1.10$$

and at constant pressure, from *1.6*, by:

$$C_p = \left(\frac{\partial H}{\partial T}\right)_P \qquad 1.11$$

$$= \left(\frac{\partial U}{\partial T}\right)_P + P\left(\frac{\partial V}{\partial T}\right)_P. \qquad 1.12$$

Subtracting *1.10* from *1.12* and substituting identical differentials* yields:

$$C_p - C_v = \left[P + \left(\frac{\partial U}{\partial V}\right)_T\right] \cdot \left(\frac{\partial V}{\partial T}\right)_P. \qquad 1.13$$

Substitution of:

$$\alpha = \frac{1}{V} \cdot \left(\frac{\partial V}{\partial T}\right)_P = \text{temperature coefficient of volume expansion}$$

and:

$$\beta = -\frac{1}{V} \cdot \left(\frac{\partial V}{\partial P}\right)_T = \text{coefficient of isothermal compressibility}$$

yields:

$$C_p - C_v = \frac{\alpha^2 VT}{\beta}$$

---

* Some of the fundamental relations of partial differentiation are outlined in appendix 5.

for a system with a generalized equation of state $U = f(P, T, V)$. For an ideal gas, defined by the equation of state $PV = RT$, it is observed experimentally that $(\partial U / \partial V)_T = 0$ and substituting this in *1.13* yields:

$$C_p - C_v = R. \qquad 1.14$$

The variation of C_p with temperature is adequately expressed for most substances by an empirical relation of the form:

$$C_p = a + bT + cT^n \qquad 1.15$$

where a, b and c are constants for a particular substance.

The change in the enthalpy of a system due to a change in its temperature is given by integration of *1.11*:

$$H_{(T_1 \to T_2)} = \int_{T_1}^{T_2} C_p \, dT \qquad 1.16$$

which, on substitution of *1.15* gives:

$$H_{(T_1 \to T_2)} = \int_{T_1}^{T_2} (a + bT + cT^n) \, dT. \qquad 1.17$$

The heat of a reaction (ΔH) is dependent on temperature, the variation being given by the change in heat capacity in the reaction. Thus it follows from *1.11* that:

$$\left(\frac{\partial \Delta H}{\partial T} \right)_P = \Delta C_p, \qquad 1.18$$

(the **Kirchhoff** equation) where

$$\Delta C_p = \sum C_p \, (\text{Products}) - \sum C_p \, (\text{Reactants}). \qquad 1.19$$

In indefinite integral form:

$$\Delta H = \int \Delta C_p \, dT. \qquad 1.20$$

This equation is solved by substitution of the combined equations *1.15* and *1.19*. The heat of reaction at temperature T is:

$$\begin{aligned} \Delta H_T &= \int \Delta C_p \, dT \\ &= \int \left[\sum_{\text{Products}} (a + bT + cT^n) - \sum_{\text{Reactants}} (a + bT + cT^n) \right] dT \\ &= \Delta H_0 + (\sum a_P - \sum a_R) T + \frac{(\sum b_P - \sum b_R) T^2}{2} \\ &\quad + \frac{(\sum c_P - \sum c_R) T^{(n+1)}}{n+1}. \end{aligned}$$

The value of the integration constant ΔH_0 is obtained if ΔH is known at one temperature (e.g. 298°K). Alternatively, equation *1.18* can be expressed as a definite integral:

$$\Delta H_{T_2} - \Delta H_{T_1} = \int_{T_1}^{T_2} \Delta C_p \, \mathrm{d}T \qquad\qquad 1.21$$

$$= (\sum a_P - \sum a_R)(T_2 - T_1) + \left(\frac{\sum b_P - \sum b_R}{2}\right)(T_2^2 - T_1^2)$$

$$+ \left(\frac{\sum c_P - \sum c_R}{n+1}\right)(T_2^{(n+1)} - T_1^{(n+1)}).$$

If any of the components undergo a phase change (at temperature T_t with a latent heat L_t where $T_1 < T_t < T_2$) then *1.21* becomes:

$$\Delta H_{T_2} - \Delta H_{T_1} = \int_{T_1}^{T_t} \Delta C_{p\,(T_1 \to T_t)} \cdot \mathrm{d}T \pm L_t + \int_{T_t}^{T_2} \Delta C_{p\,(T_t \to T_2)} \cdot \mathrm{d}T. \quad 1.22$$

The **entropy** (S) of a system is defined through application of the Second Law of Thermodynamics, such that the change in entropy when the system undergoes a reversible process is given by:

$$\mathrm{d}S = \frac{\delta Q}{T} \qquad\qquad 1.23$$

where δQ is the reversible heat transferred at the temperature T. Combination with *1.3* yields:

$$\mathrm{d}U = T\mathrm{d}S - P\mathrm{d}V \qquad\qquad 1.24$$

for a system undergoing a reversible process where only mechanical work is done.

The entropy change when a system changes its temperature is given by integration of *1.23* and substitution of *1.9*. Thus, at constant volume:

$$S_{v\,(T_1 \to T_2)} = \int_{T_1}^{T_2} \frac{C_v}{T} \cdot \mathrm{d}T, \qquad\qquad 1.25$$

and at constant pressure:

$$S_{p\,(T_1 \to T_2)} = \int_{T_1}^{T_2} \frac{C_p}{T} \cdot \mathrm{d}T. \qquad\qquad 1.26$$

When a phase transformation (latent heat L_t at T_t) occurs in the system in the temperature range considered, the entropy change:

$$\Delta S_t = \frac{L_t}{T_t} \qquad\qquad 1.27$$

must be incorporated at the transformation temperature. Combination of *1.27* and *1.26* applied to the components of a reaction yield a relation analogous to *1.22* for the difference in the entropy of the reaction at temperatures T_1 and T_2:

$$\Delta S_{T_2} - \Delta S_{T_1} = \int_{T_1}^{T_t} \frac{\Delta C_{p\,(T_1 \to T_t)}}{T}.\,\mathrm{d}T \pm \frac{L_t}{T_t} + \int_{T_t}^{T_2} \frac{\Delta C_{p\,(T_t \to T_2)}}{T}.\,\mathrm{d}T. \qquad 1.28$$

The **Helmholtz free energy** (A) of a system is defined by the relation:

$$A = U - TS \qquad 1.29$$

which, when differentiated completely and added to *1.24*, yields:

$$\mathrm{d}A = -S\,\mathrm{d}T - P\,\mathrm{d}V. \qquad 1.30$$

Thus isothermally, $\mathrm{d}A = -P\,\mathrm{d}V$, or the reversible change in the Helmholtz free energy equals the isothermal work content of the system (maximum work function).

The **Gibbs free energy** (G) of a system is defined by the relation:

$$G = H - TS \qquad 1.31$$

$$= U + PV - TS. \qquad 1.32$$

Complete differentiation of *1.32* and addition of *1.24* yields:

$$\mathrm{d}G = V\,\mathrm{d}P - S\,\mathrm{d}T. \qquad 1.33$$

The isobaric variation of the Gibbs free energy with temperature follows, for:

$$\left(\frac{\partial G}{\partial T}\right)_P = -S.$$

Substitution of *1.31* and rearranging differentials leads to the **Gibbs–Helmholtz** relation:

$$\left[\frac{\partial}{\partial T}\left(\frac{G}{T}\right)\right]_P = -\frac{H}{T^2} \qquad 1.34$$

or, in indefinite integral form:

$$\frac{G}{T} = -\int \frac{H}{T^2}.\,\mathrm{d}T. \qquad 1.35$$

This is solved on substitution of the indefinite integral form of *1.17* and integration of the resultant relation:

$$G = -T \int \frac{1}{T^2}\left[H_0 + \int (a + bT + cT^n).\,\mathrm{d}T\right].\,\mathrm{d}T \qquad 1.36$$

to give:

$$G = f(T) + H_0 + IT$$

where H_0 and I are integration constants determined from a knowledge either of G at two temperatures, or of G and H at one temperature.

Alternatively the variation of G with temperature is obtained by substitution of *1.17* and *1.26* in the defining equation *1.31*. Thus, in indefinite form:

$$G = \int C_p \, dT - T . \int \frac{C_p}{T} . dT. \qquad 1.37$$

Again, integration yields two constants which are fixed by a knowledge of G at two temperatures, or of G and H or S at one temperature.

It may readily be shown that when a reaction or process takes place in any system, the change in free energy of the system is given by:

$$\Delta G \leqslant 0 \qquad 1.38$$

where the inequality sign applies when the system reacts and tends spontaneously towards equilibrium, and the equality sign applies when the system reaches the equilibrium state. Thus in any real process, the free energy of a system decreases, reaching a minimum value when equilibrium is attained.

Partial molar quantities*

The total free energy of a multicomponent system (containing n_A, n_B, n_C, etc., moles of components A, B, C, etc., respectively) is given by:

$$G' = f(P, T, n_A, n_B, n_C, \ldots). \qquad 1.39$$

When a small quantity δn_i of component i is added to the system at constant pressure and temperature, the total free energy of the system changes by an amount $\delta G'$. The ratio of these quantities ($\delta G'$ and δn_i), when both tend to zero, is defined as the **partial molar free energy** of component i. That is:

$$\lim_{\delta n_i \to 0} \left(\frac{\delta G'}{\delta n_i} \right)_{P, T, n_j} = \left(\frac{\partial G'}{\partial n_i} \right)_{P, T, n_j} \equiv \bar{G}_i. \qquad 1.40$$

Hence, for a system at constant temperature and pressure, the total free energy of the system is given by:

$$G' = \sum n_i . \bar{G}_i, \qquad 1.41$$

---

* This section is given in terms of the Gibbs free energy (G), but it applies equally to any of the state variables of the system.

and the free energy per mole of the system (the integral molar free energy) is:

$$G = \sum N_i . \bar{G}_i \qquad 1.42$$

where N_i is the mole fraction of component i.

Subtraction of the complete differential of *1.41* from *1.40*, expressed as a partial differential equation, yields the **Gibbs–Duhem** equation:

$$\sum n_i d\bar{G}_i = \sum N_i d\bar{G}_i = 0. \qquad 1.43$$

Partial (and integral) molar quantities are related by the equations previously derived for a system of fixed composition. For example:

$$\bar{G}_i = \bar{H}_i - T\bar{S}_i \qquad 1.44$$

and:

$$\frac{\partial}{\partial T}\left(\frac{\bar{G}_i}{T}\right)_P = -\frac{\bar{H}_i}{T^2}. \qquad 1.45$$

For two and three component systems the values of the partial molar quantities at a particular composition are readily found if values of the

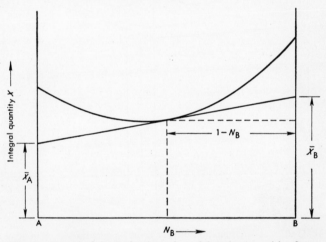

Fig. 1a. Graphical determination of partial molar quantities from integral molar quantity in a binary system.

integral molar quantity are known over an adequate composition range which includes that particular composition. Thus for a binary system, complete differentiation of *1.42* and subtraction of the Gibbs–Duhem relation *1.43* yields:

$$dG = \bar{G}_A dN_A + \bar{G}_B dN_B.$$

Multiplication throughout by:

$$\frac{N_A}{dN_B} = -\frac{N_A}{dN_A} \text{ (as } dN_A = -dN_B)$$

and elimination of $\bar{G}_A$ by addition of *1.42* yields:

$$\bar{G}_B = G + (1 - N_B)\frac{dG}{dN_B}. \qquad 1.46$$

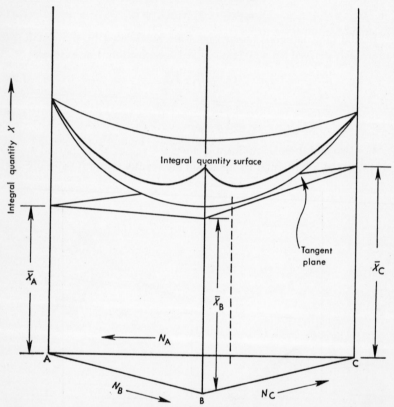

Fig. 1b. Graphical determination of partial molar quantities from integral molar quantity in a ternary system.

Similarly:

$$\bar{G}_A = G + (1 - N_A)\frac{dG}{dN_A}. \qquad 1.47$$

Thus, as shown in Fig. 1a, the partial molar quantity for a component i, at a particular composition, is given by the intercept of the tangent to the curve for the integral molar quantity at that composition with the axis $N_i = 1$.

For a ternary system (represented by an equilateral right triangular prism) the intercept of the tangent plane to the integral molar quantity surface with the axis $N_i = 1$ gives the value of the patrial molar quantity for the component i at the contiguous composition (Fig. 1b).

In the study of multicomponent heterogeneous systems, the partial molar free energy is of special significance. The necessary condition for chemical equilibrium in such systems is best expressed in terms of an independently defined quantity, the Gibbs chemical potential. If, for a system containing an arbitrary number of moles, $\delta U'$ is the change in the internal energy of the whole system when δn_i moles of component i are added, then:

$$\lim_{\delta n_i \to 0} \left(\frac{\delta U'}{\delta n_i} \right) = \left(\frac{\partial U'}{\partial n_i} \right) \equiv \mu_i \qquad 1.48$$

where μ_i is the **Gibbs chemical potential** of component i.

It may readily be shown that chemical equilibrium exists between phases of a multicomponent system when equality of the Gibbs chemical potential for any particular component exists between the phases. Thus for a system of components 1, 2, 3, etc., consisting of phases A, B, C, etc., at equilibrium:

$$\left. \begin{aligned} \mu_1^A &= \mu_1^B = \mu_1^C \text{ etc.} \\ \mu_2^A &= \mu_2^B = \mu_2^C \text{ etc.} \end{aligned} \right\} \qquad 1.49$$

Further, expression of the Gibbs chemical potential is possible in terms of any of the extensive state variables. That is:

$$\mu_i = \left(\frac{\partial U'}{\partial n_i} \right)_{S', V', n_j} = \left(\frac{\partial H'}{\partial n_i} \right)_{S', P, n_j} = \left(\frac{\partial A'}{\partial n_i} \right)_{T, V', n_j}$$

$$= \left(\frac{\partial G'}{\partial n_i} \right)_{T, P, n_j} \text{ which by definition} \equiv \bar{G}_i. \qquad 1.50$$

Thus the Gibbs chemical potential is equivalent to the partial molar free energy of the component, and equality of the partial molar free energy of a component in the various phases of a heterogeneous system is a necessary and sufficient condition for these phases to be in chemical equilibrium.

The equilibrium constant

From *1.33*, for a system doing mechanical work only:

$$dG = V dP - S dT$$

or, isothermally for 1 mole of an ideal gas (defined by $PV = RT$):

$$dG = V dP$$

$$= RT\frac{dP}{P} = RT d \ln P. \qquad 1.51$$

A quantity, the **fugacity** (f) of a real, non-ideal gas is defined such that $fV = RT$ and hence:

$$dG = RT d \ln f \qquad 1.52$$

$$(f \to P \text{ as } P \to 0)$$

for a real gas.

Integration of *1.52* at constant temperature and pressure between the state of interest and a standard state designated by the superscript ^{0} yields:

$$G - G^0 = RT \ln \frac{f}{f^0}. \qquad 1.53$$

The ratio, f_i/f_i^0 for a substance i, is called the **activity** (a) of the substance. Thus:

$$\bar{G}_i - G_i^0 = RT \ln a_i \qquad 1.54$$

where the partial molar free energy ($\bar{G}_i$) is the free energy of the substance i in the state of interest, and the standard molar free energy G_i^0 is the free energy of i in a standard state, usually (although not always) chosen as the pure component.

The applicability of the activity concept is demonstrated by consideration of the generalized reaction:

$$bX + cY + dZ + \ldots \rightleftharpoons mP + nQ + lR + \ldots$$

where b, c, d, m, n, etc., are the number of moles of components X, Y, Z, P, Q, etc. The free-energy change for this reaction is given generally by:

$$\Delta G = (m\bar{G}_P + n\bar{G}_Q + l\bar{G}_R + \ldots) - (b\bar{G}_X + c\bar{G}_Y + d\bar{G}_Z + \ldots) \qquad 1.55$$

or, more specifically, when all components are in their standard states:

$$\Delta G^0 = (mG_P^0 + nG_Q^0 + lG_R^0 + \ldots) - (bG_X^0 + cG_Y^0 + dG_Z^0 + \ldots). \qquad 1.56$$

Subtracting *1.56* from *1.55* and substituting *1.54* for each of the components gives, at equilibrium (when $\Delta G = 0$):

$$\Delta G^0 = -RT \ln \frac{a_P^m . a_Q^n . a_R^l \ldots}{a_X^b . a_Y^c . a_Z^d \ldots} \qquad 1.57$$

$$= -RT \ln K_p \qquad 1.58$$

where K_p is the equilibrium constant for the reaction and ΔG^0 is the **standard free-energy change** for the reaction (i.e. the free-energy change when all components are in their standard states).

The variation with temperature of the equilibrium constant for a reaction is given by substitution of *1.58* in the Gibbs–Helmholtz equation *1.34*:

$$\left(\frac{\mathrm{d}\ln K_p}{\mathrm{d}T}\right)_p = \frac{\Delta H^0}{RT^2} \quad \text{(the \textbf{van't Hoff} equation)} \qquad 1.59$$

where ΔH^0 is the standard enthalpy change for the reaction (i.e. the enthalpy change when all components are in their standard states). Solution of *1.59* is obtained by substitution of *1.20* and integration as an indefinite or, when possible, as a definite integral. As an indefinite integral:

$$\ln K_p = \frac{1}{R}\left(\mathrm{I} + \frac{\Delta H_0}{T} + \Delta a\ln T + \Delta bT + \Delta cT^n\right) \qquad 1.60$$

where ΔH_0 and I are integration constants which are found either by insertion of known values of K_p at two temperatures, or of K_p and ΔH at one temperature, in similar manner to the solution of the free energy–temperature relation *1.36*.

Over a small temperature interval, it is often permissible to assume that ΔH^0 is independent of temperature. In this approximate form, *1.59* can be written as:

$$\ln\left(\frac{K_1}{K_2}\right) = \frac{\Delta H^0}{R}\left(\frac{1}{T_2} - \frac{1}{T_1}\right) \qquad 1.61$$

or:

$$\log\left(\frac{K_1}{K_2}\right) = \frac{\Delta H^0}{4 \cdot 575}\left(\frac{1}{T_2} - \frac{1}{T_1}\right).$$

Alternatively:

$$\Delta H^0 = \frac{4 \cdot 575\, T_1 T_2 (\log K_1 - \log K_2)}{T_1 - T_2}. \qquad 1.62$$

Solutions

The difference between the free energy of a component i in a solution and in the chosen standard state is given by *1.54*:

$$\bar{G}_i - G_i^0 = RT\ln a_i.$$

For convenience, the difference on the left-hand side of this equation is called the **partial molar free energy of mixing** or the **relative partial molar**

free energy of the component i, $\bar{G}_i^M$ (or $\varDelta G_i$). Partial molar entropies and enthalpies of mixing are similarly defined, these being related through all the expressions previously derived. For example:

$$\bar{G}_i^M = \bar{H}_i^M - T\bar{S}_i^M \qquad 1.63$$

and:

$$\frac{\partial}{\partial T}\left(\frac{\bar{G}_i^M}{T}\right) = -\frac{\bar{H}_i^M}{T^2}. \qquad 1.64$$

Integral molar quantities of mixing are related to the partial molar quantities of mixing by expressions of the type *1.42*. Thus the integral molar entropy of mixing for a binary solution AB is given by:

$$S^M = N_A \bar{S}_A^M + N_B \bar{S}_B^M$$
$$= (N_A \bar{S}_A + N_B \bar{S}_B) - (N_A S_A^0 + N_B S_B^0) \qquad 1.65$$

from the definition of the partial molar entropy of mixing. The first term in parentheses is the integral molar entropy of the solution (S) and the second is the entropy of the unmixed pure components A and B.

The study of solutions is facilitated by the use of the concept of the **ideal solution**, originally defined by Raoult in terms of the equality of the partial pressure of a component with its mole fraction–vapour pressure product. Thus, for a component i in an ideal solution:

$$p_i = p_i^0 N_i.$$

Replacing the partial pressure by fugacities (which removes the limitation of ideal gas behaviour of the vapours):

$$\frac{f_i}{f_i^0} = N_i = a_i \text{ by definition.} \qquad 1.66$$

(Raoult's law)

From this definition of an ideal solution, further special qualities are derivable. Substituting *1.66* in *1.54*:

$$\bar{G}_i^M = \bar{G}_i - G_i^0 = RT \ln N_i \qquad 1.67$$

for an ideal solution. Substituting this in *1.64*:

$$\frac{\partial}{\partial T}(R \ln N_i) = -\frac{\bar{H}_i^M}{T^2}.$$

As $\partial/\partial T(R \ln N_i) = 0$, that is, the composition of the ideal solution is independent of temperature, then:

$$\bar{H}_i^M = 0 \qquad 1.68$$

and hence:

$$H^M = \sum N_i \bar{H}_i^M = 0. \qquad 1.69$$

Thus, the heat of mixing of an ideal solution is zero. Also, as from *1.33*:

$$\left(\frac{\partial G}{\partial P}\right)_T = V,$$

then:

$$\left(\frac{\partial \bar{G}_i^M}{\partial P}\right)_T = \bar{V}_i^M$$

$$= \frac{\partial}{\partial P}(RT \ln N_i)$$

for an ideal solution. But as the composition is independent of pressure, then:

$$\frac{\partial}{\partial P}(RT \ln N_i) = 0$$

or:

$$\bar{V}_i^M = 0 \qquad 1.70$$

and:

$$V^M = \sum N_i \bar{V}_i^M = 0, \qquad 1.71$$

that is, the molar volume of mixing of an ideal solution is zero.

From *1.68* and *1.31* applied to partial molar quantities of mixing:

$$\bar{S}_i^M = -\frac{\bar{G}_i^M}{T}$$

for an ideal solution. Substituting *1.67* for $\bar{G}_i^M$:

$$\bar{S}_i^M = -R \ln N_i \qquad 1.72$$

and the ideal entropy of mixing is given by:

$$S^M = \sum N_i \bar{S}_i^M$$

$$= -R \sum N_i \ln N_i. \qquad 1.73$$

The concept of the ideal solution is of limited usefulness as a means of expressing the approximate behaviour of real solutions. However, the exact behaviour of real solutions may be expressed in terms of their deviations from ideal behaviour. This expression may be made in several ways.

The **activity coefficient** for a component of any solution is defined by:

$$\gamma_i = \frac{a_i}{N_i}.\qquad 1.74$$

For an ideal solution $a_i = N_i$ and $\gamma_i = 1$, so the magnitude of the activity coefficient is a measure of the deviation of a non-ideal solution from ideality. Solutions having values of γ less than or greater than unity deviate from ideal behaviour in a negative or a positive manner respectively.

It is sometimes more convenient to express the non-ideal behaviour of a solution in terms of one or other of the molar thermodynamic properties of a component or of the whole solution. For this purpose, partial and integral excess quantities are defined as the difference between the value of the quantity in the real solution and the value the quantity would have in a hypothetical ideal solution of the same composition and under the same conditions of temperature and pressure. For example, the **excess partial molar free energy** is defined as:

$$\bar{G}_i^E \text{ (or } \bar{G}_i^{xs}) = \bar{G}_i - \bar{G}_i^I, \qquad 1.75$$

where $\bar{G}_i^I$ is the partial molar free energy of the component i in a hypothetical ideal solution. Thus, $\bar{G}_i^E = 0$ when the component i is in an ideal solution. Similarly, the excess integral molar entropy is defined as

$$S^E \text{ (or } S^{xs}) = S - S^I, \qquad 1.76$$

where S is the integral molar entropy of the solution under consideration and S^I is the entropy of the hypothetical ideal solution of the same composition. Thus $S^E = 0$ for an ideal solution.

Excess partial and integral quantities are related through the thermodynamic relations previously derived, for example:

$$\bar{G}_i^E = \bar{H}_i^E - T\bar{S}_i^E, \qquad 1.77$$

and (the Gibbs–Helmholtz relation):

$$\frac{\partial}{\partial T}\left(\frac{G^E}{T}\right) = -\frac{H^E}{T^2}. \qquad 1.78$$

Substituting *1.54* and *1.67* in *1.75* yields:

$$\bar{G}_i^E = (G_i^0 + RT\ln a_i) - (G_i^0 + RT\ln N_i)$$
$$= RT\ln\gamma_i \qquad 1.79$$

from which it is apparent that the sign of the excess partial molar (and hence excess integral) free energy will be positive or negative depending on whether the solution in question shows positive ($\gamma_i > 1$) or negative ($\gamma_i < 1$) deviations from ideal behaviour. These excess free-energy quantities are therefore very useful for describing the deviations of real solutions from ideal behaviour.

Many real solutions deviate from ideal behaviour in their enthalpy of mixing values (these being non-zero) but behave ideally with regard to their entropy of mixing values. On this basis Hildebrand [3] defined a **regular solution** by the expressions:

and:
$$\left.\begin{aligned} H^M &= \sum N_i \bar{H}_i^M \neq 0 \\ S^M &= \sum N_i \bar{S}_i^M = S_{\text{Ideal}}^M = -R \sum N_i \ln N_i. \end{aligned}\right\} \qquad 1.80$$

Substituting 1.54 and 1.81 in the definitional relation 1.31 applied to integral quantities of mixing yields, for a regular solution:

$$\begin{aligned} H^M &= G^M + TS^M \\ &= RT \sum N_i \ln a_i - RT \sum N_i \ln N_i \\ &= RT \sum N_i \ln \gamma_i \end{aligned} \qquad 1.81$$

where γ_i is the activity coefficient of component i. It follows, of course, that for a regular solution:

$$\bar{H}_i^M = RT \ln \gamma_i \qquad 1.82$$

which, by comparison with 1.79 yields:

and:
$$\left.\begin{aligned} \bar{H}_i^M &= \bar{G}_i^E \\ H^M &= G^E \end{aligned}\right\} \qquad 1.83$$

for a regular solution. However, from 1.33 it follows that, generally:

$$\left(\frac{\partial \bar{G}_i^E}{\partial T}\right)_P = -\bar{S}_i^E$$

and so, for a regular solution, for which $\bar{S}_i^E$, (from its definition and 1.81) is zero, then:

$$\left(\frac{\partial \bar{G}_i^E}{\partial T}\right)_P = 0.$$

Hence it follows from 1.79 that for a regular solution the quantity $RT \ln \gamma_i$ is independent of temperature.

The use of a function α, defined by:

$$\alpha_i = \frac{\ln \gamma_i}{(1 - N_i)^2} \qquad 1.84$$

for a component i of a solution, has proved of considerable benefit in the treatment of some thermodynamic relations. This function is generally found to be 'well-behaved' with respect to composition, in some cases the relation being linear or even independent of composition. As will be demonstrated (examples *5.6*, *5.8*, *5.9* and *8.3*), expression of thermodynamic relations in terms of this function often leads to their simplification and enhancement of the ease of their application. It may be shown, with certain assumptions, that for a regular solution defined by *1.80*, the quantity α is independent of composition and has the same value for all the components of the solution. That is:

$$\ln \gamma_i = \alpha(1 - N_i)^2,$$

which form is commonly used to express the composition-dependence of the activity coefficient of a component of a regular solution. It should be emphasized, however, that the fitting of a parabolic relation of this type to the data for a particular system is not in itself a sufficient condition for the assumption of regular solution behaviour.

Dilute solutions

It is found experimentally that at extreme dilution, the partial pressure of a solute is proportional to its mole fraction. That is:

$$p_i = k' N_{i\,(N_i \to 0)}$$

where k' is a constant for the solute in a particular solution. This is a statement of **Henry's law** which, however, assumes ideal behaviour of the solute vapour. For the more general case when the solute vapour is non-ideal, the use of fugacity is more strictly correct. Thus if f_i is the fugacity of the solute, then:

$$f_i = k' N_{i\,(N_i \to 0)}.$$

Dividing through by f_i^0 and noting that $f_i/f_i^0 = a_i$:

$$a_i = \frac{k'}{f_i^0} N_{i\,(N_i \to 0)}$$
$$= k N_{i\,(N_i \to 0)}. \qquad 1.85$$

(since f_i^0 is a constant at any given temperature).

The constant k is equal to the slope of the activity–composition curve at infinite dilution (i.e. the tangent to the activity–composition curve at the origin). However, the ratio $[a_i/N_i]_{(N_i \to 0)}$ is equal to the value of the solute activity coefficient at infinite dilution. That is:

$$\left[\frac{a_i}{N_i}\right]_{(N_i \to 0)} = \gamma_i^0 \qquad 1.86$$

where the symbol γ_i^0 is used to designate the activity coefficient at the origin. For many solutes it is found experimentally that a_i/N_i is constant up to at least one atom-per cent concentration.

It may readily be shown that if, in a binary solution (A–B), the low concentration solute B conforms to Henry's law up to a concentration N_B, then the solvent A will behave ideally (i.e. conform to Raoult's law) over the same composition range, between $N_A = (1 - N_B)$ and pure solvent A.

Alternative standard states

For non-ideal dilute solutions it is frequently more correct and convenient to express the thermodynamic properties of a component in relation to a standard state which lies within or adjacent to the composition range of interest, in preference to the pure substance as standard state. Indeed, with some solutions the latter has no real significance; for example, where a solute in a *solid* solution normally exists in the pure state as a liquid or a gas at the same temperature and pressure as the solution. In such cases it is most convenient to use thermodynamic quantities referred not to the pure substance but to a dilute solution conforming to Henry's law as the standard state. The use of two such 'alternative standard states' is described here. Others are also in common use, notably in relation to aqueous solutions, but the manipulation of quantities referred to these other standard states does not differ in principle from the two states selected for consideration.

The **infinitely dilute solution** standard state is defined such that the activity approaches the atom fraction at infinite dilution. That is:

$$\frac{a_i}{N_i} \to 1 \text{ as } N_i \to 0$$

or:

$$a_i = N_{i(N_i \to 0)}.$$

However, as the activity of a solute i is defined by:

$$a_i = \frac{f_i}{f_i^0},$$

then:

$$a_i = \frac{1}{k''} f_i$$

where k'' is a constant, the value of which will depend on the standard state to which f_i^0 refers. Let k'' refer to the infinitely dilute standard state, for which, by definition $a_i = N_i$ at infinite dilution. If the solute vapour behaves ideally, and $f_i = p_i$, then:

$$N_i = \frac{1}{k''}p_i \text{ at infinite dilution.}$$

This relation is, of course, Henry's law, *1.85*. Thus, as the condition $a_i = N_i$ (at infinite dilution) leads to the Henry's law relation for the solute i, it follows that any solute obeying Henry's law up to a particular concentration will conform to $a_i = N_i$ up to that same concentration, where a_i is the activity of the solute on the infinitely dilute solution standard state scale. Within this concentration range, therefore, when the standard state for the solute is so defined, the atom fraction can be substituted directly in equations involving the activity of the solute.

Beyond the concentration range where Henry's law is obeyed by the solute, the activity can be referred to the infinitely dilute solution standard state by means of a Henry's law activity coefficient (f), defined such that:

$$f_i = \frac{a_i}{N_i}. \qquad 1.87$$

It follows that $f_i = 1$ in the range where Henry's law is obeyed.

At any chosen concentration, N_i, the activity coefficient of the solute, relative to the infinitely dilute solution standard state, is given by *1.87*, whilst that relative to the pure substance standard state is given by *1.74*:

$$\gamma_i = \frac{a_i}{N_i}.$$

Hence the relation between the activities of the solute in terms of the two standard states is given by division of *1.74* by *1.87*:

$$\left[\frac{a_{i\,(pure)}}{a_{i\,(dilute)}} = \frac{\gamma_i}{f_i}\right]_{N_i=const.}$$

where the subscripts (dilute) and (pure) relate to the activity scales corresponding to the two standard states. In the concentration range where Henry's law is obeyed by the solute, $f_i = 1$ and $\gamma_i = \gamma_i^0$ (from *1.86*). Hence:

$$\left[\frac{a_{i\,(pure)}}{a_{i\,(dilute)}} = \gamma_i^0\right]_{N_i=const.} \qquad 1.88$$

when Henry's law applies.

Because the partial molar free energy (i.e. the chemical potential) of the solute in the solution is not determined by the choice of the standard state, it is readily shown that the ratio of the activities of the solute at two arbitrarily selected compositions of the solution, relative to any one standard state, must be identical to the ratio in terms of any other standard state.

For, at composition I: $\bar{G}_i^I - G_i^0 = RT \ln a_i^I$,

and at composition II: $\bar{G}_i^{II} - G_i^0 = RT \ln a_i^{II}$.

Subtracting: $\bar{G}_i^I - \bar{G}_i^{II} = RT \ln \dfrac{a_i^I}{a_i^{II}}$.

As $(\bar{G}_i^I - \bar{G}_i^{II})$ is independent of standard state, the ratio

$$\left[\frac{a_i^I}{a_i^{II}}\right]$$

must also be independent. Hence it follows that *1.88* gives the ratio of the activities, relative to the two standard states under consideration, for all compositions from $N_i = 0$ to $N_i = 1$.

The conversion of the standard state involves a corresponding change in the standard free energy (G_i^0) of the solute. The free-energy change accompanying the transfer of one mole of a solute B from the pure B standard state to the infinitely dilute solution standard state, that is:

$$B_{(pure)} \rightarrow B_{(dilute)}$$

is given by:

$$\Delta G_B^0 = G_{B\,(dilute)}^0 - G_{B\,(pure)}^0.$$

Because the partial molar free energy of the solute at a constant concentration is independent of the choice of standard state, the value of ΔG_B^0 remains unchanged if $\bar{G}_{B\,(pure)}$ is added and $\bar{G}_{B\,(dilute)}$ is subtracted from the right-hand side of this equation. Thus:

$$\Delta G_B^0 = G_{B\,(dilute)}^0 - G_{B\,(pure)}^0 + \bar{G}_{B\,(pure)} - \bar{G}_{B\,(dilute)}$$

or:

$$\Delta G_B^0 = (\bar{G}_B - G_B^0)_{pure} - (\bar{G}_B - G_B^0)_{dilute}.$$

But:

$$(\bar{G}_B - G_B^0) = RT \ln a_B \quad \text{(from 1.54)}.$$

Hence:

$$\Delta G_B^0 = RT \ln \left[\frac{a_{B\,(pure)}}{a_{B\,(dilute)}}\right]_{N_B = constant} \qquad 1.89$$

$$= RT \ln \gamma_B^0 \quad \text{(from 1.88)}. \qquad 1.90$$

Thus:

$$G_{B\,(dilute)}^0 = G_{B\,(pure)}^0 + RT \ln \gamma_B^0. \qquad 1.91$$

For a solute i which obeys Raoult's law, $\gamma_i^0 = 1$ and $\Delta G_i^0 = 0$.

The **infinitely dilute, weight-per cent** standard state is particularly useful in the concentration range where the activity (referred to the pure solute as standard state) is a linear function of the weight-per cent concentration of the solute. For such a solute, the weight-per cent concentration can be used directly in thermodynamic calculations without the necessity of converting analysed compositions into atom fractions (as is necessary when the standard state is defined in terms of the infinitely dilute atom fraction).

The dilute weight-per cent standard state is defined such that:

$$\frac{a_i}{\text{wt}\%i} \to 1 \quad \text{as} \quad \text{wt}\%i \to 0$$

or:

$$a_i = \text{wt}\%i_{(\text{wt}\%i \to 0)}.$$

If the activity equals the concentration up to 1 weight-per cent of component i, then $a_i = 1$ at $\text{wt}\%i = 1$ and this 1 weight-per cent solution is then the standard state.

Deviations from this equality of activity and concentration are measured in terms of a Henry's law activity coefficient (f), defined by:

$$f_i = \frac{a_i}{\text{wt}\%i}. \qquad 1.92$$

As with the infinitely dilute atom fraction standard state, the free-energy change accompanying the transfer of standard state from the pure solute to the dilute, weight-per cent solution is given by a relation identical to *1.89*. That is:

$$\Delta G_B^0 = RT\ln\left[\frac{a_{B\,(\text{pure})}}{a_{B\,(\text{dilute})}}\right]_{N_B = \text{constant}} \qquad 1.93$$

Proceeding in analogous manner to that used in the derivation of the free-energy change to the infinitely dilute, atom fraction standard state, at any chosen composition the activity of the solute is given by *1.92*, relative to the dilute, weight-per cent standard state, and by *1.74*, relative to the pure substance standard state. Hence the ratio of the activity coefficients on the two scales is:

$$\frac{\gamma_B}{f_B} = \left[\frac{(a_B/N_B)_{\text{pure}}}{(a_B/\text{wt}\%B)_{\text{dilute}}}\right]_{\text{constant composition}}$$

and, at infinite dilution where $f_B = 1$, $\gamma_B = \gamma_B^0$, the activity coefficient of the solute at infinite dilution relative to the pure substance standard state. Therefore:

$$\left[\frac{a_{B\,(\text{pure})}}{a_{B\,(\text{dilute})}}\right]_{\text{constant composition}} = \left[\gamma_B^0 \cdot \frac{N_B}{\text{wt}\%B}\right]_{\text{constant composition}} \qquad 1.94$$

The extension of this relation to finite solute concentrations follows from the non-dependence on the choice of standard state of the partial molar free energy of the solute, as described in the treatment of the infinitely dilute atom fraction standard state.

In dilute solution, the ratio $N_B/\text{wt}\%B$ can be expressed as a real number for any given system, using the relation:

$$N_B = \frac{\dfrac{\text{wt}\%B}{M_B}}{\dfrac{\text{wt}\%B}{M_B} + \dfrac{(100 - \text{wt}\%B)}{M_A}}$$

where M_A and M_B are the atomic weights respectively of the solvent A and the solute B. For small concentrations of B, the first term in the denominator is small compared to the second, and this relation may be simplified to:

$$N_B \simeq \frac{\text{wt}\%B \cdot M_A}{100 \cdot M_B}.$$

Therefore:

$$\frac{N_B}{\text{wt}\%B} = \frac{M_A}{100 \cdot M_B}. \qquad 1.95$$

Substituting *1.94* and *1.95* in *1.93* yields the free-energy change accompanying the change in standard state:

$$B_{(\text{pure})} \rightarrow B_{(\text{wt}\% \text{ dilute})}$$

$$\Delta G^0 = RT \ln \gamma_B^0 + RT \ln \frac{M_A}{100 \cdot M_B} \qquad 1.96$$

or:

$$G_{(\text{dilute})}^0 = G_{(\text{pure})}^0 + RT \ln \gamma^0 \cdot \frac{M_A}{100 \cdot M_B}. \qquad 1.97$$

Hence, by comparison with *1.93*:

$$\frac{a_{B(\text{pure})}}{a_{B(\text{dilute})}} = \frac{\gamma_B^0 \cdot M_A}{100 \cdot M_B}. \qquad 1.98$$

The term γ_B^0 in *1.90*, *1.97* and *1.98* is usually a function of temperature and must be represented as such if free-energy changes are required over a range of temperatures. However, frequently the value of γ_B^0 is known for only one temperature, and the assumption of regular solution behaviour must be made. At high dilution this is acceptable. Following such an assumption, the partial molar heat of mixing of the solute at infinite dilution $[\bar{H}_B^M]^0$ can be regarded as a constant over a restricted

3

temperature range (see page 15). It follows from *1.82* that $RT\ln\gamma_B^0$ is a constant, or $\ln\gamma_B^0$ is inversely proportional to the temperature. The standard free-energy change in *1.96* is then expressible as a function of temperature by:

$$\Delta G_B^0 = [\bar{H}_B^M]^0 + RT\ln\frac{M_A}{100.M_B} \qquad 1.99$$

where $[\bar{H}_B^M]^0 = RT\ln\gamma_B^0$.

If the pure solute normally exists in a different physical state to that which it adopts in the solution at the same temperature and pressure, a further term must be added to *1.90* or *1.97* to account for this change in physical state. For example, if the pure solute normally exists as a solid at a given temperature and pressure, but the solution of interest is a liquid, the free-energy change accompanying the fusion process for this solute must be added to the free-energy change for the standard state transfer. As the free-energy of fusion (G_f) is zero at the true melting point, therefore:

$$S_f = \frac{L_f}{T_f} \qquad 1.100$$

and:

$$G_f = L_f - TS_f$$

where S_f and L_f, the entropy and enthalpy of fusion at the melting point T_f, are assumed to be independent of temperature.

Multicomponent solutions

The thermodynamic behaviour of a particular solute in a solution is usually affected by the presence of other solutes, even at low concentrations. Thus the activity coefficient, f_X, of a solute X is both a function of the concentration of X and of the concentrations of the other solutes. In a solution containing two solutes X and Y this interdependence can be expressed as:

$$f_X = f_X^X \times f_X^Y \qquad 1.101$$

or:

$$\log f_X = \log f_X^X + \log f_X^Y$$

where f_X is the activity coefficient of X at a given concentration in the ternary alloy, f_X^X is the activity coefficient of X at the same concentration of X in the absence of Y and f_X^Y, called an **interaction coefficient**, is a measure of the effect of Y on the activity coefficient of X. In most of the dilute solutions which have been studied to date the interaction coefficient f_X^Y is found to be a logarithmic function of the concentration of Y, but is independent of the concentration of X. Thus, this concentration-dependence is expressed by:

$$\frac{\partial \log f_X^Y}{\partial \text{wt}\% Y} = e_X^Y \qquad\qquad 1.102$$

$$\frac{\partial \ln f_X^Y}{\partial N_Y} = \epsilon_X^Y \qquad\qquad 1.103$$

where the **interaction parameters** e_X^Y and ϵ_X^Y have values calculated on the basis of the activity coefficients being defined respectively in terms of the weight-per cent, or atom fraction, dilute solution standard states.

For dilute solutions containing more than two solutes, it is generally found that values of the experimentally determined interaction parameters e_X^Y or ϵ_X^Y are unaffected by the presence in the solution of other (third, fourth, etc.) solutes. Where this condition applies, Wagner [4] has derived the following relation for the activity coefficient of a component X in a multicomponent solution containing solutes X, Y, Z, etc., in terms of the interaction coefficients:

$$\ln f_X = N_X \cdot \frac{\partial \ln f_X}{\partial N_X} + \left[N_Y \cdot \frac{\partial \ln f_X}{\partial N_Y} + N_Z \cdot \frac{\partial \ln f_X}{\partial N_Z} + \ldots \right]$$
$$+ \frac{1}{2} \left[N_X^2 \cdot \frac{\partial^2 \ln f_X}{\partial N_X^2} + N_X \cdot N_Y \cdot \frac{\partial^2 \ln f_X}{\partial N_X \partial N_Y} + \ldots \right] + \ldots$$

where the derivatives are taken for the limiting case of zero concentration of all solutes. However, at low concentrations, the terms involving second- or higher-order derivatives become very small and can be neglected. Making this approximation and substituting *1.102* or *1.103* for the first derivatives, the relation simplifies either to:

$$\ln f_X = N_X \cdot \epsilon_X^X + N_Y \cdot \epsilon_X^Y + N_Z \cdot \epsilon_X^Z + \ldots \qquad 1.104$$

in terms of the atom fraction standard state scale, or:

$$\log f_X = \text{wt}\% X \cdot e_X^X + \text{wt}\% Y \cdot e_X^Y + \text{wt}\% Z \cdot e_X^Z \qquad 1.105$$

in terms of the weight-per cent standard state scale.

In practical systems, *1.104* and *1.105* can often be applied to represent the interaction effects between solutes at concentrations up to at least one atom- or weight-per cent. These equations have commonly been used to compute the activities of solutes in molten steels. However, the errors arising from neglect of the higher order derivatives become increasingly significant as the concentration of solutes is raised and, though equations *1.102* or *1.103* may continue to be applicable, equations *1.104* and *1.105* are usually not valid for other than relatively dilute solutions.

Wagner has shown further that, at infinite dilution, the interaction parameters are related by:

$$\epsilon_Y^X = \epsilon_X^Y \qquad\qquad 1.106$$

$$e_Y^X = \frac{M_Y}{M_X} . e_X^Y \qquad\qquad 1.107$$

where M_X and M_Y are the atomic weights of the solutes X and Y, which relations may be made to yield values of the interaction parameters when the latter are unknown or not readily amenable to experimental determination.

References

1. K. K. KELLEY, Contributions to the data on theoretical metallurgy, X., U.S. Bureau of Mines, *Bulletin* 476, 1949.
2. O. KUBASCHEWSKI and E. LL. EVANS, *Metallurgical Thermochemistry*, Pergamon Press, 1958.
3. J. H. HILDEBRAND, *J. Am. Chem. Soc.*, **51**, 1929, p. 66.
4. C. WAGNER, *Thermodynamics of Alloys*, Addison Wesley, 1952.

CHAPTER 2

Enthalpy and Heat Capacity

The heat change accompanying a reaction is an indefinite quantity, since part of the energy of the reaction may be consumed as work of expansion against an external pressure (and as energy in a form other than heat, e.g. electrical energy). However, as enthalpy is completely defined in terms of state variables (equation *1.4*), the enthalpy change in a reaction, which is equal to the heat change at constant pressure when only mechanical work is done (equation *1.6*), is dependent only on the initial and final states and not on the reaction path. The additive properties of enthalpy, originally formulated empirically as **Hess's law**, follow as a consequence of enthalpy being a variable of state. Thus, enthalpies or enthalpy changes may be added and subtracted parallel with the same manipulations performed on their respective components or reactions.

The enthalpies of the elements in their normal states are conventionally made equal to zero at 298°K and one atmosphere pressure. The heats of the formation reactions for compounds under the same conditions are, therefore, the standard enthalpies, or heats of formation of these compounds. Extensive tables of these values are available.

When heats of reaction are required at other than the standard temperature it is adequate for some purposes to assume that the enthalpy terms involved are independent of temperature and to use either the standard values or a mean value in the temperature range of interest. If greater accuracy is required, heats of reaction at temperatures other than 298°K are calculated using the Kirchhoff equation (*1.18*).

The following examples are selected to illustrate various ways in which these principles may be applied. As calorimetric work is usually carried out under constant pressure conditions (or pressure effects are either ignored or allowed for in the handling of the results) the readily available quantities are enthalpy and heat capacity at constant pressure. However, the principles used can, in theory at least, be applied equally well to calculations in terms of internal energy and heat capacity at constant volume.

Applications of Hess's law

2.1   *Determine the heat of reaction of pure solid* Na_2O *with HCl gas at 1 atmosphere pressure to form NaCl and water at 25°C.*

The standard heats of formation in kcal mole^{-1} are:

$$NaCl_{(s)} \quad -98{\cdot}6 \pm 0{\cdot}2 \quad : \quad HCl_{(g)} \quad -22{\cdot}0 \pm 0{\cdot}1$$

$$Na_2O_{(s)} \quad -100{\cdot}7 \pm 1{\cdot}2 \quad : \quad H_2O_{(l)} \quad -68{\cdot}32 \pm 0{\cdot}01$$

The enthalpy quantities involved in the reaction are therefore:

$$Na_2O_{(s)} + 2HCl_{(g)} \rightleftharpoons 2NaCl_{(s)} + H_2O_{(l)}$$

$$(-100{\cdot}7) \quad 2\times(-22{\cdot}0) \quad 2\times(-98{\cdot}6) \quad (-68{\cdot}32)$$

The heat of the reaction is equal to the difference between the enthalpies of the products and of the reactants (equation *1.7*), i.e.:

$$\Delta H^0_{298} = [2\times(-98{\cdot}6)+(-68{\cdot}32)] - [(-100{\cdot}7)+2\times(-22{\cdot}0)]$$

$$= -120{\cdot}82 \text{ kcal.}$$

The errors in the individual enthalpies are additive,* giving an overall error of:

$$1{\cdot}2+(2\times0{\cdot}1)+(2\times0{\cdot}2)+0{\cdot}01 = \pm1{\cdot}81 \text{ kcal.}$$

Hence:

$$\Delta H^0_{298} = -120{\cdot}82 \pm 1{\cdot}81 \text{ kcal.}$$

Because ΔH^0 is negative, the 120·82 ($\pm$1·81) kcal are evolved when 1 mole of Na_2O and 2 mole of HCl gas are reacted *completely* at 25°C to form 2 mole of NaCl and 1 mole of water. Thus the heat of reaction is equal to:

$$-120{\cdot}82 \ (\pm1{\cdot}81) \text{ kcal per mole of } Na_2O \text{ or of } H_2O$$

or:

$$-60{\cdot}41 \ (\pm0{\cdot}91) \text{ kcal per mole of HCl gas or of NaCl.}$$

If the heat of reaction per gram of one of the components is required, the molar heat is divided by the molecular weight of that component.

---

* This is one of the major disadvantages of the application of Hess's law. In this example the error is only 1·5 per cent of the heat of reaction, but when the latter is small the error in its determination by this means may be of comparable magnitude, and very much larger than that obtained from a direct experimental determination of the enthalpy change.

2.2 *Calculate the standard heat of formation of solid* PbO_2 *from solid lead and oxygen gas at* 1 *atmosphere pressure, given the following data valid at* 298°K:

Reaction		Heat of Reaction	
$Pb_{(s)} + \frac{1}{2}O_{2(g)} \rightleftharpoons PbO_{(s)}$	:	$-52\cdot4$ kcal	*2.2.1*
$3PbO_{(s)} + \frac{1}{2}O_{2(g)} \rightleftharpoons Pb_3O_{4(s)}$	:	$-18\cdot4$ kcal	*2.2.2*
$Pb_3O_4 + O_{2(g)} \rightleftharpoons 3PbO_{2(g)}$	:	$-22\cdot7$ kcal	*2.2.3*

This is an example of a reaction which can be represented as being made up from a series of reactions for which data are available. The overall reaction is:

$$Pb_{(s)} + O_{2(g)} \rightleftharpoons PbO_{2(s)} \qquad\qquad 2.2.4$$

this being equivalent to the sum of equation *2.2.1* and one-third the sum of *2.2.2* and *2.2.3*. Following Hess's law, the heats of reaction are also additive, i.e.

$$\Delta H^0_{(2.2.4)} = \Delta H^0_{(2.2.1)} + \tfrac{1}{3}\Delta H^0_{(2.2.2)} + \tfrac{1}{3}\Delta H^0_{(2.2.3)}$$

$$= -52\cdot4 - 6\cdot1 - 7\cdot6$$

$$= -66\cdot1 \text{ kcal.}$$

Historically, heats of formation are always quoted as exothermic, or negative heat, quantities. Thus the heat of the reaction for the formation of lead dioxide from its components at 298°K is $-66\cdot1$ kcal, and the standard heat of formation of solid PbO_2 is $66\cdot1$ kcal mole^{-1}.

2.3 *Calculate the heat of reaction when* 1 *mole of zinc is dissolved in a* HCl ($100H_2O$) *solution, given the following data:*

$$HCl_{(g)} + 100H_2O_{(l)} \rightleftharpoons HCl(100H_2O)_{(l)} \quad : \quad \Delta H_{298} = -17\cdot5 \text{ kcal} \quad 2.3.1$$

$$ZnCl_{2(s)} + 200H_2O_{(l)} \rightleftharpoons ZnCl_2(200H_2O)_{(l)} \quad : \quad \Delta H_{298} = -14\cdot9 \text{ kcal}$$
$$\qquad\qquad\qquad\qquad\qquad\qquad\qquad\qquad\qquad\qquad\qquad\qquad 2.3.2$$

$$ZnCl_{2(s)} \quad : \quad \Delta H^0_{298} = -99\cdot5 \text{ kcal mole}^{-1}$$

$$HCl_{(g)} \quad : \quad \Delta H^0_{298} = -22\cdot0 \text{ kcal mole}^{-1}$$

The reaction in question is:

$$Zn_{(s)} + 2[HCl(100H_2O)]_{(l)} \rightleftharpoons ZnCl_2 \cdot (200H_2O)_{(l)} + H_{2(g)} \qquad 2.3.3$$

The reactions *2.3.1* and *2.3.2* are the solution reactions for HCl and $ZnCl_2$, i.e. the enthalpy values are the heats of solution in water. For the reaction between zinc and hydrochloric acid gas; i.e.

$$Zn_{(s)} + 2HCl_{(g)} \rightleftharpoons ZnCl_{2(s)} + H_{2(g)} \qquad\qquad 2.3.4$$

the heat of reaction is found (as in example *2.1*) to be:

$$\Delta H_{298} = (-99 \cdot 5) - 2 \times (-22 \cdot 0) = -55 \cdot 5 \text{ kcal.}$$

Reaction *2.3.3* can then be obtained by subtracting twice reaction *2.3.1* from the sum of *2.3.2* and *2.3.4*. Hess's law gives:

$$\begin{aligned}
\Delta H_{(2.3.3)} &= \Delta H_{(2.3.2)} + \Delta H_{(2.3.4)} - 2\Delta H_{(2.3.1)} \\
&= -14 \cdot 9 - 55 \cdot 5 - 2 \times (-17 \cdot 5) \\
&= -35 \cdot 4 \text{ kcal mole}^{-1} \text{ (of zinc)}
\end{aligned}$$

which is the heat of reaction when 1 mole of zinc is dissolved in 2 mole of the HCl solution.

Heats of reaction at elevated temperatures

The following examples illustrate the application, in various forms, of the Kirchhoff equation.

2.4   *Evaluate (a) the enthalpy of* Cr_2O_3 *at* 1,900°C, *(b) the heat required to raise the temperature of* 1 *mole of* Cr_2O_3 *from* 10°C *to* 1,900°C.

(a)   The solution of equation *1.16* to obtain the enthalpy of Cr_2O_3 at an elevated temperature requires knowledge of the standard heat of formation and the heat capacity of Cr_2O_3. These are:

$$\Delta H^0_{298} = -270,000 \text{ cal mole}^{-1}$$

$$C_{p_{Cr_2O_3}} = 28 \cdot 53 + 2 \cdot 20 \times 10^{-3}T - 3 \cdot 74 \times 10^5 T^{-2} \text{ cal deg}^{-1} \text{ mole}^{-1}$$

The calculation of the enthalpy or enthalpy increment at, or between temperatures other than, the standard temperature of 298°K can be carried out in two ways.

METHOD 1: A completely general expression for the enthalpy as a function of temperature is first obtained by solving *1.17* as an indefinite integral and finding the value of the integration constant by substitution of the standard heat of formation and the temperature of 298°K. Thus:

$$\begin{aligned}
\Delta H^0_T &= \int C_p . \mathrm{d}T \\
&= \int [28 \cdot 53 + 2 \cdot 20 \times 10^{-3}T - 3 \cdot 74 \times 10^5 T^{-2}] \mathrm{d}T \\
&= \Delta H_0 + 28 \cdot 53T + 1 \cdot 10 \times 10^{-3}T^2 + 3 \cdot 74 \times 10^5 T^{-1} \text{ cal mole}^{-1}
\end{aligned}$$

where ΔH_0 is an integration constant, found by substituting:

$$\Delta H_{298}^0 \text{ for Cr}_2\text{O}_3 = -270,000 \text{ cal mole}^{-1},$$

i.e.

$$\Delta H_0 = -270,000 - (28 \cdot 53 \times 298) - \left(\frac{1 \cdot 1 \times 298^2}{10^3}\right) - \left(\frac{3 \cdot 74 \times 10^5}{298}\right)$$

$$= -279,900.$$

Therefore:

$$\Delta H_T^0 = -279,900 + 28 \cdot 53T + 1 \cdot 10 \times 10^{-3}\,T^2 + 3 \cdot 74 \times 10^5\,T^{-1} \text{ cal mole}^{-1}$$

which may be solved for any value of T. Thus, at $T = 1,900°\text{C}$ $(2,173°\text{K})$:

$$\Delta H_{2,173}^0 = -279,900 + (28 \cdot 53 \times 2,173) + (1 \cdot 10 \times 10^{-3} \times 2,173^2)$$

$$+ \left(\frac{3 \cdot 74 \times 10^5}{2,173}\right)$$

$$= -212,500 \text{ cal mole}^{-1}.$$

METHOD 2: Equation *1.17* may be solved as a definite integral between the limits $T = 298$ and $2,173°\text{K}$.*

Thus:

$$\Delta H_{2,173}^0 - \Delta H_{298}^0 = \int_{298}^{2,173} C_p\,.\,dT$$

$$= \int_{298}^{2,173} [28 \cdot 53 + 2 \cdot 20 \times 10^{-3}\,T - 3 \cdot 74 \times 10^5\,T^{-2}]\,dT$$

$$= [28 \cdot 53T + 1 \cdot 10 \times 10^{-3}\,T^2 + 3 \cdot 74 \times 10^5\,T^{-1}]_{298}^{2,173}$$

The value of ΔH_{298}^0 is given as $-270,000$ cal mole^{-1}. Therefore:

$$\Delta H_{2,173}^0 = -270,000 + 28 \cdot 53(2,173 - 298) + 1 \cdot 10 \times 10^{-3}(2,173^2 - 298^2)$$

$$+ 3 \cdot 74 \times 10^5 \left(\frac{1}{2,173} - \frac{1}{298}\right)$$

$$= -270,000 + 53,500 + 5,100 - 1,100$$

$$= -270,000 + 57,500$$

$$= -212,500 \text{ cal mole}^{-1}.$$

* While, in general, temperatures in this book are quoted to the nearest degree Kelvin, it should be appreciated that, in practice, the accuracy of temperature measurement is often much less than this at high temperatures.

The two methods are, of course, equivalent and require the same information for solution. The first method is preferable when enthalpy values are required at more than one temperature.

(b)   The calculation of the enthalpy *increment* when a substance is heated from one temperature to another does not require knowledge of the standard heat of formation. The amount of heat required to raise the temperature of 1 mole of Cr_2O_3 from 10°C to 1,900°C is:

$$\Delta H^0 = \Delta H^0_{2,173} - \Delta H^0_{283} = \int_{283}^{2,173} C_p \cdot dT$$

$$= \int_{283}^{2,173} [28 \cdot 53 + 2 \cdot 20 \times 10^{-3}\,T - 3 \cdot 74 \times 10^5\,T^{-2}]\,dT$$

$$= 28 \cdot 53(2{,}173 - 283) + 1 \cdot 10 \times 10^{-3}(2{,}173^2 - 283^2)$$

$$+ 3 \cdot 74 \times 10^5 \left(\frac{1}{2{,}173} - \frac{1}{283} \right)$$

$$= 53{,}900 + 5{,}100 - 1{,}200$$

$$= 57{,}800 \text{ cal mole}^{-1}.$$

In the previous calculation (a), method 2, the enthalpy increment between the standard temperature 298°K and 2,173°K was calculated (i.e. as above) and added to the standard heat of formation (ΔH^0_{298}) to give the enthalpy of Cr_2O_3 at 2,173°K. The difference between the two enthalpy increments (i.e. $57{,}800 - 57{,}500 = 300$ cal mole^{-1}) is, of course, equal to the enthalpy increment between 283 and 298°K.

2.5   *A bath of molten copper is supercooled to 5°C below its true melting point. Nucleation of solid copper then takes place and solidification proceeds under adiabatic conditions. What percentage of the bath solidifies?*

The following data are required:

The latent heat of fusion of copper (L_f) = 3,100 cal mole^{-1} at 1,083°C.

$$C_{p_{Cu(l)}} = 7 \cdot 5 \text{ cal deg}^{-1} \text{ mole}^{-1}$$

$$C_{p_{Cu(s)}} = 5 \cdot 41 + 1 \cdot 5 \times 10^{-3}\,T \text{ cal deg}^{-1} \text{ mole}^{-1}.$$

This type of problem is essentially a variation on the classical heat balance problem of dropping a hot object into a bucket of water, etc. Because no heat is exchanged with the surroundings, solidification proceeds only until the latent heat evolved causes the temperature of the bath to rise to the true melting point, when solidification ceases. Thus, the heat balance arises between the heat evolved during solidification and the heat required to raise the temperature of the bath (now a mixture of liquid and solid copper) to the true melting point; i.e. through the 5°C of supercooling. This quantity of heat is given by:

$$\int_{1,351}^{1,356} 7 \cdot 5 \, dT = 7 \cdot 5 \times (1,361 - 1,356)$$

$$= 37 \cdot 5 \text{ cal mole}^{-1} \text{ of liquid copper}$$

plus:

$$\int_{1,351}^{1,356} (5 \cdot 41 + 1 \cdot 5 \times 10^{-3} \, T) \, dT = [5 \cdot 41T + 0 \cdot 75 \times 10^{-3} \, T^2]_{1,351}^{1,356}$$

$$= 37 \cdot 2 \text{ cal mole}^{-1} \text{ of solid copper.}$$

As for every mole of copper which solidifies, 3,100 cal of latent heat are evolved, this will raise the temperature of:

$$\left[\frac{3,100 - 37 \cdot 2}{37 \cdot 5} + 1 \right] = 82 \cdot 7$$

mole of copper back to the melting point. That is, 81·7 mole of liquid copper and 1 mole of solidified copper can be heated from 1,078 to 1,083°C by the latent heat evolved on the solidification of 1 mole of copper. Therefore, the fraction of the bath which solidifies is 1/82·7 or 1·21 per cent.

2.6   *Find the heat of reaction when γ-iron is oxidized by pure oxygen gas to form ferrous oxide* (FeO) *at 1,350°C.*

The tabulated data for the heat of oxidation of iron apply at 298°K, but between this temperature and the required temperature iron undergoes a ferromagnetic to paramagnetic change at 760°C and a phase transformation (from α to γ form) at 910°C. To calculate the high temperature heat of oxidation of iron it is necessary, therefore, to use relations of the form of equation *1.22*. Between each of the transformation temperatures the enthalpy increments are calculated by essentially the same procedure as that outlined in example 2.4a, method 1, i.e., the integration constant, ΔH_0, in the general equation is evaluated from a known value of ΔH_T^0, valid in the temperature range of interest. Hence these calculations are shown only in outline and emphasis is given to the procedure for adding or subtracting the latent heats at the various transformation points.

The standard heat of formation of FeO is given as $-63\cdot2$ kcal mole^{-1}, i.e. for the reaction:

$$Fe_{(\alpha)} + \tfrac{1}{2}O_{2(g)} \rightleftharpoons FeO_{(s)} \qquad\qquad 2.6.1$$

the heat of reaction is:

$$\Delta H^0_{298} = -63{,}200 \text{ cal.}$$

The Kirchhoff equation 1.20 is used to extend this value to higher temperatures. The relevant heat capacity relations are:

$$C_{p\,Fe\,(\alpha,\,\text{magnetic})} = 4\cdot18 + 5\cdot92 \times 10^{-3}\,T \text{ cal deg}^{-1} \text{ mole}^{-1}$$

$$C_{p\,FeO(s)} = 11\cdot66 + 2\cdot00 \times 10^{-3}\,T - 0\cdot67 \times 10^5\,T^{-2} \text{ cal deg}^{-1} \text{ mole}^{-1}$$

$$C_{p\,O_2(g)} = 7\cdot16 + 1\cdot00 \times 10^{-3}\,T - 0\cdot40 \times 10^5\,T^{-2} \text{ cal deg}^{-1} \text{ mole}^{-1}.$$

Thus, for reaction $2.6.1$:

$$\Delta C_p = C_{p\,FeO(s)} - C_{p\,Fe\,(\alpha,\,\text{magnetic})} - \tfrac{1}{2}C_{p\,O_2(g)}$$

$$= 3\cdot90 - 4\cdot42 \times 10^{-3}\,T - 0\cdot47 \times 10^5\,T^{-2}.$$

Substituting this in 1.20:

$$\Delta H^0_T = \int \Delta C_p . \, dT$$

$$= \Delta H_0 + 3\cdot90T - 2\cdot21 \times 10^{-3}\,T^2 + 0\cdot47 \times 10^5\,T^{-1}$$

where ΔH_0, the integration constant, is evaluated by substituting $\Delta H^0_{298} = -63{,}200$ cal.

Hence:

$$\Delta H^0_T = -64{,}300 + 3\cdot90T - 2\cdot21 \times 10^{-3}\,T^2 + 0\cdot47 \times 10^5\,T^{-1} \text{ cal.} \qquad 2.6.2$$

At 760°C, α-Fe changes from the ferro-magnetic to the para-magnetic state (i.e. the Curie point). This change is accompanied by an absorption of heat over a range of temperature from about 300° to 900°C, which is evidenced by an abnormally high heat capacity for iron over this temperature range and is characteristic of what is known as a second-order transformation. However, when the enthalpy of iron is required at a temperature above 900°C, as in the present case, the heat change associated with the magnetic change can be represented by a 'latent heat of transformation' (L_t) which is absorbed at a constant temperature of 760°C (the temperature of maximum heat capacity).

For the reaction:

$$Fe_{(\alpha,\,\text{ferro-magnetic})} \rightleftharpoons Fe_{(\alpha,\,\text{para-magnetic})} \qquad\qquad 2.6.3$$

the 'latent heat of transformation' at 760°C is given as:

$$\Delta H^0_{\text{trans}} = +660 \text{ cal.}$$

The heat of reaction 2.6.1 at 760°C (1,033°K) is, (from 2.6.2):

$$\Delta H^0_{1,033} = -62,600 \text{ cal.}$$

Applying Hess's law at 1,033°K to reactions 2.6.1 and 2.6.3 yields the reaction:

$$\text{Fe}_{(\alpha, \text{ para-mag.})} + \tfrac{1}{2}O_{2(g)} \rightleftharpoons \text{FeO}_{(s)} \qquad 2.6.4$$

for which the heat of reaction is:

$$\Delta H^0_{1,033} = \Delta H^0_{(2.6.1)} - \Delta H^0_{(2.6.3)}$$

$$= -62,600 - 660$$

$$= -63,260 \text{ cal.}$$

As $\text{Fe}_{(\alpha, \text{ para-mag.})}$ has a different heat capacity–temperature relation to $\text{Fe}_{(\alpha, \text{ ferro-mag.})}$, i.e.

$$C_{p\text{Fe} (\alpha, \text{ non-mag.})} = 9 \cdot 0 \text{ cal deg}^{-1} \text{ mole}^{-1},$$

the heat capacity change in reaction 2.6.4 is different to that in 2.6.1. The value for 2.6.4, obtained from the previously quoted values of $C_{p\text{FeO}(s)}$ and $C_{pO_2(g)}$ with the $C_{p\text{Fe} (\alpha, \text{ para-mag.})}$ is:

$$\Delta C_p = -0 \cdot 92 + 1 \cdot 50 \times 10^{-3} T - 0 \cdot 47 \times 10^5 T^{-2}.$$

Hence the enthalpy change for reaction 2.6.4 is:

$$\Delta H^0_T = \int \Delta C_p . \mathrm{d}T$$

$$= \Delta H_0 - 0 \cdot 92T + 0 \cdot 75 \times 10^{-3} T^2 + 0 \cdot 47 \times 10^5 T^{-1}.$$

Solving for ΔH_0, the integration constant, by substitution of $\Delta H^0_{1,033} = -63,260$ cal gives:

$$\Delta H^0_T = -63,160 - 0 \cdot 92T + 0 \cdot 75 \times 10^{-3} T^2 + 0 \cdot 47 \times 10^5 T^{-1}.$$

At 1,183°K, the temperature of the $\alpha \rightarrow \gamma$ transformation in iron, the heat change for reaction 2.6.4 is:

$$\Delta H^0_{1,183} = -63,160 \text{ cal.}$$

The transformation from α to γ iron is a typical 'first-order transformation' with a true latent heat of transformation of $+220$ cal mole^{-1}, which is absorbed at a constant temperature of 910°C (1,183°K); i.e.

$$\text{Fe}_{(\alpha, \text{ para-mag.})} \rightleftharpoons \text{Fe}_{(\gamma)} \quad : \quad \Delta H^0 = +220 \text{ cal mole}^{-1}. \qquad 2.6.5$$

Applying Hess's law to equations *2.6.4* and *2.6.5* at 1,183°K, for the reaction:

$$Fe_{(\gamma)} + \tfrac{1}{2}O_{2(g)} \rightleftharpoons FeO_{(s)} \qquad\qquad 2.6.6$$

the heat of reaction is:

$$\Delta H^0_{1,183} = \Delta H^0_{(2.6.4)} - \Delta H^0_{(2.6.5)}$$
$$= -63,160 - 220$$
$$= -63,380 \text{ cal.}$$

The heat of capacity of γ-iron is given by:

$$C_{pFe(\gamma)} = 1{\cdot}84 + 4{\cdot}66 \times 10^{-3}\,T \text{ cal deg}^{-1} \text{ mole}^{-1}$$

and the heat capacity change for reaction *2.6.6* is therefore:

$$\Delta C_p = 6{\cdot}24 - 3{\cdot}16 \times 10^{-3}\,T - 0{\cdot}47 \times 10^5\,T^{-2}.$$

Hence:

$$\Delta H^0_T = \Delta H_0 + 6{\cdot}24T - 1{\cdot}58 \times 10^{-3}\,T^2 + 0{\cdot}47 \times 10^5\,T^{-1}$$

and, since $\qquad\qquad \Delta H^0_{1,183} = -63,380 \text{ cal,}$
therefore:

$$\Delta H^0_T = -68,580 + 6{\cdot}24T - 1{\cdot}58 \times 10^{-3}\,T^2 + 0{\cdot}47 \times 10^5\,T^{-1}$$

which is valid from 1,183°K up to 1,651°K, the melting point of FeO. At the temperature of 1,350°C (1,623°K):

$$\Delta H^0_{1,623} = -62,600 \text{ cal.}$$

Thus, when γ-iron is oxidized to form ferrous oxide at 1,350°C, 62,600 cal of heat are evolved per mole of iron oxidized.

2.7 *Blast-furnace gas containing 20 per cent CO, 10 per cent CO$_2$ and 70 per cent N$_2$ by volume is burned with the correct amount of air in a furnace. If the gases enter the furnace at 600°C and leave at 1,050°C, calculate the maximum flame temperature and the heat supplied to the furnace in B.Th.U. per cubic foot of exhaust gases.*

This is a very common type of problem of the heat-balance type. The heat evolved in a reaction is used to heat up the products of the reaction and the surroundings, the problem being to calculate one or other of the heat terms or increases in temperature. In this particular problem, the gas of known analysis burns to give up a calculable amount of heat which is used to heat the product (and any diluting) gases. Assuming adiabatic conditions, the maximum temperature of these gases in the flame can be calculated. The heat in these gases is partly transferred to the furnace and partly carried off in the exhaust. Calculation of the latter quantity will also give, by difference, the former – the heat supplied to the furnace.

The required data are:

For CO: Standard heat of formation $= -26,400$ cal mole^{-1}

Heat capacity $C_p = 6\cdot79 + 0\cdot98 \times 10^{-3}T - 0\cdot11 \times 10^5 T^{-2}$ cal deg^{-1} mole^{-1}

For CO$_2$:   Standard heat of formation $= -94,050$ cal mole^{-1}

Heat capacity $C_p = 10\cdot55 + 2\cdot16 \times 10^{-3}T - 2\cdot04 \times 10^5 T^{-2}$ cal deg^{-1} mole^{-1}

For O$_2$:   Heat capacity $C_p = 7\cdot16 + 1\cdot00 \times 10^{-3}T - 0\cdot40 \times 10^5 T^{-2}$ cal deg^{-1} mole^{-1}

For N$_2$:   Heat capacity $C_p = 6\cdot66 + 1\cdot02 \times 10^{-3}T$ cal deg^{-1} mole^{-1}

For the reaction:

$$2CO_{(g)} + O_{2(g)} \rightleftharpoons 2CO_{2(g)} \qquad\qquad 2.7.1$$

the heat of reaction at 298°K is obtained by application of Hess's law to the formation reactions for CO$_2$ and CO.

Thus:

$$\Delta H^0_{298} = [2 \times (-94,050) - 2 \times (-26,400) - 0]$$
$$= -135,300 \text{ cal.}$$

Now, following *1.20*:

$$\Delta H^0 = \int \Delta C_p . \mathrm{d}T$$

and for the above reaction:

$$\Delta C_p = 2C_{p\text{CO}_2(g)} - 2C_{p\text{CO}(g)} - C_{p\text{O}_2(g)}$$
$$= 0\cdot36 + 1\cdot36 \times 10^{-3}T - 3\cdot46 \times 10^5 T^{-2}.$$

Therefore:

$$\Delta H^0_T = \Delta H_0 + 0\cdot36T + 0\cdot68 \times 10^{-3} T^2 + 3\cdot46 \times 10^5 T^{-1}$$

where ΔH_0, the integration constant $(= -136,600)$, is found by substituting $\Delta H^0_{298} = -135,300$ cal.

Hence:

$$\Delta H^0_T = -136,600 + 0\cdot36T + 0\cdot68 \times 10^{-3} T^2 + 3\cdot46 \times 10^5 T^{-1}.$$

Solving this for a temperature of 600°C (873°K), the temperature of the gas entering the furnace, the heat liberated by reaction *2.7.1* is:

$$\Delta H^0_{873} = -135,400 \text{ cal.}$$

This heat of reaction heats the products, together with the diluting nitrogen and carbon dioxide in the incoming gas, to the maximum flame temperature. Note that this heat will be a positive quantity with respect to the exhaust gas.

In reaction 2.7.1, 2 mole of CO combine with 1 mole of oxygen from the air to form 2 mole of CO_2. Therefore, the exhaust gas will consist of:

$$\left.\begin{array}{l} \text{2 mole of } CO_2 \text{ from reaction } 2.7.1 \\ \text{1 mole of } CO_2 \text{ in the blast furnace gas} \end{array}\right\} \text{3 mole } CO_2$$

$$\left.\begin{array}{l} \text{7 mole of } N_2 \text{ in the blast furnace gas} \\ \text{4 mole of } N_2 \text{ in the air} \end{array}\right\} \text{11 mole } N_2$$

and these are heated to the maximum flame temperature (T_M) by the heat supplied from the combustion of the 2 mole of CO at 873°K.

Thus, available heat $= 135,400 \text{ cal} = \int_{873}^{T_M} [3C_{p_{CO_2}} + 11C_{p_{N_2}}] \mathrm{d}T$.

For 3 mole of CO_2: $C_p = 31 \cdot 65 + 6 \cdot 48 \times 10^{-3} T - 6 \cdot 12 \times 10^5 T^{-2}$ cal deg^{-1}

For 11 mole of N_2: $C_p = 73 \cdot 26 + 11 \cdot 22 \times 10^{-3} T$ cal deg^{-1}.

Hence:

$$[104 \cdot 91 T + 8 \cdot 85 \times 10^{-3} T^2 + 6 \cdot 12 \times 10^5 T^{-1}]_{873}^{T_M} = 135,400$$

and:

$$104 \cdot 91 T_M + 8 \cdot 85 \times 10^{-3} T_M^2 + 6 \cdot 12 \times 10^5 T_M^{-1} = 234,350$$

which can be solved for T_M. However, to simplify the solution it is possible to neglect the third term on the left-hand side of the equation. Because T_M must be greater than 1,320°K (the exit temperature of the gases), then:

$$6 \cdot 12 \times 10^5 T_M^{-1} < 500 \text{ cal, or} < 0 \cdot 25\% \text{ of the available heat.}$$

Thus:

$$8 \cdot 85 \times 10^{-3} T_M^2 + 104 \cdot 91 T_M - 234,350 \simeq 0,$$

a quadratic in T_M, which is solved by the formula method:*

$$T_M = \frac{-104 \cdot 91 \pm \sqrt{[(104 \cdot 91)^2 + (4 \times 8 \cdot 85 \times 234 \cdot 35)]}}{2 \times 8 \cdot 85 \times 10^{-3}}$$

$$= \left(\frac{-104 \cdot 9 \pm 139 \cdot 0}{17 \cdot 7}\right) \times 10^3 = 1,927°\text{K or } 1,654°\text{C}.$$

* See appendix 5.

Thus, the maximum flame temperature is 1,654°C.

The heat supplied to the furnace is the difference between the heat evolved in the reaction (135,400 cal at 873°K) and the heat carried away in the exhaust gases. The latter is the quantity of heat required to raise the exhaust gases to the exit temperature of 1,050°C (1,323°K) from the inlet temperature of 600°C. Thus, the heat carried away is:

$$\int_{873}^{1,323} \underset{\text{exhaust}}{\sum} C_p . dT = [104 \cdot 91T + 8 \cdot 85 \times 10^{-3}T^2 + 6 \cdot 12 \times 10^5 T^{-1}]_{875}^{1,323}$$

$$= 47,100 + 8,740 - 240$$

$$= 55,600 \text{ cal,}$$

and the heat supplied to the furnace is:

$$135,400 - 55,600 = 79,800 \text{ cal.}$$

This is the heat corresponding to 3 mole of CO_2 and 11 mole of N_2 (= 14 mole of exhaust gas). Assuming these gases behave ideally, the volume of this gas at N.T.P. is $14 \times 22 \cdot 4$ litre. At 1,050°C (1,323°K) and a constant pressure of 1 atmosphere, the gas expands to a volume of:

$$14 \times 22 \cdot 4 \times \frac{1,323}{273} = 1,521 \text{ litre}$$

$$= 53 \cdot 7 \text{ cu ft of exhaust gas.}$$

Therefore, the heat supplied to the furnace per cu ft of exhaust gas is:

$$\frac{79,800}{53 \cdot 7} = 1,485 \text{ cal}$$

$$= 5 \cdot 89 \text{ B.Th.U.}$$

2.8 *Pure chromic oxide (Cr_2O_3) reacts with the stoichiometric amount of pure aluminium, both initially at 25°C, to produce alumina and pure liquid chromium. If the maximum temperature attained in the crucible is 1,900°C, calculate the heat lost to the surroundings per kilogram of aluminium.*

This problem can be approached from two different viewpoints. Possibly the simpler method is to assume that the reaction takes place at 25°C, part of the heat generated being used to heat the products of reaction to 1,900°C and the remainder being lost to the surroundings. The reaction at room temperature is:

$$2Al_{(s)} + Cr_2O_{3(s)} \rightleftharpoons 2Cr_{(s)} + Al_2O_{3(s)} \qquad 2.8.1$$

4

The standard heats of formation of Cr_2O_3 and Al_2O_3 are -270 and -400 kcal mole^{-1} respectively. Hence the heat of reaction at 298°K is:

$$\Delta H^0_{298} = -400,000 - (-270,000)$$

$$= -130,000 \text{ cal (heat evolved)}.$$

This heat is used partly to heat 2 mole of chromium and 1 mole of Al_2O_3 to 1,900°C (2,173°K).

Heat required for Al_2O_3.

$$\Delta H^0_{(298 \to 2,173°K)} = \int_{298}^{2,173} C_{p_{Al_2O_3}} . dT$$

and:

$$C_{p_{Al_2O_3(s)}} = 27\cdot38 + 3\cdot08 \times 10^{-3} T - 8\cdot20 \times 10^5 T^{-2} \text{ cal deg}^{-1} \text{ mole}^{-1}.$$

Therefore:

$$\Delta H^0_{(298 \to 2,173°K)} = 51,350 + 7,140 - 2,375$$

$$= 56,115 \text{ cal mole}^{-1}.$$

Heat required for chromium.

Chromium melts at 1,850°C (2,123°K) and the heat required to raise the *two* mole of chromium from 298°K to 2,173°K will include the latent heat of fusion. Noting that:

$$C_{p_{Cr(s)}} = 5\cdot84 + 2\cdot36 \times 10^{-3} T - 0\cdot88 \times 10^5 T^{-2} \text{ cal deg}^{-1} \text{ mole}^{-1}$$

$$C_{p_{Cr(l)}} = 9\cdot40 \text{ cal deg}^{-1} \text{ mole}^{-1}$$

$$L_f = 4,600 \text{ cal mole}^{-1} \text{ at } 2,123°K,$$

then, following *1.22*:

$$\Delta H^0_{(298 \to 2,173°K)} = \int_{298}^{2,123} [11\cdot68 + 4\cdot72 \times 10^{-3} T - 1\cdot76 \times 10^5 T^{-2}] dT$$

$$+ (2 \times 4,600) + \int_{2,123}^{2,173} 18\cdot80 . dT$$

$$= 21,300 + 10,430 - 508 + 9,200 + 940$$

$$= 41,360 \text{ cal.}$$

The heat lost to the surroundings (for each unit of reaction) is the difference between the heat of reaction and the sensible heat of the products. Thus heat loss

$$= 130,000 - 56,100 - 41,400$$

$$= 32,500 \text{ cal.}$$

K

This heat will correspond to 2 mole of aluminium reacted. Thus, the heat loss per kilogram of aluminium is:

$$\frac{32{,}500}{2} \times \frac{1{,}000}{26{\cdot}97} = 603{,}000 \text{ cal}$$

where $26{\cdot}97$ is the atomic weight of aluminium.

In practice, of course, the overall process would not take place so discretely as this. For once the reaction is initiated, the temperature of the reacting mass would rise and at any time during the reaction, un-consumed reactants and just-generated products would be at some temperature less than $1{,}900°C$. However, as enthalpy is a variable of state of any thermodynamic system, changes in enthalpy as the system passes from one state to another will be independent of the way in which this happens. Hence in this instance, the difference between the heat generated by the reaction and the sensible heat requirements of the products, i.e. the heat evolved, will be a constant, independent of just how or at what temperature the reaction takes place. To illustrate this, consider the 'opposite extreme' from the process stipulated for the calculation just made. Let heat be supplied to the reactants to raise their temperature to $1{,}900°C$ and let the reaction take place at that temperature to give alumina and liquid chromium as the final product. Then, if the initial heat supplied is subtracted from the heat of reaction to give the net heat evolved, the latter should be equal to the value just calculated.

Consider reaction *2.8.1* at $1{,}900°C$.

The heat required to raise the temperature of 2 mole of aluminium to $1{,}900°C$ is obtained from:

$$C_{p_{Al(s)}} = 4{\cdot}94 + 2{\cdot}96 \times 10^{-3}\,T \text{ cal deg}^{-1}\text{ mole}^{-1}$$

$$C_{p_{Al(l)}} = 7{\cdot}00 \text{ cal deg}^{-1}\text{ mole}^{-1}$$

$$L_f \text{ at } 659°C = 2{\cdot}5 \text{ kcal mole}^{-1}$$

and is calculated as shown previously to obtain:

$$\Delta H^0_{(298 \to 2{,}173°K)} = 30{,}940 \text{ cal.}$$

The heat required to raise the temperature of 1 mole of chromium oxide to $1{,}900°C$ has been calculated in example 2.4a, method 2 (p. 29), as:

$$\Delta H^0_{(298 \to 2{,}173°K)} = 57{,}500 \text{ cal.}$$

Thus the total heat required to raise the temperature of the reactants to $1{,}900°C$ is:

$$\Delta H^0 = 30{,}940 + 57{,}500$$

$$= 88{,}440 \text{ cal.}$$

Because of the occurrence of phase transformations in the temperature range $298 \rightarrow 2{,}173°K$ (i.e. aluminium melts at $932°K$, chromium melts at $2{,}123°K$) calculation of the variation with temperature of the heat of reaction *2.8.1* necessitates the use of *1.22*. Following the procedure elaborated in example *2.6*:

$$\Delta H^0_{2,173} - \Delta H^0_{298} = \int_{298}^{932} [2C_{p_{Cr(s)}} + C_{p_{Al_2O_3(s)}} - 2C_{p_{Al(s)}} - C_{p_{Cr_2O_3(s)}}]\, dT$$

$$-(2 \times 2{,}500) + \int_{932}^{2,123} [2C_{p_{Cr(s)}} + C_{p_{Al_2O_3(s)}} - 2C_{p_{Al(l)}} - C_{p_{Cr_2O_3(s)}}]\, dT$$

$$+(2 \times 4{,}600) + \int_{2,123}^{2,173} [2C_{p_{Cr(l)}} + C_{p_{Al_2O_3(s)}} - 2C_{p_{Al(l)}} - C_{p_{Cr_2O_3(s)}}]\, dT.$$

Using the C_p values given previously and:

$$C_{p_{Cr_2O_3(s)}} = 28·53 + 2·20 \times 10^{-3}\, T - 3·74 \times 10^5\, T^{-2} \text{ cal deg}^{-1} \text{ mole}^{-1},$$

the heat of reaction at $2{,}173°K$ is calculated as:

$$\Delta H^0_{2,173} = -121{,}000 \text{ cal.}$$

The difference between this and the sensible heat requirements of the reactants will be the heat lost to the surroundings, i.e.

$$\text{heat loss} = 121{,}000 - 88{,}440$$

$$= 32{,}560 \text{ cal per unit of reaction.}$$

Thus the heat loss per kilogram of aluminium

$$= \frac{37·08}{2} \times 32{,}560$$

$$= 603{,}000 \text{ cal}$$

which is equal to the value calculated previously, when the reaction was assumed to take place at $25°C$.

The use of the Clapeyron equations

The preceding examples have involved the Kirchhoff equation, giving the temperature dependence of the heat of a reaction at constant pressure. However, if pressure is introduced as a second independent variable, in addition to temperature, useful relations may be deduced expressing the interdependence of these three quantities. In particular, the Clapeyron, or the approximate Clausius–Clapeyron, equation may be used to calculate the pressure variation of an equilibrium transformation temperature or, alternatively, the temperature variation with pressure may be used to deduce the heat of reaction. The following two examples illustrate typical applications of these equations. Further applications to transformations in condensed systems are involved in the derivation of thermodynamic data from constitutional diagrams considered in chapter 7.

2.9   *At 1 atmosphere pressure, sodium melts at 97·8°C with a latent heat of fusion of 630 cal mole^{-1} and an increase in specific volume of 0·0279 cc g^{-1}. Calculate the melting point of sodium at 10 atmosphere pressure.*

The effect of pressure on a phase change in a one-component system is given by the Clapeyron equation. One derivation of the relation (applied to the fusion reaction considered in the problem) is as follows.

At equilibrium:

$$G_{(s)} = G_{(l)}$$

where G is the Gibbs free energy of the phase. Hence, if the pressure and temperature of the system are changed infinitesimally, such that the system stays at equilibrium, then:

$$dG_{(s)} = dG_{(l)}$$

or, from *1.33*:

$$V_{(s)}.dP - S_{(s)}.dT = V_{(l)}.dP - S_{(l)}.dT.$$

Hence:

$$\frac{dT}{dP} = \frac{V_{(l)} - V_{(s)}}{S_{(l)} - S_{(s)}} = \frac{\Delta V}{\Delta S}$$

where ΔV and ΔS are the volume and entropy differences, respectively, between the two phases at equilibrium (in this case liquid and solid).

However, as at equilibrium, $\Delta S = \Delta H/T$, from *1.27*, then:

$$\frac{dT}{dP} = \frac{T\Delta V}{\Delta H} \qquad\qquad 2.9.1$$

where ΔH is the enthalpy change at the equilibrium transformation temperature T (in this case, the heat of fusion (L_f) at the 1 atmosphere melting point, 97·8°C or 371°K).

Particular care should be taken in selecting the units of the quantities substituted in equation *2.9.1*. In the present problem, for consistency, the latent heat of fusion must be expressed in cal g^{-1}. As the atomic weight of sodium is 23, then:

$$\Delta H = \frac{630}{23} = 27·4 \text{ cal g}^{-1}.$$

Substituting in *2.9.1*:

$$\frac{dT}{dP} = \frac{371 \times 0\cdot0279}{27\cdot4}$$

$$= 0\cdot378 \text{ deg cc cal}^{-1}.$$

The units deg cc cal^{-1}, deduced from consideration of the substituted quantities, must now be converted into more conventional and convenient ones, for example deg atm^{-1}. To do this, it is necessary to multiply by a quantity in units of cal cc^{-1} atm^{-1} (i.e. deg cc cal^{-1} $\times$ cal cc^{-1} atm^{-1} = deg atm^{-1}).

As 1 cal = 41·293 cc atm, therefore:

$$\frac{dT}{dP} = 0\cdot378 \times \frac{1}{41\cdot293}$$

$$= 0\cdot00915 \text{ deg atm}^{-1}$$

which, if assumed to be independent of pressure, yields an increase of 0·09 degrees in the melting point of sodium when the pressure is increased to 10 atmospheres. This value is comparable with the limits of accuracy of the determination of the melting point and is fairly typical of the small effect of pressure on the melting points of pure metals.

2.10   *The vapour pressure of liquid carbon tetrachloride is given as a function of temperature by:*

$$\log p = -2,400T^{-1} - 5\cdot30 \log T + 23\cdot60$$

where p is in mm Hg.

Calculate the latent heat of vaporization of CCl_4 *at its boiling point,* 77°C.

The Clapeyron equation was derived in the previous example for any phase change in a single component system. For the particular case of the vaporization of a liquid, the volume of the latter is small relative to that of the vapour and the volume change on vaporization will approximate closely to the volume of the vapour. If it is further assumed that this vapour behaves as an ideal gas (defined by $PV = RT$) then, from equation *2.9.1*:

$$\frac{dP}{dT} = \frac{P\Delta H}{RT^2}$$

or:

$$\frac{d \ln P}{dT} = \frac{\Delta H}{RT^2}$$

and:

$$\frac{\mathrm{d}\log P}{\mathrm{d}T} = \frac{\Delta H}{4 \cdot 575 T^2}.$$

This is one form of the Clausius–Clapeyron equation.

For this problem:

$$\frac{\mathrm{d}\log P}{\mathrm{d}T} = +2{,}400 T^{-2} - \frac{5 \cdot 30}{2 \cdot 303} T^{-1}, \deg^{-1}.*$$

Hence:

$$\Delta H = 4 \cdot 575 T^2 . (2{,}400 T^{-2} - 2 \cdot 3 T^{-1})$$

the units of which are cal mole^{-1}, as $R = 1 \cdot 987$ cal deg^{-1} mole^{-1} or RT^2 is in units of cal deg mole^{-1}. Thus at 77°C (350°K):

$$\Delta H = 7{,}300 \text{ cal mole}^{-1}.$$

This value for the latent heat of vaporization of carbon tetrachloride at the boiling point compares well with the value of 7,150 cal mole^{-1} quoted in the literature.

---

* The units of $\dfrac{\mathrm{d}\log P}{\mathrm{d}T}$ are deg^{-1}, for it should be recalled that $\log P$ is dimensionless,

or alternatively that:

$$\frac{\mathrm{d}\log P}{\mathrm{d}T} = \frac{1}{2 \cdot 303 P} . \frac{\mathrm{d}P}{\mathrm{d}T} = \frac{\text{pressure}}{\text{pressure} \times \text{temperature}}$$

$$= \frac{1}{\text{temperature}}$$

Note also that P is given in mm Hg. However, the units are immaterial when $(\log P)$ is differentiated for substitution in the Clausius–Clapeyron equation. For example:

$$\log P = -2{,}400 T^{-1} - 5 \cdot 3 \log T + 23 \cdot 6$$

or:

$$P = \text{antilog}\,[-2{,}400 T^{-1} - 5 \cdot 3 \log T + 23 \cdot 6]\,\text{mm Hg.}$$

Converting to atmospheres:

$$P = \frac{\text{antilog}\,[-2{,}400 T^{-1} - 5 \cdot 3 \log T + 23 \cdot 6]}{760}$$

or:

$$\log P = -2{,}400 T^{-1} - 5 \cdot 3 \log T + 23 \cdot 6 - \log 760$$

and:

$$\frac{\mathrm{d}\log P}{\mathrm{d}T} = +2{,}400 T^{-2} - \frac{5 \cdot 3}{2 \cdot 303} T^{-1}, \deg^{-1} \text{ as before.}$$

That is, conversion of the $(\log P)$ expression to any system of units changes only the temperature independent term, which disappears on differentiation.

Exercises

2.A   Twenty gram of ice at a temperature of $-2°C$ is dropped into a calorimeter containing 100 gram of water at 25°C. The water equivalent of the calorimeter is 18 gram and the final temperature of the bath, corrected for heat losses, is 9·7°C. Find the specific heat of ice.

2.B   Steam at 100°C is blown into a swimming bath of dimensions 80 ft × 30 ft × 5 ft to raise the temperature of the water from 15°C to 20°C. Find the weight of steam required. (Latent heat of steam = 960 B.Th.U. lb^{-1}, 1 B.Th.U. = heat required to raise 1 lb of water 1°F, 1 cu ft of water weighs 62·5 lb.)

2.C   Assuming no heat is lost to the surroundings, calculate the amount of heat required to just melt 1,000 gram of lead initially at 15°C.

2.D   Fifty gram of steam at 100°C are passed into an adiabatic calorimeter containing 200 gram of ice and 100 gram of water at 0°C. Find the final temperature of the water. (Use data given in 2.B.)

2.E   A bath of pure molten aluminium is cooled towards its melting point of 659°C at a constant rate of $5·0°C\ min^{-1}$. Assuming that the rate of heat loss from the bath remains constant and that equilibrium is maintained throughout the solidification process, calculate the time for isothermal solidification of the bath and the cooling rate immediately after solidification.

2.F   A skater weighing 120 lb glides in a straight line on one skate, decelerating uniformly to rest in 20 yd from a speed of 10 m.p.h. on ice at $-5°C$. If the width of her skate is 5 mm, what is the maximum depth of groove in the ice that she could leave behind her? The specific heat and density of ice are 0·5 cal $deg^{-1}\ g^{-1}$ and 0·917 g cc^{-1} respectively.

2.G   An aircraft is fitted with an auxiliary ramjet engine of 2,000 cm^2 cross-section which is ignited at an air speed of 400 m.p.h. at an altitude of 6,500 ft. At this altitude the air density is 1,000 g m^{-3} and its pressure 0·82 atm and temperature 0°C. Purified kerosine fuel is burnt in the ramjet, being supplied at 3·11 litre sec^{-1} which is just sufficient to combine completely with the oxygen of the air. The kerosine is of analysis 86·4 per cent C and 13·6 per cent H_2 by weight, of density 0·79 g cc^{-1}, and has a heat of combustion of 11·14 kcal g^{-1}. If the weight of the aircraft is 2,000 kg and 5 per cent of the theoretical thrust is available to drive it forward, calculate the instantaneous acceleration of the aircraft in level flight when the ramjet is fired. It should be assumed that the exhaust gases behave ideally and that the error arising from the use of C_p rather than C_v data is negligible.

2.H   The mean value of the coefficient of cubical expansion (α) of liquid mercury in the temperature range 0–100°C is $18 \cdot 1 \times 10^{-5}$ deg^{-1} and the coefficient of isothermal compressibility (β) is 45×10^{-6} atm^{-1}. If the density of mercury is $13 \cdot 35$ g cc^{-1}, calculate the difference in its molar heat capacities at constant pressure and constant volume.

2.I   The latent heat of vaporization of zinc is $27 \cdot 3$ kcal mole^{-1} at the boiling point, 907°C. Find the vapour pressure over pure zinc at 850°C.

2.J   Calculate the approximate pressure required to distil mercury at 100°C if the latent heat of vaporization is $14 \cdot 14$ kcal mole^{-1} at the boiling point 357°C.

2.K   A drop calorimeter employs boiling liquid nitrogen as the calorimetric fluid, values of the integrated heat capacity of a metal sample dropped into the calorimeter from various temperatures being calculated from the extra volume of nitrogen gas boiled off. If this boil-off is to be metered by a simple U-tube type of manometric flow-meter, calculate the approximate correction (per mm Hg) which must be applied to the integrated heat capacity calculation to take into account the necessary pressure drop across this flowmeter. The latent heat of vaporization of nitrogen is $1 \cdot 33$ kcal mole^{-1} at the boiling point of $77 \cdot 6$°K (760 mm pressure) and the specific volume difference between liquid and gaseous nitrogen is $6 \cdot 39$ litre mole^{-1} at that temperature.

2.L   Given the following data, calculate the heat of reaction when solid magnesium is dissolved in a solution consisting of HCl (100 H$_2$O)

$$Mg_{(s)} + 2HCl_{(g)} = MgCl_{2(s)} + H_{2(g)}; \quad \Delta H = -109 \cdot 4 \text{ kcal}$$
$$HCl_{(g)} + 100H_2O = HCl(100H_2O); \quad \Delta H = -17 \cdot 4 \text{ kcal}$$
$$MgCl_{2(s)} + 200H_2O = MgCl_2(200H_2O); \quad \Delta H = -35 \cdot 5 \text{ kcal}.$$

2.M   Calculate the heat of formation of Fe$_2$O$_3$ at 298°K, given that the heat of reaction of Fe$_2$O$_3$ with carbon monoxide to form solid iron and carbon dioxide is $-6 \cdot 65$ kcal mole^{-1} of Fe$_2$O$_3$.

2.N   Given the following data, calculate the standard heat of formation of solid aluminium carbide (Al_4C_3), and the limits of error in this value.

Heat of formation of: $CO_{(g)} = -26\cdot40 \pm 0\cdot03$ kcal mole^{-1}

$CO_{2\,g)} = -94\cdot05 \pm 0\cdot01$ kcal mole^{-1}

$Al_2O_{3\,s)} = -400\cdot0 \pm 1\cdot5$ kcal mole^{-1}.

The heat of reaction between 1 mole of Al_4C_3 and 9 mole of CO_2 to produce alumina and carbon monoxide at 25°C is $-223\cdot7 \pm 11\cdot7$ kcal.

2.O   Calculate the heat of formation of ferrous oxide (FeO) from pure iron and oxygen gas at 1,390°C, making use of the calculation given in example 2.6.

2.P   Calculate the heat of formation of calcium oxide (CaO) at 1,000°C from the appropriate enthalpy and heat capacity data of appendix 3.

2.Q   If a mass of ferrous oxide is heated to 1,000°C and then exposed to a gas mixture of carbon monoxide and hydrogen in suitable proportions, the oxide can be reduced to the metal without any further heat supply (i.e. the process is autogenous or thermally self-supporting). Find the optimum ratio p_{CO}/p_{H_2} (where $p_{CO}+p_{H_2} = 1$) for the inlet gas in order to achieve this condition, assuming a heat loss from the charge to the surroundings of 5,000 cal per lb of oxide reduced.

2.R   Regenerated producer gas of composition 5 per cent CO_2, 25 per cent CO, 2 per cent H_2O, 14 per cent H_2, and 54 per cent N_2 by volume is fed into a furnace at 700°C. It is desired to heat up the furnace as rapidly as possible, but the maximum flame temperature must not exceed 1,600°C or the furnace refractories would soften. What is the minimum volume of air to be fed into the furnace with each 1,000 cu ft of producer gas to achieve this? (For the purposes of this calculation, the heat capacities of the gases should be assumed to be linear functions of temperature: i.e. the terms in T^{-2} should be ignored.)

2.S   During the grinding of steels, sparks are generated as a result of particles of molten iron, ejected at high speed, combining with the oxygen of the air to form molten FeO. Assuming that the grinding action raises the temperature of the iron particles to 1,600°C, and using the relations obtained in example 2.6, what is the maximum temperature attainable in the spark in air at 25°C? What assumptions are made concerning the data used in this calculation?

2.т The most commonly used Thermit or exothermic material for fusion welding is a finely divided mixture of aluminium and iron oxide (Fe_3O_4) in the ratio $1:3\cdot2$ respectively which, after initiation, reacts to give 66,300 B.Th.U. for every lb of aluminium used. In preparing a melt or pouring on to a butted steel joint, it is found that a 60-lb charge of the mixture in the above proportions would reach a maximum temperature of 2,600°C in the reaction crucible. As this temperature is too high for pouring, pieces of steel scrap are mixed with the charge at room temperature (25°C), before the initiation of the reaction, to give a maximum temperature of 2,400°C. Assuming that heat losses from the charge and the heat capacity of the crucible are independent of temperature in the temperature range 2,000–3,000°C, calculate the approximate weight of steel scrap to be added to the charge. The heat capacity and heats of transformation of the steel may be taken as equal to those for pure iron.

CHAPTER 3

Entropy and Free Energy

Calculations of the entropies or free energies of substances or reactions from heat capacity data follow similar lines to the calculations of enthalpy detailed in the last chapter. For example, equations *1.26* for Entropy and *1.37* for Gibbs Free Energy correspond roughly to equation *1.20* used previously. The solution of these equations may be obtained in a manner similar to the two methods used previously to solve the enthalpy equations, either treating the integrals as indefinite and solving for the integration constants, or as definite integrals between temperature limits. As before, both methods require knowledge of the appropriate values at one of the limits.

As the third law of thermodynamics proposes that the entropy of all substances in complete internal equilibrium is zero at 0°K, the 'standard' entropies of elements at 298°K are non-zero. In calculations involving standard entropies of reactions, these non-zero values for the elements must be substituted together with those for compounds.

3.1 *Determine the standard free-energy change for the oxidation of methane by water vapour to form carbon monoxide at 25°C.*

This is an illustration of the extension of the principle outlined in example 2.1 (Hess's law) to the calculation of the free-energy change. The reaction may be written as:

$$CH_{4(g)} + H_2O_{(g)} \rightleftharpoons CO_{(g)} + 3H_{2(g)}$$

for which the following data are required:

	ΔH^0_{298} kcal mole^{-1}	S^0_{298} cal deg^{-1} mole^{-1}
$CH_{4(g)}$	$-17 \cdot 89$	$44 \cdot 5$
$CO_{(g)}$	$-26 \cdot 40$	$47 \cdot 3$
$H_{2(g)}$	0	$31 \cdot 2$
$H_2O_{(g)}$	$-57 \cdot 80$	$45 \cdot 1$

From the defining relation *1.31*:

$$\Delta G^0 = \Delta H^0 - T\Delta S^0$$

ΔG^0 can be obtained from knowledge of ΔH^0 and ΔS^0. Expressing ΔH^0 for the reaction in similar form to that in problem 2.1:

$$\Delta H^0 = (\Delta H^0_{CO} + 3\Delta H^0_{H_2}) - (\Delta H^0_{CH_4} + \Delta H^0_{H_2O})$$

$$= (-26 \cdot 40) + (0) - (-17 \cdot 89) - (-57 \cdot 80)$$

$$= +49 \cdot 29 \text{ kcal mole}^{-1} \text{ or } 49,290 \text{ cal mole}^{-1}.$$

Similarly:

$$\Delta S^0 = (S^0_{CO} + 3S^0_{H_2}) - (S^0_{CH_4} + S^0_{H_2O})$$

$$= (47 \cdot 3) + (3 \times 31 \cdot 2) - (44 \cdot 5) - (45 \cdot 1)$$

$$= 51 \cdot 3 \text{ cal deg}^{-1} \text{ mole}^{-1}.$$

Hence:

$$\Delta G^0_{298} = +49,290 - 51 \cdot 3T$$

$$= +49,290 - 15,280$$

$$= +34,000 \text{ cal mole}^{-1}.$$

The value of the standard free-energy change for the reaction at 298°K is positive. As any 'going' process is always accompanied by a decrease in free energy (equation *1.38*), this value suggests that methane will not be oxidized by water vapour at 298°K, but rather that carbon monoxide and hydrogen will react to give methane and water vapour, i.e. the reaction as written will go from right-to-left.* However, it should be noted that as both ΔH^0 and ΔS^0 for the reaction are positive at 298°K then, if these values do not change much with temperature, $\Delta G^0 (= \Delta H^0 - T\Delta S^0)$ will become negative at sufficiently high temperatures. For example, on the basis of ΔH^0 and ΔS^0 being temperature independent, ΔG^0 becomes zero at 961°K, and at higher temperatures the reaction will proceed spontaneously from left to right. In fact the values of both ΔH^0 and ΔS^0 are temperature dependent, and the accurate evaluation of the minimum temperature of this reaction involves the determination of ΔG^0 as a function of temperature. Such determinations are involved in some of the following examples, and evaluations of minimum reaction temperatures are illustrated in chapter 4.

---

* It will be recalled that ΔG^0 is the free-energy change when all the components are in their standard states (equation *1.56*). Thus, the sign of ΔG^0 is not an infallible indication of the direction of a reaction in practice, for one or more of the components of the reaction may not be in its standard state. In an all-gas reaction such as that presently considered, any deductions from calculated values of ΔG^0 must necessarily involve the proviso that the gases are present in the system in their standard states, i.e. at one atmosphere pressure.

3.2   *The freezing point for pure copper is generally accepted as 1,083°C, but small droplets of liquid copper have been supercooled to 847°C before spontaneous solidification occurs. Calculate the entropy change for the isothermal solidification of copper at the latter temperature.*

At the true melting point (1,083°C) the entropy difference between the solid and liquid forms of copper is equal to the entropy of fusion (S_f). That is, for the reaction:

$$Cu_{(l)} \rightleftharpoons Cu_{(s)} \qquad\qquad 3.2.1$$

$$\Delta S^0_{(l\to s)} = -S_f \text{ at } 1,356°K.$$

The latent heat of fusion of copper is 3,100 cal mole^{-1}, and therefore, from *1.27*:

$$\Delta S^0_{1,356} = -\frac{(3,100)}{1,356} = -2\cdot28 \text{ cal deg}^{-1} \text{ mole}^{-1}.$$

The heat capacities of solid and liquid copper are:

$$C_{pCu(l)} = 7\cdot50 \text{ cal deg}^{-1} \text{ mole}^{-1}$$

$$C_{pCu(s)} = 5\cdot41 + 1\cdot50 \times 10^{-3}\,T \text{ cal deg}^{-1} \text{ mole}^{-1}.$$

Hence:

$$\Delta C_{p(3.2.1)} = -2\cdot09 + 1\cdot50 \times 10^{-3}\,T \text{ cal deg}^{-1} \text{ mole}^{-1}$$

and the change in the entropy of the reaction between 1,083°C (1,356°K) and 847°C (1,120°K) is given, following equation *1.26*, by:

$$\Delta S^0_{1,120} - \Delta S^0_{1,356} = \int\limits_{1,356}^{1,120} \frac{\Delta C_p}{T}.dT$$

$$= [-2\cdot09 \ln T + 1\cdot5 \times 10^{-3}\,T]^{1,120}_{1,356}$$

$$= -2\cdot09 \ln\frac{1,120}{1,356} + 1\cdot5 \times 10^{-3}(1,120 - 1,356)$$

$$= +0\cdot046 \text{ cal deg}^{-1} \text{ mole}^{-1}.$$

Therefore:

$$\Delta S^0_{1,120} = -2\cdot28 + 0\cdot046$$

$$= -2\cdot23 \text{ cal deg}^{-1} \text{ mole}^{-1}.$$

3.3 *Using the data given in the previous problem, determine the Gibbs free-energy change for the reaction* $Cu_{(l)} = Cu_{(s)}$ *at the temperature of spontaneous solidification, 847°C.*

This problem is most readily solved by application of the indefinite integral form of the Gibbs–Helmholtz relation, equation 1.35, applied to the reaction in question. That is:

$$\frac{\Delta G_T^0}{T} = -\int \frac{\Delta H^0}{T^2}.dT$$

or:

$$\Delta G_T^0 = -T \int \left[\frac{\Delta H_0}{T^2} + \frac{1}{T^2}\int \Delta C_p\,dT\right]dT.$$

Substituting the ΔC_p relation for reaction 3.2.1:

$$\Delta G_T^0 = -T\int\left[\frac{\Delta H_0}{T^2}+\frac{1}{T^2}\int(-2\cdot09+1\cdot5\times10^{-3}\,T)\,dT\right]dT$$

$$= -T\int\left[\frac{\Delta H_0}{T^2}-\frac{2\cdot09}{T}+0\cdot75\times10^{-3}\right]dT$$

$$= \Delta H_0+2\cdot09T\ln T-0\cdot75\times10^{-3}\,T^2+IT \qquad 3.3.1$$

where ΔH_0 and I are integration constants, the former arising from the integration of the Kirchhoff equation and the latter from the integration of the expression for ΔH^0. These are determined, as detailed in chapter 1, from a knowledge either of ΔG^0 at two temperatures or of ΔG^0 and ΔH^0 at one temperature. The latter information is presently available for reaction 3.2.1, for at the equilibrium melting point (1,083°C or 1,356°K):

$$\Delta H^0 = -L_f = -3,100 \text{ cal}$$

and:

$$\Delta G^0 = 0 \text{ (from } 1.38).$$

Hence:

$$\Delta H_{1,356}^0 = -3,100 = \Delta H_0+\int(-2\cdot09+1\cdot50\times10^{-3}\,T)\,dT$$

$$= \Delta H_0-2\cdot09\times1,356+0\cdot75\times10^{-3}(1,356)^2$$

and:

$$\Delta H_0 = -1,650.$$

Substituting this value in 3.3.1:

$$\Delta G_T^0 = -1,650+2\cdot09T\ln T-0\cdot75\times10^{-3}\,T^2+IT \text{ cal mole}^{-1}.$$

But $\Delta G^0_{1,356} = 0$. Therefore, substituting $T = 1,356°K$ and equating to zero yields:

$$I = -12·85.$$

Hence:

$$\Delta G^0_T = -1,650 + 2·09T \ln T - 0·75 \times 10^{-3} T^2 - 12·85T \text{ cal mole}^{-1}$$

and the required free-energy change at $847°C$ $(1,120°K)$ is:

$$\Delta G^0_{1,120} = -540 \text{ cal mole}^{-1}.$$

This calculation of the free-energy difference between two coexisting phases of a pure component from data for the latent heat of the transformation is used again in chapter 7, where it is applied to the derivation of thermodynamic data from constitutional phase diagrams (cf. examples 7.5 and 7.7).

Alternatively, $\Delta H^0_{1,120°K}$ can be determined in the manner described in example 2.4 and $\Delta G^0_{1,120°K}$ is then obtained by inserting this value and that for $\Delta S^0_{1,120°K}$, determined in the previous example, in equation 1.31. The procedure is demonstrated in the following example.

3.4   *Evaluate the entropy and Gibbs free-energy change at* $1,350°C$ *for the formation of ferrous oxide from pure iron and oxygen gas at* 1 *atmosphere pressure* (cf. *example 2.6*).

The reaction at $298°K$ is:

$$\text{Fe}_{(\alpha)} + \tfrac{1}{2}\text{O}_{2(g)} \rightleftharpoons \text{FeO}_{(s)}. \qquad \textit{3.4.1}$$

The standard entropies of the components are:

	S^0_{298}, cal deg^{-1} mole^{-1}
$\text{Fe}_{(\alpha)}$	6·49
$\text{FeO}_{(s)}$	14·05
$\text{O}_{2(g)}$	49·02

Hence, at $298°K$, the entropy change for reaction *3.4.1* is:

$$\Delta S^0_{298} = S^0_{\text{FeO}(s)} - S^0_{\text{Fe}(\alpha)} - \tfrac{1}{2}S^0_{\text{O}_2(g)}$$

$$= -16·95 \text{ cal deg}^{-1}.$$

At temperatures up to $760°C$ $(1,033°K)$, the Curie temperature for iron, the value of ΔC_p for reaction *3.4.1*, given in example 2.6, is:

$$\Delta C_p = 3·90 - 4·42 \times 10^{-3}T - 0·47 \times 10^5 T^{-2}.$$

Substituting this in equation *1.26*, the entropy change over the temperature interval 298 to $1,033°K$ is given by:

$$\Delta S^0_{1,033} - \Delta S^0_{298} = \int_{298}^{1,033} \frac{\Delta C_p}{T}. \, \mathrm{d}T$$

$$= \int_{298}^{1,033} [3 \cdot 90 T^{-1} - 4 \cdot 42 \times 10^{-3} - 0 \cdot 47 \times 10^5 \, T^{-3}] \, \mathrm{d}T$$

$$= 4 \cdot 85 - 3 \cdot 25 - 0 \cdot 25.$$

Therefore:

$$\Delta S^0_{1,033} + 16 \cdot 95 = 1 \cdot 35$$

or:

$$\Delta S^0_{1,033} = -15 \cdot 60 \text{ cal deg}^{-1}.$$

At $1,033°K$ the ferro- to para-magnetic change can be regarded as being accompanied by a latent heat of transformation of $+660$ cal mole^{-1} (cf. example 2.6, p. 32). Thus, for the reaction:

$$\text{Fe}_{(\alpha, \text{ ferro-magnetic})} \rightleftharpoons \text{Fe}_{(\alpha, \text{ para-magnetic})} \qquad 3.4.2$$

at $1,033°K$ the entropy change is:

$$\Delta S^0 = \frac{660}{1,033} = 0 \cdot 64 \text{ cal deg}^{-1} \text{ mole}^{-1}.$$

Applying Hess's law to the entropy changes for reactions *3.4.1* and *3.4.2*, for the reaction:

$$\text{Fe}_{(\alpha, \text{ para-magnetic})} + \tfrac{1}{2}\text{O}_{2(g)} \rightleftharpoons \text{FeO}_{(s)} \qquad 3.4.3$$

the entropy change at $1,033°K$ is:

$$\Delta S^0_{1,033} = \Delta S^0_{(3.4.1)} - \Delta S^0_{(3.4.2)}$$

$$= -15 \cdot 60 - 0 \cdot 64$$

$$= -16 \cdot 24 \text{ cal deg}^{-1}.$$

Reaction *3.4.3* applies up to $910°C$ ($1,183°K$), at which temperature the reaction:

$$\text{Fe}_{(\alpha, \text{ para-magnetic})} \rightleftharpoons \text{Fe}_{(\gamma)} \qquad 3.4.4$$

occurs, with a latent heat of transformation of $+220$ cal mole^{-1}, or an entropy of transformation of $220/1,183 = 0 \cdot 19$ cal deg^{-1} mole^{-1}. The entropy change for reaction *3.4.3* at this temperature is obtained by substituting ΔC_p for this reaction, from example 2.6:

$$\Delta C_p = -0 \cdot 92 + 1 \cdot 50 \times 10^{-3} \, T - 0 \cdot 47 \times 10^5 \, T^{-2}$$

5

into equation *1.26* and determining the entropy increment in the temperature range 1,033 to 1,183°K, i.e.:

$$\Delta S^0_{1,183} - \Delta S^0_{1,033} = -0.92 \ln \frac{1,183}{1,033} + 1.5 \times 10^{-3}(1,183 - 1,033)$$

$$+ 0.24 \times 10^5 \times \left(\frac{1}{(1,183)^2} - \frac{1}{(1,033)^2} \right).$$

Therefore:

$$\Delta S^0_{1,183} + 16.24 = 0.10$$

or:

$$\Delta S^0_{1,183} = -16.14 \text{ cal deg}^{-1}.$$

Applying Hess's law to reactions *3.4.3* and *3.4.4* at 1,183°K, for the reaction:

$$\mathrm{Fe}_{(\gamma)} + \tfrac{1}{2}\mathrm{O}_{2(g)} \rightleftharpoons \mathrm{FeO}_{(s)} \qquad\qquad 3.4.5$$

the entropy change is:

$$\Delta S^0_{1,183} = \Delta S^0_{(3.4.3)} - \Delta S^0_{(3.4.4)}$$

$$= -16.14 - 0.19$$

$$= -16.33 \text{ cal deg}^{-1}.$$

For this reaction (from example 2.6):

$$\Delta C_p = 6.24 - 3.16 \times 10^{-3}T - 0.47 \times 10^5 T^{-2}$$

which applies up to 1,378°C (1,651°K), the melting point of FeO. Hence the entropy change at 1,623°K, the temperature for which the answer is required, is:

$$\Delta S^0_{1,623} = \Delta S^0_{1,183} + 6.24 \ln \frac{1,623}{1,183} - 3.16 \times 10^{-3}(1,623 - 1,183)$$

$$+ 0.24 \times 10^5 \times \left(\frac{1}{(1,623)^2} - \frac{1}{(1,183)^2} \right)$$

$$= -16.33 + 0.57$$

$$= -15.76 \text{ cal deg}^{-1}.$$

Alternatively, the integrated heat capacity equations could be solved as indefinite integrals, the integration constants being found by substitution of the known values of entropy at known temperatures, as (for enthalpy) in example 2.6. The two procedures, as emphasized previously, are equivalent and yield the same answer.

The Gibbs free-energy change for the formation of ferrous oxide at $1,350°C$ is calculated from the value of the entropy of formation and the enthalpy of formation at the same temperature. That is:

$$\Delta G^0_{1,623} = \Delta H^0_{1,623} - 1,623\Delta S^0_{1,623}.$$

Substituting the value of ΔH^0 (from example 2.6) and the value of ΔS^0 just calculated:

$$\Delta G^0_{1,623} = -62,600 - (1,623 \times -15·76)$$

$$= -37,000 \text{ cal mole}^{-1} \text{ of FeO.}$$

Alternatively, the Gibbs free-energy change can be evaluated by the use of the Gibbs–Helmholtz relation *1.34* as in example 3.3. That is, the variation of enthalpy with temperature, calculated in example 2.6, may be substituted in the integral form *1.35*, the resulting integration constants being found by substitution of the known enthalpy and free-energy data at one temperature in each temperature range. The solution by this method is illustrated again in the next example.

3.5 *At 882°C, titanium transforms from the low-temperature hexagonal, close-packed (α) form to a body-centred cubic (β) structure. Calculate the hypothetical melting point of the α form of titanium.*

This type of calculation can be made for any substance which has more than one allotropic form and for which adequate data exist. The accuracy of the answer depends very largely on the magnitude of the temperature extrapolation which is made in the calculation (i.e. the difference between the temperatures of the allotropic transformation and the hypothetical melting point).

The principle used is simple. Because the free energy is a function only of the state of a system, its variation in any process is independent of the path of the process. Thus the free-energy change accompanying the change from α to liquid titanium can be written as:

$$\Delta G^0_{(\alpha \to l)} = \Delta G^0_{(\alpha \to \beta)} + \Delta G^0_{(\beta \to l)}$$

which is equal to zero at the hypothetical equilibrium melting point of α titanium. The problem is to find the temperature at which:

$$\Delta G^0_{(\alpha \to \beta)} = -\Delta G^0_{(\beta \to l)} = \Delta G^0_{(l \to \beta)} \qquad 3.5.1$$

by expressing both ΔG^0 terms as functions of temperature.

The reaction:

$$\text{Ti}_{(\alpha)} \rightleftharpoons \text{Ti}_{(\beta)} \qquad 3.5.2$$

occurs normally at 882°C (1,155°K) with a latent heat of transformation of 830 cal mole^{-1}. The heat capacities of the two allotropes are:

$$C_{p\,(Ti,\,\alpha)} = 5\cdot28 + 2\cdot4 \times 10^{-3}\,T \text{ cal deg}^{-1} \text{ mole}^{-1}$$

$$C_{p\,(Ti,\,\beta)} = 6\cdot91 \text{ cal deg}^{-1} \text{ mole}^{-1}.$$

Therefore, for the reaction *3.5.2*:

$$\Delta C_p = 1\cdot63 - 2\cdot4 \times 10^{-3}\,T \text{ cal deg}^{-1} \text{ mole}^{-1}.$$

Substituting this in *1.36*, the free-energy change for *3.5.2* is:

$$\Delta G_T^0 = -T \int \left[\frac{\Delta H_0}{T^2} + \frac{1}{T^2} \int (1\cdot63 - 2\cdot4 \times 10^{-3}\,T)\,\mathrm{d}T \right] \mathrm{d}T$$

$$= -T \int \left[\frac{\Delta H_0}{T^2} + \frac{1\cdot63}{T} - 1\cdot2 \times 10^{-3} \right] \mathrm{d}T$$

$$= \Delta H_0 - 1\cdot63\,T\ln T + 1\cdot2 \times 10^{-3}\,T^2 + IT$$

where ΔH_0 and I are integration constants which are obtained as follows.

As $\Delta H_{1,155}^0$ for reaction *3.5.2* is 830 cal mole^{-1} and

$$\Delta H^0 = \Delta H_0 + \int \Delta C_p.\,\mathrm{d}T,$$

therefore:

$$830 = \Delta H_0 + (1\cdot63 \times 1,155) - 1\cdot2 \times (1,155)^2 \times 10^{-3}$$

or:

$$\Delta H_0 = 548$$

and:

$$\Delta G_T^0 = 548 - 1\cdot63\,T\ln T + 1\cdot2 \times 10^{-3}\,T^2 + IT.$$

But $\Delta G^0 = 0$ at the equilibrium transformation temperature of 1,155°K. Therefore:

$$I = 9\cdot65$$

and:

$$\Delta G_{(\alpha \to \beta)}^0 = 548 - 1\cdot63\,T\ln T + 1\cdot2 \times 10^{-3}\,T^2 + 9\cdot65\,T \text{ cal mole}^{-1}.$$

For the reaction:

$$Ti_{(\beta)} \rightleftharpoons Ti_{(l)} \qquad\qquad 3.5.3$$

the latent heat of fusion is 4,500 cal mole^{-1} at 1,660°C (1,933°K), and the heat capacity of liquid titanium, $C_{p\,(Ti,\,l)} = 8\cdot00$ cal deg^{-1} mole^{-1}.

The change in the heat capacity for reaction *3.5.3* is:

$$\Delta C_p = 1\cdot09 \text{ cal deg}^{-1} \text{ mole}^{-1}$$

and:

$$\Delta G_T^0 = -T \int \left[\frac{\Delta H_0}{T^2} + \frac{1}{T^2} \int 1 \cdot 09 \, \mathrm{d}T \right] \mathrm{d}T$$
$$= \Delta H_0 - 1 \cdot 09 T \ln T + IT.$$

Solving for the integration constants in a similar manner to before:

$$\Delta H_0 = 4{,}500 - (1 \cdot 09 \times 1{,}933) = 2{,}400$$

$$I = \frac{-2{,}400 + 1 \cdot 09 \times 1{,}933 \times 7 \cdot 57}{1{,}933} = 7 \cdot 01.$$

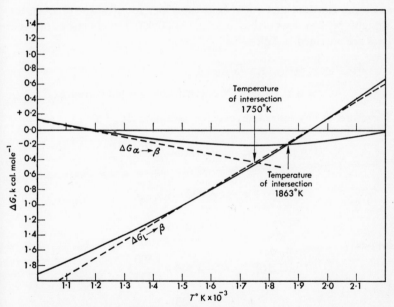

Fig. 3.5a. Determination of hypothetical melting point of α-titanium.

Therefore:

$$\Delta G_{(\beta \to \mathrm{l})}^0 = 2{,}400 - 1 \cdot 09 T \ln T + 7 \cdot 01 T \text{ cal mole}^{-1}$$

or:

$$\Delta G_{(\mathrm{l} \to \beta)}^0 = -2{,}400 + 1 \cdot 09 T \ln T - 7 \cdot 01 T \text{ cal mole}^{-1}.$$

Equation 3.5.1 is applicable at the hypothetical melting point of α-titanium. The temperature at which the two free-energy values, $\Delta G_{(\alpha \to \beta)}^0$ and $\Delta G_{(\mathrm{l} \to \beta)}^0$ are equal is best found graphically. Plots of the two free-energy functions are shown in Fig. 3.5a, from which the temperature of intersection of the two curves is read-off as $1,863°K$ or $1,590\,(\pm7)°C$, the hypothetical melting point of α-titanium. However, although the thermodynamic treatment is perfectly valid, the hypothetical melting point may be grossly in error, for it is apparent from the graph that the values for $\Delta G^0_{(\alpha\to\beta)}$ for $T>1,400°K$ are very much in doubt. This error arises from the extrapolation of the C_p data for the α-phase to higher temperatures than those to which the empirical relation is applicable, and also probably from the assumed linear temperature dependence of the C_p relations for $Ti_{(\beta)}$ and $Ti_{(l)}$.

If the enthalpies and entropies of transformation and fusion are assumed to be independent of temperature (which corresponds to assuming constant and equal heat capacities for all three phases), the straight, broken lines of Fig. 3.5a are obtained. The equations of these lines are obtained as follows:

$$\Delta G^0_{(\alpha\to\beta)} = \Delta H^0_{(\alpha\to\beta)} - T\Delta S^0_{(\alpha\to\beta)}$$

$$= 0 \text{ at } 1,155°K, \text{ the transformation temperature } (T_t).$$

Therefore, at any other temperature, assuming $\Delta C_p = 0$:

$$\Delta G^0_{(\alpha\to\beta)} = \Delta H_t - \frac{T\Delta H_t}{T_t}$$

$$= 830 - \frac{T\times830}{1,155}$$

$$= 830 - 0{\cdot}719T.$$

Similarly:

$$\Delta G^0_{(l\to\beta)} = -4,500 + \frac{4,500}{1,933}T$$

$$= -4,500 + 2{\cdot}33T.$$

The intersection of these lines gives a value for the hypothetical melting point of α-titanium of $1,750°K$ or $1,477°C$. This value is probably more accurate, in this instance, than that calculated using the C_p data. This situation is unusual, however, and arises from the large extrapolation of the latter. Generally, the assumption of non-temperature-dependent enthalpies and entropies of reaction leads to a less accurate value than that obtained by taking into account their variations with temperature, but in some circumstances, as in the present case, the approximation can be justified. It is interesting to note that the value of $1,750°K$ obtained from the linear G/T relations is in excellent agreement with the estimate made by Kaufman [1] of 1,730 ($\pm$ 30)°K for the hypothetical melting point, based on free-energy calculations using the Debye theory of specific heats.

Exercises

3.A   Using the appropriate data given in appendix 3, calculate the enthalpy, entropy and free-energy changes at 1,000°K for the water–gas reaction:

$$C + H_2O \rightleftharpoons CO + H_2.$$

3.B   Assuming that values of the standard entropies of formation of the components are not available, recalculate the free-energy change in the previous example, given that the free-energy change at 500°K is 15·2 kcal.

3.C   Derive relations for the variation of the free-energy change for the oxidation of aluminium with temperature applicable over the range 900–1,000°K which includes the melting point of the metal.

3.D   Given that the free energy of formation of ammonia from nitrogen and hydrogen is 8·35 and 13·95 kcal mole^{-1} at 500 and 700°C, respectively, calculate the standard heat of formation of ammonia at 298°K.

3.E   If the latent heat of vaporization of zinc is 27·3 kcal mole^{-1} at the boiling point 907°C, and using the data given in appendix 3, draw a graph of the variation of the entropy of zinc between 25 and 920°C.

3.F   On slow cooling, iron containing 0·01 weight-per cent carbon transforms at around 908°C from the high-temperature F.C.C. austenite phase to the B.C.C. ferrite phase. However, as is well known, rapid quenching of the austenite suppresses the transformation until at some lower temperature the austenite transforms by a shear mechanism to the phase known as martensite. The thermodynamics of this process are of obvious importance, one quantity which must be considered being the free-energy change for the suppressed austenite $\rightarrow$ ferrite transformation. Calculate this free-energy change as a function of temperature below the Curie temperature.

3.G   Pure solid manganese has four allotropes, designated α, β, γ and δ, stable in the temperature ranges as shown in appendix 3, Heat Capacity data. It has been found that the γ-phase cannot be completely retained by quenching to room temperature, but transforms, at least partially, to the low-temperature α-form. Calculate the theoretical transformation temperature $\gamma \rightarrow \alpha$, assuming that:

(a) the enthalpies and entropies of transformation are independent of temperature,
(b) the C_p data for the α- and γ-phases can be extrapolated to higher and lower temperatures respectively. (Use 5-figure logs.)

3.H   The following data are smoothed values of the temperature variation of the heat capacity for an ordered alloy of composition Cu_3Au on heating from 100°C to above the critical disordering temperature, 390°C. Calculate the approximate 'entropy of ordering' of this alloy as given by these data:

T °C	100	150	200	250	275	300	325	350
C_p cal deg^{-1} mole^{-1}	24·8	25·5	26·2	26·9	27·3	30·0	32·9	36·5

T °C	375	385	395	425	450	500	550
C_p cal deg^{-1} mole^{-1}	50·4	62·0	33·0	30·2	29·2	29·9	30·7

3.I   On heating, the metal thallium undergoes a phase transformation from a hexagonal to a body-centred cubic structure at 234°C. Calculate the entropy of fusion of hexagonal thallium at its hypothetical melting point, using the Cp data in appendix 3. (Use 5-figure logs.)

References

1. L. KAUFMAN, *Acta Met.*, 7, No. 8, 1958, p. 575.

CHAPTER 4

The Equilibrium Constant

Possibly the commonest application of the principles of chemical thermodynamics is to be found in consideration of systems in which all the components or phases are in complete thermodynamic equilibrium. The equilibrium composition of the phases of a heterogeneous system under a given set of prescribed conditions, or the effects of changes in the applied conditions on the equilibrium compositions, is readily calculable from a knowledge of certain simple thermodynamic data of the system. When, after reaction between the components or phases of a system, thermodynamic equilibrium is attained, the concentrations of the components or the compositions of the phases then present are related (irrespective of their initial concentrations) through the component fugacities or activities at equilibrium. This relation is inherent in the definition of the equilibrium constant for the reaction in terms of the standard free-energy change, equation *1.58*, for the latter is a function of temperature only and, being an intensive property, is independent of the amount of the reacting species present.

The thermodynamic approach can only yield information relating to the equilibrium condition, giving no indication of the rate of approach of the system towards equilibrium. As an illustration of this limitation, consider that in air at atmospheric pressure all the common metals should completely oxidize at room temperature. Their commercial use in metallic form is possible only because the equilibrium condition is approached at a very slow rate at this temperature.

Consideration of heterogeneous systems at equilibrium (i.e. systems comprising more than one phase) involves an important principle of thermodynamics, for the conditions for equilibrium will, in general, apply to the whole system, and not only to one phase thereof. For example, if a liquid or solid metal and its oxide are exposed to a gas containing oxygen, then at equilibrium the partial pressure of oxygen in equilibrium with the condensed phases must also equal that in equilibrium with the other components of the gas phase (cf. examples 4.5, 4.11, 4.12).

As shown in earlier chapters, often a reaction can be regarded as arising from a series of more elementary reactions. Thus, following Hess's law, the standard free-energy changes for the more elementary reactions may be manipulated to yield the value for the reaction of interest. From the logarithmic relation *1.58* between the standard free-energy change and the equilibrium constant, the value of the latter for such a reaction can be obtained by appropriate multiplication and division of the equilibrium constants for the elementary reactions, corresponding to the addition and subtraction of the standard free-energy changes for the latter (cf. example 4.11).

Although, to be thermodynamically precise, the equilibrium constant must be expressed in terms of the fugacities or activities of the components of the reaction at equilibrium, it can often be assumed that a gas behaves ideally when its pressure is not greater than 1 atmosphere and the temperature is well in excess of the boiling point of the gas. In such circumstances, the expression for the equilibrium constant can be simplified if the fugacity is replaced by the partial pressure of a gaseous component.* In addition, it is sometimes justifiable to assume that little or no reaction occurs between solid components in a system and, if these are present initially as pure elements or compounds, their activities may be taken as unity (i.e. the component is in its pure standard state). For example, in a gaseous oxidation reaction the metal and its oxide may appear at unit activity in the expression for the equilibrium constant for the reaction.

These principles are demonstrated in the following examples.

4.1   *Determine the lowest temperature at which copper oxide* (Cu_2O) *can dissociate in a vacuum of* 10^{-5} mm Hg.

There are several ways in which this example could be solved, all of which are essentially equivalent. The basic step in calculating the minimum temperature for a reaction to proceed is to determine the free-energy change for the reaction as a function of temperature. Under a particular set of conditions, the minimum temperature is that at which the free-energy change is related to the value of the equilibrium constant for the reaction (under the same conditions) by equation *1.58*:

$$\Delta G^0 = -RT \ln K_p.$$

The dissociation reaction:

$$Cu_2O_{(s)} \rightleftharpoons 2Cu_{(s)} + \tfrac{1}{2}O_{2(g)} \qquad\qquad 4.1.1$$

is accompanied by a standard free-energy change:

$$\Delta G^0 = 40,500 + 3 \cdot 92 T \log T - 29 \cdot 5 T \text{ cal.} \qquad 4.1.2$$

---

* Indeed, sometimes there is no alternative to this replacement, for the fugacity of the gas may be unknown.

For reaction *4.1.1*, equation *1.58* is expressed as:

$$\Delta G^0 = -RT \ln \frac{f_{O_2}^{1/2} \cdot a_{Cu}^2}{a_{Cu_2O}}$$

$$= -4 \cdot 575 T \log p_{O_2}^{1/2} \qquad \qquad 4.1.3$$

assuming that the Cu and Cu_2O are in the pure state (i.e. $a = 1$), and the oxygen behaves as an ideal gas (i.e. $f_{O_2} = p_{O_2}$).

In a vacuum of 10^{-5} mm Hg, taking the partial pressure of oxygen in air as 0·2 atmosphere:

$$p_{O_2} = 0 \cdot 2 \times 10^{-5} \times \frac{1}{760} = 2 \cdot 635 \times 10^{-9} \text{ atmosphere.}$$

(This, of course, ignores vacuum pump vapours, etc.) Therefore:

$$\Delta G^0 = -2 \cdot 288 T \log (2 \cdot 635 \times 10^{-9})$$

$$= +19 \cdot 6T. \qquad \qquad 4.1.4$$

The minimum temperature (T_d) for dissociation of Cu_2O is given by the equality of relations *4.1.2* and *4.1.4*. That is:

$$40,500 + 3 \cdot 92 T_d \log T_d - 29 \cdot 5 T_d = 19 \cdot 6 T_d$$

or:

$$3 \cdot 92 T_d \log T_d = 49 \cdot 1 T_d - 40,500$$

which is best solved graphically. Thus by plotting $(49 \cdot 1T - 40,500)$ and $(3 \cdot 92 T \log T)$ versus T, the minimum temperature of dissociation of Cu_2O is obtained as the intersection of the line and the (very slight) curve at $T = 1,085°K$, or $812(\pm 3)°C$.

This value can be checked by solving *4.1.3* for the value of p_{O_2} at this temperature. At $1,085°K$, ΔG^0 (from *4.1.2*) is $+21,400$ and hence, from *4.1.3*, p_{O_2} is $2 \cdot 38 \times 10^{-9}$ atmosphere. This is somewhat smaller than the value calculated earlier and it follows that the equilibrium temperature is too high by about 2°C, which is, however, within the error limits of the value determined graphically.

4.2 *In separate experiments, pure nitrogen at atmospheric pressure is passed over either mercury or a mercury–thallium amalgam (68·4 atom-per cent thallium). At temperatures less than 100°C the vapour pressure of thallium is negligible, relative to that of mercury. The flow rate of the nitrogen is controlled such that the gas is just saturated with mercury vapour as it passes over the pure mercury or the amalgam. The vapour carried over in the gas stream is condensed in a cold trap and weighed. In experiments with the samples at 26°C, the weights of mercury trapped from the pure mercury and the amalgam were respectively 2·20 and 0·75 mg per hundred litres of nitrogen, the nitrogen volume being measured at 20°C and 1 atmosphere pressure. Assuming that equilibrium is continuously maintained over the samples, calculate the partial pressure of mercury over the amalgam and the activity coefficient of mercury in the amalgam at 26°C.*

This example is concerned with the carrier-gas experiment, where the partial pressure of a volatile component over a solution is measured by sweeping away the vapour of the component, under equilibrium conditions, with an inert carrier gas and weighing the condensate. The activity of the volatile component in the solution is directly calculable from measurement of the partial pressures of the component over the solution and over the pure component. The reactions may be written as follows. For pure mercury:

$$Hg_{(pure,\ l)} \rightleftharpoons Hg_{(g\ in\ N_2)}$$

$$K_p = \left(\frac{f_{Hg}}{a_{Hg}}\right)_{(pure\ Hg)}$$

$$= p_{Hg\ (pure\ Hg)}$$

assuming that mercury vapour behaves as an ideal gas, and as $a_{Hg} = 1$ when referred to pure liquid mercury as the standard state. Over the amalgam:

$$Hg_{(l\ in\ amalgam)} \rightleftharpoons Hg_{(g\ in\ N_2)}$$

$$K_p = \left(\frac{p_{Hg}}{a_{Hg}}\right)_{(amalgam)}$$

again assuming that the mercury vapour behaves ideally.

Since the equilibrium constant K_p for a reaction in a system is independent of the initial composition of the system, it follows that:

$$a_{Hg\ (amalgam)} = \frac{p_{Hg\ (amalgam)}}{p_{Hg\ (pure\ Hg)}}. \qquad 4.2.1$$

(Note that this relation is equivalent to the definition of activity for the mercury through *1.53* and *1.54* if the fugacities in the latter are replaced by partial pressures.)

The volume of the nitrogen was measured at 20°C, whereas the experiment was performed at 26°C. This latter is the temperature for which the partial pressure must be calculated. Thus (assuming the nitrogen behaves ideally):

$$\text{Volume (of 100 litre at 20°C) at 26°C} = 100 \times \frac{299}{293} = 102 \text{ litre.}$$

When passed over the pure mercury, this volume of nitrogen contains 2·20 mg mercury. As 200·6 g of mercury (= gram atomic weight of Hg) occupies 22·4 litre volume at N.T.P., therefore:

$$2 \cdot 2 \text{ mg Hg occupies } \frac{22 \cdot 4}{200 \cdot 6} \times 2 \cdot 2 = 0 \cdot 239 \text{ cc at N.T.P.}$$

$$= 0 \cdot 239 \times \frac{299}{273} \text{ cc at } 26°C$$

$$= 0 \cdot 262 \text{ cc at } 26°C.$$

Thus, the partial pressure of Hg over pure mercury

$$= \frac{0 \cdot 262}{102,000} \times 760$$

$$= 19 \cdot 5 \times 10^{-4} \text{ mm Hg.}$$

When passed over the mercury-thallium amalgam, 102 litre of nitrogen contains 0·75 mg mercury, which occupies a volume of:

$$\frac{22 \cdot 4}{200 \cdot 6} \times 0 \cdot 75 \text{ cc} = 0 \cdot 082 \text{ cc at N.T.P.}$$

$$= 0 \cdot 089 \text{ cc at } 26°C.$$

Thus the partial pressure of Hg over the Hg–Tl amalgam

$$= \frac{0 \cdot 089}{102,000} \times 760$$

$$= 6 \cdot 65 \times 10^{-4} \text{ mm Hg.}$$

Therefore, from *4.2.1*:

$$a_{\text{Hg}} = \frac{p_{\text{Hg}}}{p°_{\text{Hg}}}$$

$$= \frac{6 \cdot 65 \times 10^{-4}}{19 \cdot 5 \times 10^{-4}}$$

$$= 0 \cdot 34$$

and, from *1.74*:

$$\gamma_{\text{Hg}} = \frac{a_{\text{Hg}}}{N_{\text{Hg}}} = \frac{0 \cdot 34}{0 \cdot 316}$$

$$= 1 \cdot 08.$$

The detailed calculations and corrections of the volume of the N_2 to the temperature of the experiment are unnecessary to calculate the activity of the mercury alone. For this value is given by the ratio of the weights of mercury carried over by equal volumes of carrier gas from the alloy and pure metal. Thus:

$$a_{Hg} = \frac{0 \cdot 75}{2 \cdot 20} = 0 \cdot 34 \text{ as calculated previously.}$$

4.3   *A methane–hydrogen mixture at 1 atmosphere pressure is allowed to come to equilibrium with a steel containing 0·60 weight-per cent carbon at 925°C. On analysis, the gas is found to contain 0·64 per cent methane and 99·36 per cent hydrogen by volume.*

Calculate the activity of carbon in the alloy and the expected analysis (by volume) of a carbon monoxide–carbon dioxide mixture which would be in equilibrium with the steel at the same temperature and pressure.

When data are available for the equilibrium condition for a reaction in a given system, it is often possible to determine the equilibrium condition for a similar reaction in a related system from knowledge of the equilibrium constants for the two reactions. This is a typical example of this principle. The activity of carbon in the alloy is determined by the hydrogen–methane gas composition and the equilibrium constant for the carburizing reaction. Using this value of the activity, the composition of a carbon monoxide–carbon dioxide gas mixture can be determined from knowledge of the equilibrium constant for the carburizing reaction with these gases. The determination of activity by partitioning between two liquid phases is a further example of this principle.

The standard free-energy change for the reaction:

$$C_{(s, \text{ graphite})} + 2H_{2(g)} \rightleftharpoons CH_{4(g)} \qquad 4.3.1$$

is given by:

$$\Delta G^0 = -21,600 + 26 \cdot 2T \text{ cal.}$$

Hence, from *1.58*:

$$4 \cdot 575 T \log K_p = +21,600 - 26 \cdot 2T$$

or, at 925°C (1,198°K):

$$K_p = 0 \cdot 0162.$$

The equilibrium constant for reaction *4.3.1* is given by:

$$K_p = \frac{f_{CH_4}}{f_{H_2}^2 \cdot a_C}$$

$$= \frac{p_{CH_4}}{p_{H_2}^2 \cdot a_C}$$

when the gases are assumed to behave ideally. Substituting the given gas composition in equilibrium with the steel:

$$K_p = 0.0162 = \frac{0.0064}{(0.9936)^2 . a_C}$$

or:

$$a_C = \frac{1}{0.0162} . \frac{0.0064}{(0.9936)^2}$$

$$= 0.40$$

i.e. the activity of the carbon in the steel, relative to graphite as the standard state, is 0.40.

The composition of the carbon monoxide–carbon dioxide atmosphere in equilibrium with carbon at this activity is obtained from the equilibrium constant for the reaction:

$$CO_{2(g)} + C_{(s, \, graphite)} \rightleftharpoons 2CO_{(g)}. \qquad 4.3.2$$

The standard free-energy change for this reaction is:

$$\Delta G^0 = +40,800 - 41.7T \text{ cal}$$

and hence, from *1.58*:

$$4.575T \log K_p = -40,800 + 41.7T$$

or, at 925°C (1,198°K):

$$K_p = 46.8.$$

The equilibrium constant for *4.3.2* is:

$$K_p = \frac{f_{CO}^2}{f_{CO_2} . a_C}$$

$$= \frac{p_{CO}^2}{p_{CO_2} . a_C}$$

assuming ideal behaviour of the gases. Substituting the calculated values for K_p and a_C:

$$\frac{p_{CO}^2}{p_{CO_2}} = 18.72$$

or, because $p_{CO} + p_{CO_2} = 1$:

$$p_{CO}^2 = 18.72(1 - p_{CO})$$

or:

$$p_{CO}^2 + 18.72 p_{CO} - 18.72 = 0$$

which is a quadratic in p_{CO}. Solving by the formula method:*

$$p_{CO} = \frac{-18\cdot72 \pm \sqrt{[(18\cdot72)^2 + (4 \times 18\cdot72)]}}{2}$$

$$= 0\cdot952 \text{ atmosphere}$$

and:

$$p_{CO_2} = 0\cdot048 \text{ atmosphere.}$$

That is, a gas comprising 95·2 per cent CO and 4·8 per cent CO_2 (by volume) at 1 atmosphere pressure is in equilibrium with the steel containing 0·60 weight-per cent carbon at 925°C.

4.4 *The stability of ammonia gas depends on pressure as well as on temperature. Show that this is so by calculating the extent of the dissociation of ammonia to form hydrogen and nitrogen at 200°C at 1·0 and 0·8 atmosphere total pressure.*

In general, the solution of a problem containing x unknown quantities requires knowledge of x independent simultaneous equations relating these unknowns. In the present examples one of these relations can be obtained from the equilibrium constant. A second relation may usually be derived from an imposed restriction of constant pressure or volume. Thus, in the previous example the values of the two unknowns, p_{CO} and p_{CO_2}, were obtained from knowledge of the value of the equilibrium constant and the imposed restriction that the total pressure ($p_{CO} + p_{CO_2}$) equalled 1 atmosphere. In the present instance there are three unknowns, p_{NH_3}, p_{H_2} and p_{N_2}, and three independent simultaneous equations are required. In addition to the two relations used previously, a third relation arises from the consideration that the mass is conserved within the system, i.e. the reaction occurs in a closed system, with no gain or loss of mass to the surroundings.†

The dissociation reaction is:

$$NH_{3(g)} \rightleftharpoons \tfrac{1}{2}N_{2(g)} + 1\tfrac{1}{2}H_{2(g)} \qquad\qquad 4.4.1$$

and the standard free-energy change is:

$$\Delta G^0 = 10,400 - 7\cdot1T\log T - 3\cdot79T \text{ cal.}$$

Thus, at 200°C (473°K):

$$\Delta G^0 = -380 \text{ cal.}$$

* See appendix 5.

† The derivation and manipulation of the simultaneous equations when four or more unknowns are involved are considered in example 4.10.

Now, from *1.58*:

$$\Delta G^0 = -RT \ln K_p$$

and hence, at 473°K, the equilibrium constant is given by:

$$K_p = \text{antilog}\left[\frac{+380}{4 \cdot 575 \times 473}\right]$$

$$= 1 \cdot 49_{(4)}.$$

But the equilibrium constant for reaction 4.4.1 is given by:

$$K_p = 1 \cdot 49_{(4)} = \frac{f_{H_2}^{3/2} \cdot f_{N_2}^{1/2}}{f_{NH_3}}$$

$$= \frac{p_{H_2}^{3/2} \cdot p_{N_2}^{1/2}}{p_{NH_3}} \qquad 4.4.2$$

if the gases are assumed to behave ideally.

The two additional relations between the partial pressures are obtained by consideration of the restrictions on the system. Thus, as the dissociation of ammonia always results in the formation of 3 mole of hydrogen to 1 of nitrogen, it follows that:

$$3p_{N_2} = p_{H_2}. \qquad 4.4.3$$

In addition, the total pressure is fixed at first $1 \cdot 0$ and then $0 \cdot 8$ atmosphere pressure; i.e. for 1 atmosphere pressure:

$$p_{N_2} + p_{H_2} + p_{NH_3} = 1. \qquad 4.4.4$$

Substituting first *4.4.4* and then *4.4.3* for p_{NH_3} and p_{N_2} respectively into *4.4.2* and rearranging:

$$0 \cdot 577 p_{H_2}^2 + 1 \cdot 992 p_{H_2} - 1 \cdot 494 = 0$$

or:

$$p_{H_2} + 3 \cdot 46 p_{H_2} - 2 \cdot 59 = 0.$$

Hence:

$$p_{H_2} = \frac{-3 \cdot 46 \pm \sqrt{[(3 \cdot 46)^2 + (4 \times 2 \cdot 59)]}}{2}$$

$$= \frac{-3 \cdot 46 + \sqrt{(1 \cdot 95 + 10 \cdot 36)}}{2}$$

$$= \frac{-3 \cdot 46 + \sqrt{(22 \cdot 31)}}{2}$$

$$= \frac{-3 \cdot 46 + 4 \cdot 72}{2} = 0 \cdot 63_{(4)}.$$

6

Substituting in *4.4.3* and *4.4.4*:

$$p_{N_2} = 0.21_{(1)}$$

$$p_{NH_3} = 0.15_{(5)}.$$

Hence at 1 atmosphere pressure, 84·5 per cent (by volume) of the ammonia will dissociate.

When the total pressure is 0·8 atmosphere:

$$p_{N_2} + p_{H_2} + p_{NH_3} = 0.8. \qquad\qquad 4.4.5$$

Substituting in a manner similar to that adopted previously and rearranging:

$$0.577p_{H_2}^2 + 1.992p_{H_2} - 1.195 = 0$$

or:

$$p_{H_2}^2 + 3.46p_{H_2} - 2.073 = 0.$$

Hence:

$$p_{H_2} = \frac{-3.46 \pm \sqrt{[(3.46)^2 + 8.292]}}{2}$$

$$= \frac{-3.46 + 4.51}{2} = 0.52_{(1)}$$

and from *4.4.3*: $\qquad\qquad p_{N_2} = 0.17_{(4)},$

from *4.4.5*: $\qquad\qquad p_{NH_3} = 0.10_{(5)}.$

Hence, at 0·8 atmosphere pressure, 86·4 per cent (by volume) of the ammonia will dissociate.

The effect of pressure on the degree of dissociation of ammonia follows the Le Chatelier principle. Consideration of *4.4.1*, in which 1 mole of ammonia dissociates to give 2 mole of nitrogen and hydrogen, would indicate that the degree of dissociation increases with decrease in total pressure. This has been calculated to be so.

4.5   *The equilibrium between carbon and its oxides is such that above about* 900°C *the formation of carbon dioxide is negligible at* 1 *atmosphere pressure. With this in mind, calculate the approximate minimum temperature for the reduction of pure manganese oxide by solid carbon to form pure manganese metal in a vacuum of* 10^{-3} *mm Hg. If the reduced metal enters into solution in iron and the minimum temperature of reduction is thereby lowered* 53°C, *calculate the activity of the manganese in solution in the iron.*

The product of the reaction between the metal oxide (MnO) and solid carbon is the metal (Mn), carbon monoxide and/or carbon dioxide.

That is:

$$MnO_{(s)} + C_{(s)} \rightleftharpoons Mn_{(s)} + CO_{(g)} \qquad 4.5.1$$

$$2MnO_{(s)} + C_{(s)} \rightleftharpoons Mn_{(s)} + CO_{2(g)}. \qquad 4.5.2$$

The partial pressures of CO and CO_2 at equilibrium with the metal and its oxide are related through a further reaction:

$$CO_2 + C \rightleftharpoons 2CO. \qquad 4.5.3$$

It is stated that the equilibrium partial pressure of CO_2 is negligible at temperatures above 900°C when the total pressure of the carbon gases is 1 atmosphere. According to the principle of Le Chatelier, the equilibrium in reaction *4.5.3* will be displaced to the right as the pressure is lowered. Hence in the present example, where the total pressure of the carbon gases is 10^{-3} mm Hg, the temperature above which p_{CO_2} is negligible will be significantly less than 900°C. As a first approximation, therefore, it is reasonable to assume that reaction *4.5.2* occurs to a negligible extent, and that the reduction is adequately represented by *4.5.1*. If the minimum temperature is determined at which the latter reaction can occur when $p_{CO} = 10^{-3}$ mm Hg, then substitution of this temperature and this value of p_{CO} in the equilibrium constant for *4.5.3* will indicate whether or not the assumption that p_{CO_2} is negligible is justified.*

The standard free-energy change for reaction *4.5.1* is obtained from data for the reactions:

$$MnO_{(s)} \rightleftharpoons Mn_{(s)} + \tfrac{1}{2}O_{2(g)} : \Delta G^0 = 91{,}950 - 17 \cdot 4T \text{ cal} \qquad 4.5.4$$

$$C_{(s)} + \tfrac{1}{2}O_{2(g)} \rightleftharpoons CO_{(g)} : \Delta G^0 = -26{,}700 - 20 \cdot 95T \text{ cal}. \qquad 4.5.5$$

Adding reactions *4.5.4* and *4.5.5* yields reaction *4.5.1*, for which, therefore:

$$\Delta G^0 = +65{,}250 - 38 \cdot 35T \text{ cal}.$$

The minimum temperature for reaction *4.5.1* to proceed will be that at which this expression equals $(-RT \ln K_p)$ for the reaction, where K_p is determined by the conditions prescribed (i.e. pure carbon, manganese and manganese oxide and carbon monoxide at 10^{-3} mm Hg pressure), i.e. when:

$$65{,}250 - 38 \cdot 35T = -4 \cdot 575T \log \frac{a_{Mn} \cdot f_{CO}}{a_{MnO} \cdot a_C} \qquad 4.5.6$$

$$= -4 \cdot 575T \log p_{CO}$$

---

* Alternatively the simultaneous formation of both CO and CO_2 in the reduction process can be allowed for in the precise determination of the minimum temperature for reaction. The more complicated procedure necessary in this case is demonstrated in example 4.12.

when all the condensed phases are pure and the carbon monoxide behaves ideally. Thus:

$$65{,}250 - 38{\cdot}35T = -4{\cdot}575\,T\log\frac{10^{-3}}{760}$$

$$= +26{\cdot}90T$$

or:
$$65{,}250 = 65{\cdot}25T.$$

Hence the minimum temperature for the reduction of MnO is 1,000°K or 727°C.

The partial pressure of carbon dioxide in equilibrium at this temperature with solid carbon and carbon monoxide at 10^{-3} mm Hg pressure, is now obtained from the equilibrium constant for reaction 4.5.3. For this reaction:

$$\Delta G^0 = +40{,}800 - 41{\cdot}7T \text{ cal}$$

$$= -900 \text{ cal at } 1{,}000°K$$

and:

$$K_p = 1{\cdot}574 = \frac{p^2_{CO}}{p_{CO_2}}$$

assuming ideal behaviour of the gases and the purity of the solid carbon. Hence:

$$p_{CO_2} = \frac{10^{-3}}{760} \times \frac{1}{1{\cdot}574}$$

$$= 1{\cdot}1 \times 10^{-12} \text{ atm}$$

$$= 8{\cdot}4 \times 10^{-10} \text{ mm Hg.}$$

As this value is negligible, relative to p_{CO}, the error in the calculated equilibrium temperature of 1,000°K will not be significant.

The solution of the manganese in the iron results in a depression of the minimum temperature of reduction by 53°C, i.e. this temperature becomes 947°K. Equation 4.5.6 becomes:

$$65{,}250 - (38{\cdot}35 \times 947) = -4{\cdot}575 \times 947 \log a_{Mn} \cdot p_{CO}$$

where the MnO and the solid carbon are again assumed pure and the carbon dioxide to behave ideally. Thus:

$$\log a_{Mn} = \frac{-28{,}900}{4{,}330} + 5{\cdot}88$$

or:

$$a_{Mn} = 0{\cdot}159.$$

The activity of the manganese in solution in the iron is 0·159.

4.6 *A gas consisting of 60·2 per cent H_2, 39·8 per cent H_2O at 1 atmosphere pressure is in equilibrium with pure γ-iron at 910°C. At the same temperature the gas composition in equilibrium with an iron–nickel alloy (containing 0·721 atom fraction of iron) is 51·9 per cent H_2 and 48·1 per cent H_2O. Determine the activity of iron in the alloy.*

This technique, in which the oxygen potential over a metal or an alloy is controlled by the gas atmosphere, can be used to determine the activity of a component of an alloy when that component forms an oxide which is considerably more stable (i.e. has a more negative free energy of formation) than the oxides of the other elements present in the alloy. At 910°C (1,183°K) the standard free energies of formation of nickel oxide (NiO) and ferrous oxide (FeO) are $-34,800$ and $-44,350$ cal mole^{-1} respectively. Hence it is evident that the iron will oxidize in preference to the nickel. It is essential from the point of view of the calculation that the oxide formed is pure and does not enter into solid solution in the alloy. These conditions are well satisfied in the present system and the activity of the ferrous oxide may be taken as unity.

In equilibrium with pure iron, the reaction is:

$$Fe_{(s)} + H_2O_{(g)} \rightleftharpoons FeO_{(s)} + H_{2(g)}$$

for which:

$$K_p = \frac{a_{FeO} \cdot f_{H_2}}{a_{Fe} \cdot f_{H_2O}}.$$

Because both Fe and FeO are in their standard states (i.e. at unit activity) and the gases may be assumed to be ideal, this simplifies to:

$$K_p = \left(\frac{p_{H_2}}{p_{H_2O}} \right)_{\text{Fe, pure}}.$$

The corresponding reaction with the alloy is:

$$Fe_{(Fe-Ni)} + H_2O_{(g)} \rightleftharpoons FeO_{(s)} + H_{2(g)}. \qquad 4.6.1$$

The activity of the pure ferrous oxide is again unity, but the activity of the iron is now less than unity in the alloy. Thus:

$$K_p = \left(\frac{p_{H_2}}{a_{Fe} \cdot p_{H_2O}} \right)_{\text{Fe-Ni}}.$$

However, as the value of the equilibrium constant for the reaction is unchanged on solution of the iron in the alloy, then:

$$\left(\frac{p_{H_2}}{p_{H_2O}} \right)_{\text{Fe, pure}} = \left(\frac{p_{H_2}}{a_{Fe} \cdot p_{H_2O}} \right)_{\text{Fe-Ni}}.$$

Rearranging terms:

$$a_{Fe} = \frac{(p_{H_2}/p_{H_2O})_{Fe-Ni}}{(p_{H_2}/p_{H_2O})_{Fe, pure}}$$

and substituting the gas compositions given:

$$a_{Fe} = \frac{(0\cdot519/0\cdot481)}{(0\cdot602/0\cdot398)}$$

$$= 0\cdot713.$$

That is, the activity of the iron in the iron–nickel alloy, relative to pure iron as the standard state, is $0\cdot713$.

It should be noted that the ratio:

$$\left(\frac{p_{H_2}}{p_{H_2O}}\right)_{Fe, pure} \left(= \frac{0\cdot602}{0\cdot398} = 1\cdot52\right),$$

which is equal to the equilibrium constant for reaction *4.6.1*, can be obtained from a knowledge of the standard free-energy change for the reaction (cf. example 4.5). However, the gas composition in equilibrium with the *alloy* can be obtained only by experimental measurement.

4.7 *At* $1,600°C$, *liquid solutions of* MnO *in* FeO *and* Mn *in* Fe *are approximately ideal. Determine the weight-per cent concentration of manganese in iron which is in equilibrium with an oxide melt (slag) containing* $0\cdot30$ *mole fraction of* MnO *and* $0\cdot70$ *mole fraction of* FeO *at this temperature.*

This example (though a simplified version) is of practical importance in relation to the refining of steel, and demonstrates how the equilibrium relation may be applied to wholly condensed systems in an exactly similar manner to that used in previous examples involving gaseous phases. In addition, the example illustrates the conversion of concentration in terms of mole fraction to per cent by weight, an often-necessary procedure in practical systems.

The exchange of iron and manganese between metal and slag is controlled by the reaction:

$$FeO_{(l)} + Mn_{(l)} \rightleftharpoons MnO_{(l)} + Fe_{(l)}. \qquad 4.7.1$$

The free-energy change for this reaction is obtained by subtracting:

$$Fe_{(l)} + \tfrac{1}{2}O_{2(g)} \rightleftharpoons FeO_{(l)} : \Delta G^0 = -55,620 + 10\cdot83T \text{ cal}$$

from:

$$Mn_{(l)} + \tfrac{1}{2}O_{2(g)} \rightleftharpoons MnO_{(l)} : \Delta G^0 = -84,700 + 14\cdot5T \text{ cal}$$

to give:

$$\Delta G^0_{(4.7.1)} = -29,080 + 3 \cdot 67T \text{ cal}$$
$$= -22,200 \text{ cal at } 1,873°K \text{ } (1,600°C).$$

From *1.58* the equilibrium constant for reaction *4.7.1* is expressed by:

$$+\left(\frac{22,200}{4 \cdot 575 \times 1,873}\right) = \log K_p = \log\left(\frac{a_{MnO} \cdot a_{Fe}}{a_{FeO} \cdot a_{Mn}}\right).$$

However, because the two liquid solutions are approximately ideal, the activities of the reaction components can be replaced by their atom fractions (equation *1.66*). Hence:

$$\log\left(\frac{N_{MnO} \cdot N_{Fe}}{N_{FeO} \cdot N_{Mn}}\right) = 2 \cdot 59.$$

Substituting the given values of N_{FeO} and N_{MnO}:

$$\frac{N_{Fe}}{N_{Mn}} = \frac{0 \cdot 70}{0 \cdot 30} \cdot \text{antilog } 2 \cdot 59$$
$$= 908$$

and, as:

$$N_{Fe} + N_{Mn} = 1$$

therefore:

$$N_{Fe} = 0 \cdot 9989$$
$$N_{Mn} = 0 \cdot 0011.$$

The concentration of manganese in iron is required in terms of weight-per cent and the atom fraction may be converted as follows.

For any binary system the ratio of the weight percentages is equal simply to the product of the ratios of the atomic weights and the atom fractions of the two components, i.e. for the Mn–Fe system:

$$\frac{\text{wt\%Mn}}{\text{wt\%Fe}} = \frac{M_{Mn}}{M_{Fe}} \cdot \frac{\text{at\%Mn}}{\text{at\%Fe}}$$

where M_{Mn} and M_{Fe} are the atomic weights of manganese and iron.

In the present example:

$$\frac{\text{wt\%Mn}}{100 - \text{wt\%Mn}} = \frac{54 \cdot 94}{55 \cdot 85} \cdot \frac{0 \cdot 0011}{0 \cdot 9989}.$$

Hence:

$$\text{wt\%Mn} = 0 \cdot 108.$$

Thus the concentration of manganese in iron in equilibrium with the oxide melt is $0 \cdot 108$ weight-per cent.

4.8   *From measurements of the equilibrium between hydrogen and hydrogen chloride gas with liquid sodium and solid sodium chloride, it is calculated that the partial pressure of chlorine gas in equilibrium with the two condensed phases is $2 \cdot 2 \times 10^{-46}$ atmosphere at 500°C. If the standard heat of formation of sodium chloride is assumed to be independent of temperature and equal to $-98 \cdot 6$ kcal mole^{-1}, calculate the equilibrium partial pressure of chlorine under the same conditions at 600°C.*

This example demonstrates the application of the approximate form of the van't Hoff relation, *1.61*. The known value of the partial pressure of chlorine is first used to deduce the value of the equilibrium constant for the sodium chloride formation reaction at 500°C. That is:

$$Na_{(l)} + \tfrac{1}{2}Cl_{2(g)} \rightleftharpoons NaCl_{(s)}$$

$$K_p = \frac{a_{NaCl}}{a_{Na} \cdot f_{Cl_2}^{1/2}}$$

$$= \frac{1}{p_{Cl_2}^{1/2}}$$

if sodium and sodium chloride are in their standard pure states and the chlorine behaves as an ideal gas. Thus:

$$K_p = \frac{1}{\sqrt{(2 \cdot 2 \times 10^{-46})}}$$

$$= 6 \cdot 74 \times 10^{22} \text{ at } 773°\text{K.}$$

Substitution of this value ($= K_1$) at the temperature T_1 in *1.61* yields the value of the equilibrium constant (K_2) at the temperature 873°K (T_2). That is:

$$\log(6 \cdot 74 \times 10^{22}) - \log K_2 = \frac{-98,600}{4 \cdot 575}\left(\frac{1}{873} - \frac{1}{773}\right)$$

or:

$$K_2 = 4 \cdot 35 \times 10^{19}.$$

Hence as:

$$p_{Cl_2} = \frac{1}{K_p^2}$$

therefore:

$$p_{Cl_2} = \frac{1}{(4 \cdot 35 \times 10^{19})^2}$$

$$= 5 \cdot 3 \times 10^{-40} \text{ atmosphere.}$$

It should be noted that this result may also be obtained by calculation of ΔG^0 at 773°K from $K_{773°K}$ and insertion of this value, and that given for ΔH^0, in the relation:

$$\Delta G^0 = \Delta H^0 - T\Delta S^0$$

to yield ΔS^0. Assuming ΔH^0 and ΔS^0 are independent of temperature (as does the method of calculation shown in detail), ΔG^0 at 873°K may now be calculated, from which $K_{873°K}$ (and hence p_{Cl_2} at this temperature) is found. The temperature independence of ΔH^0 is, of course, inherent in the approximate form of the van't Hoff equation, *1.61*, employed in the detailed calculation.

4.9 *Show that the basis of operation of the iron blast furnace – the reduction of ferrous oxide (FeO) by a* CO–CO_2 *atmosphere – is a process which is dependent upon marked deviations from equilibrium at temperatures around 600°C.*

There are several different ways in which this example can be answered. One approach is to determine whether or not the partial pressure of oxygen in equilibrium with iron and FeO is less than that in equilibrium with the CO–CO_2 atmosphere. This is the necessary condition for the reduction reaction to proceed. The equilibrium ratio p_{CO}/p_{CO_2} is fixed, however, by the equilibrium between these gases and the solid carbon in the charge. Hence a more simple approach is to determine whether or not the ratio p_{CO}/p_{CO_2} in equilibrium with graphite at the stated temperature is greater or less than the ratio in equilibrium with iron and ferrous oxide at the same temperature.

As a basis for calculation it will be assumed that the solids, iron, ferrous oxide and carbon, are present in their pure standard states and the total pressure is 1 atmosphere. The carbon monoxide and carbon dioxide are produced partly by combustion of the coke in the charge with the oxygen in the air blast and partly by reaction between the coke and the combined oxygen in the ore. It will be assumed, therefore, that the total pressure of carbon gases ($p_{CO} + p_{CO_2}$) is approximately 0·5 atmosphere, the remainder of the gas (at a total pressure of 1 atmosphere) being the diluting nitrogen from the air blast.

The free-energy change for the reaction:

$$C_{(s)} + CO_{2(g)} \rightleftharpoons 2CO_{(g)} \qquad \qquad 4.9.1$$

is given by:

$$\Delta G^0 = +40,800 - 41·7T \text{ cal.}$$

At 600°C (873°K):

$$\Delta G^0 = +4,400 \text{ cal}$$

and, from *1.58*:

$$RT \ln K_p = -4,400$$

$$= RT \ln \left(\frac{f_{CO}^2}{f_{CO_2} \cdot a_C} \right).$$

Thus, assuming the carbon is pure graphite and the gases behave ideally,

$$\log \frac{p_{CO}^2}{p_{CO_2}} = -1 \cdot 102$$

or:

$$\frac{p_{CO}^2}{p_{CO_2}} = 0 \cdot 079 \text{ at } 873°K.$$

However, as:

$$p_{CO_2} = 0 \cdot 5 - p_{CO}$$

therefore:

$$p_{CO}^2 = 0 \cdot 079 (0 \cdot 5 - p_{CO})$$

or:

$$p_{CO}^2 + 0 \cdot 079 p_{CO} - 0 \cdot 040 = 0$$

a quadratic in p_{CO}, which is solved by the formula method to give:

$$p_{CO} = \frac{-0 \cdot 079 \pm \sqrt{[(0 \cdot 079)^2 + 4(0 \cdot 040)]}}{2}$$

$$= 0 \cdot 163 \text{ atmosphere.}$$

Hence:

$$p_{CO_2} = 0 \cdot 337 \text{ atmosphere}$$

and:

$$\frac{p_{CO}}{p_{CO_2}} = 0 \cdot 484.$$

The ratio p_{CO}/p_{CO_2} in equilibrium with Fe and FeO under the stated conditions is now calculated from the equilibrium constant for the reaction:

$$Fe_{(s)} + CO_{2(g)} \rightleftharpoons FeO_{(s)} + CO_{(g)}. \qquad 4.9.2$$

The free-energy change for this reaction is obtained by adding those for reactions:

$$Fe_{(s)} + \tfrac{1}{2}O_{2(g)} \rightleftharpoons FeO_{(s)} : \Delta G^0 = -62,050 + 14 \cdot 95T \text{ cal}$$

and:

$$CO_{2(g)} \rightleftharpoons CO_{(g)} + \tfrac{1}{2}O_{2(g)} : \Delta G^0 = +67,500 - 20 \cdot 75T \text{ cal}$$

to obtain:

$$\Delta G^0_{(4.9.2)} = +5,450 - 5 \cdot 80T \text{ cal}$$

$$= +390 \text{ cal at } 873°K.$$

Hence:

$$+390 = -4.575T\log\left(\frac{p_{CO}}{p_{CO_2}}\right)$$

assuming that Fe and FeO are at unit activity and the gases are ideal. Therefore:

$$\log\left(\frac{p_{CO}}{p_{CO_2}}\right) = -0.0977$$

and:

$$\frac{p_{CO}}{p_{CO_2}} = 0.799.$$

This ratio is larger than that calculated as being in equilibrium with graphite and hence, if the latter equilibrium was attained in the blast furnace, on this basis the iron would exist only as the oxide. In practice the iron oxide is impure and the activity of ferrous oxide is usually very much lower than unity. From inspection of equation *4.9.2* it is evident that a decrease in a_{FeO} would increase proportionately the ratio p_{CO}/p_{CO_2} in equilibrium with the metal and its oxide. For example, if a_{FeO} is 0.5, the equilibrium ratio p_{CO}/p_{CO_2} is increased to 1.598.

As the activities of the iron and graphite will not be very much less than unity, it will be realized that the impurity of the solid reactants cannot be the basis for an explanation of the practical occurrence of the reduction reaction which should not, in theory, take place. The practical realization of the reduction of ferrous oxide in the lower temperature regions of the blast furnace is, therefore, only possible because of marked deviations from equilibrium conditions. These are mainly in the equilibrium in reaction *4.9.1*. The ratio p_{CO}/p_{CO_2} in equilibrium with graphite decreases from near unity at about 1,000°C to 0.484 at 600°C and to near zero at about 400°C, but the reaction occurs very slowly in relation to the time available as the gases ascend the blast furnace stack. In fact, experimentally it has been shown that finely divided iron oxide can be converted completely to cementite (Fe_3C) by exposure to a $CO–CO_2$ gas atmosphere at 600°C.

4.10 *A gas mixture of* 20 *per cent* CO, 20 *per cent* CO_2, 10 *per cent* H_2 *and* 50 *per cent* N_2 (*by volume*) *is fed into a furnace at* 900°C. *Find the equilibrium composition of the gas if the total pressure in the furnace is* 1 *atmosphere.*

This is a problem of obvious practical importance, for mixtures of these gases are used as controlled atmospheres in commercial heat-treatment furnaces. The gases will tend to react with each other at 900°C, equilibrium being finally established for the reaction:

$$CO_{(g)} + H_2O_{(g)} \rightleftharpoons CO_{2(g)} + H_{2(g)} \qquad 4.10.1$$

Data are available for the formation reactions for each of the components of this reaction. Thus:

$$C_{(s)} + \tfrac{1}{2}O_{2(g)} \rightleftharpoons CO_{(g)} \quad : \Delta G^0 = -26{,}700 - 20 \cdot 95T \text{ cal} \quad 4.10.2$$

$$C_{(s)} + O_{2(g)} \rightleftharpoons CO_{2(g)} \quad : \Delta G^0 = -94{,}200 - 0 \cdot 2T \text{ cal} \quad 4.10.3$$

$$H_{2(g)} + \tfrac{1}{2}O_{2(g)} \rightleftharpoons H_2O_{(g)} : \Delta G^0 = -58{,}900 + 13 \cdot 1T \text{ cal.} \quad 4.10.4$$

Hence, at 900°C (1,173° K):

$$\Delta G^0_{(4.10.2)} = -51{,}300 \text{ cal}$$

$$\Delta G^0_{(4.10.3)} = -94{,}400 \text{ cal}$$

$$\Delta G^0_{(4.10.4)} = -43{,}500 \text{ cal.}$$

Reaction 4.10.1 is given by 4.10.3 − {4.10.2 + 4.10.4}, and hence:

$$\Delta G^0_{(4.10.1)} = -94{,}400 - (-94{,}800)$$

$$= +400 \text{ cal at } 900°C.$$

Therefore:

$$K_{p\,(4.10.1)} = \text{antilog}\left[\frac{-\Delta G^0}{4 \cdot 575T}\right]$$

$$= \text{antilog}\left[-0 \cdot 0745\right]$$

$$= 0 \cdot 842.$$

This equilibrium constant for 4.10.1 is given by:

$$K_p = \frac{f_{CO_2} \cdot f_{H_2}}{f_{CO} \cdot f_{H_2O}}$$

or, assuming all the gases behave ideally under the prescribed conditions:

$$\frac{p_{CO_2} \cdot p_{H_2}}{p_{CO} \cdot p_{H_2O}} = 0 \cdot 842. \qquad 4.10.5$$

This is the first relation between the partial pressures of the components. As there are four of the latter, it is necessary to find three other relations between them in order to solve for their values (cf. example 4.4, p. 68).

Because the total pressure in the furnace is 1 atmosphere and the gas mixture contains 50 per cent by volume of inert nitrogen, then:

$$p_{CO} + p_{CO_2} + p_{H_2} + p_{H_2O} = 0 \cdot 5 \text{ (atm).} \qquad 4.10.6$$

In addition, the initial composition of the gas mixture is known. As the amount of any one element is conserved throughout (i.e. only its mode of association is changed), further equations relating the partial pressures may be derived. Thus if n_i denotes the number of gram-atoms or moles of the element or compound i, then, for the present mixture of gases:

$$\left.\begin{array}{l} n_C = n_{CO} + n_{CO_2} \\ n_H = 2n_{H_2} + 2n_{H_2O} \\ n_O = n_{CO} + 2n_{CO_2} + n_{H_2O} \end{array}\right\} \qquad 4.10.7$$

where n_C, n_H and n_O are constant, independent of the analysis of the gas in the system. Thus these may be related to each other from the initial analysis of the gas. For the analysis: 20 per cent CO, 20 per cent CO_2, 10 per cent H_2, it is deduced that:

$$n_C = 2n_H$$

$$n_O = 3n_H$$

$$2n_C = 3n_O$$

Therefore, substituting the appropriate relations 4.10.7:

$$n_{CO} + n_{CO_2} = 4(n_{H_2} + n_{H_2O})$$

and:

$$n_{CO} + 2n_{CO_2} + n_{H_2O} = 6(n_{H_2} + n_{H_2O}).$$

As:

$$p_i = \frac{n_i}{n_{total}} . P \quad \text{or} \quad p_i \propto n_i,$$

(where P is the total pressure), these relations may be rewritten in terms of partial pressures. Thus the relations:

$$p_{CO} + p_{CO_2} = 4p_{H_2} + 4p_{H_2O} \qquad 4.10.8$$

and:

$$p_{CO} + 2p_{CO_2} + p_{H_2O} = 6p_{H_2} + 6p_{H_2O}$$

or:

$$p_{CO} + 2p_{CO_2} = 6p_{H_2} + 5p_{H_2O} \qquad 4.10.9$$

are the remaining two equations needed to solve for the four unknowns. Of the four equations 4.10.5, 4.10.6, 4.10.8 and 4.10.9, the latter three are linear and are best used to substitute for three of the unknowns in 4.10.5.

For example, $\{4.10.6 - 4.10.8\}$ gives:

$$5p_{H_2} + 5p_{H_2O} = 0 \cdot 5$$

or:
$$p_{H_2} = 0 \cdot 1 - p_{H_2O} \qquad\qquad 4.10.10$$

and $\{4.10.9 - 4.10.6\}$ gives:
$$p_{CO_2} - 7p_{H_2} - 6p_{H_2O} = -0 \cdot 5. \qquad\qquad 4.10.11$$

Substituting for p_{H_2} from $4.10.10$ yields:
$$p_{CO_2} = 0 \cdot 2 - p_{H_2O} \qquad\qquad 4.10.12$$

Similarly, substituting $4.10.10$ and $4.10.12$ in $4.10.6$ yields:
$$p_{CO} = 0 \cdot 2 + p_{H_2O}. \qquad\qquad 4.10.13$$

Relations $4.10.10$, $4.10.12$ and $4.10.13$ may now be substituted in $4.10.5$ to obtain:
$$\frac{(0 \cdot 2 - p_{H_2O}) \cdot (0 \cdot 1 - p_{H_2O})}{(0 \cdot 2 + p_{H_2O}) \cdot p_{H_2O}} = 0 \cdot 842$$

or:
$$0 \cdot 158 p_{H_2O}^2 - 0 \cdot 468 p_{H_2O} + 0 \cdot 02 = 0$$

a quadratic in p_{H_2O}. Solving by the formula method:
$$p_{H_2O} = 0 \cdot 043.$$

Resubstituting in $4.10.10$, $4.10.12$ and $4.10.13$ in turn yields:
$$p_{H_2} = 0 \cdot 057$$
$$p_{CO_2} = 0 \cdot 157$$
$$p_{CO} = 0 \cdot 243$$

i.e. the equilibrium composition of the gas at $900°C$ is

50% N_2, $4 \cdot 3\%$ H_2O, $5 \cdot 7\%$ H_2, $15 \cdot 7\%$ CO_2 and $24 \cdot 3\%$ CO (by volume).

This type of calculation is very commonly encountered in equilibrium studies. As noted, the determination of the concentrations of n components at equilibrium involves the use of the standard free-energy change (relation 1.58) and $(n-1)$ additional relations which are formulated on the basis of the known restrictions inherent in the system (e.g. a fixed total pressure or volume, conservation of mass, etc.). These latter $(n-1)$ relations are (or can be made) of linear type.

While the value of n in the present problem is only four, and partial solution of the $(n-1)$ linear relations is a matter of simple algebraic manipulations, these become excessively tedious when four, five or six linear relations must be solved for five, six or seven unknowns. In such a case, the use of determinants* is the simplest way of solving the linear equations. Thus, in the present example, the relations *4.10.6, 4.10.8* and *4.10.9* may be rewritten:

$$p_{CO} + p_{CO_2} + p_{H_2} = (0.5 - p_{H_2O})$$

$$p_{CO} + p_{CO_2} - 4p_{H_2} = 4p_{H_2O}$$

$$p_{CO} + 2p_{CO_2} - 6p_{H_2} = 5p_{H_2O}$$

from which:

$$p_{CO} = \frac{\begin{vmatrix} (0.5 - p_{H_2O}) & 1 & 1 \\ 4p_{H_2O} & 1 & -4 \\ 5p_{H_2O} & 2 & -6 \end{vmatrix}}{\begin{vmatrix} 1 & 1 & 1 \\ 1 & 1 & -4 \\ 1 & 2 & -6 \end{vmatrix}}$$

$$= \frac{(0.5 - p_{H_2O}) \times 2 - 1(-4p_{H_2O}) + 1(3p_{H_2O})}{(+2) - (-2) + 1}$$

$$= 0.2 + p_{H_2O} \text{ as derived previously } (4.10.13).$$

Similarly p_{CO_2} and p_{H_2} may be expressed in terms of p_{H_2O}.

4.11 *It is found experimentally that a gas consisting of 1·95 per cent of CO and 98·05 per cent of CO_2 (by volume) is in equilibrium with pure solid nickel and pure solid nickel oxide at 1,500°C and 1 atmosphere total pressure. Calculate the partial pressure of oxygen in equilibrium with pure nickel and its oxide and the standard free-energy of formation of the oxide at that temperature, given only the following standard free-energy data:*

$$C_{(s)} + \tfrac{1}{2}O_{2(g)} \rightleftharpoons CO_{(g)} : \Delta G^0 = -26,700 - 20.95T \text{ cal} \qquad 4.11.1$$

$$C_{(s)} + O_{2(g)} \rightleftharpoons CO_{2(g)} : \Delta G^0 = -94,200 - 0.2T \text{ cal} \qquad 4.11.2$$

The solution to this example emphasizes one of the most important concepts of thermodynamics. That is, if the system as a whole is in thermodynamic equilibrium, parts of the system cannot be in differing states of equilibrium.† In this instance, the partial pressure of oxygen in contact with nickel and its oxide must necessarily be equal to the partial pressure of oxygen in equilibrium with the mixture of CO and CO_2.

* See appendix 5.
† This concept has been implicit in previous examples (e.g. 4.5) but appears here as the essential principle in the solution.

This principle is frequently employed for the indirect determination of partial pressures which are too small for direct measurement. Thus the small value of the partial pressure of oxygen in the system can be ascertained from the equilibrium constant for the reaction:

$$CO + \tfrac{1}{2}O_2 \rightleftharpoons CO_2.$$

The reaction for which the experimental data are given is:

$$Ni_{(s)} + CO_{2(g)} \rightleftharpoons NiO_{(s)} + CO_{(g)} \qquad 4.11.3$$

and the equilibrium constant is given by:

$$K_{p(4.11.3)} = \frac{a_{NiO} \cdot f_{CO}}{a_{Ni} \cdot f_{CO_2}}$$

$$= \frac{p_{CO}}{p_{CO_2}} \qquad 4.11.4$$

since Ni and NiO are both in their standard pure states and ideal behaviour of the gases is assumed.

Substituting the experimental values of p_{CO} and p_{CO_2} in 4.11.4:

$$K_{p(4.11.3)} = \frac{0 \cdot 0195}{0 \cdot 9805}$$

$$= 0 \cdot 0199.$$

Reaction 4.11.3 is given by the sum of the two reactions:

$$Ni_{(s)} + \tfrac{1}{2}O_{2(g)} \rightleftharpoons NiO_{(s)} \qquad 4.11.5$$

$$CO_{2(g)} \rightleftharpoons CO_{(g)} + \tfrac{1}{2}O_{2(g)}. \qquad 4.11.6$$

But 4.11.6 is given by {4.11.1 − 4.11.2} and hence the free-energy change for reaction 4.11.6 is:

$$\Delta G^0 = +67{,}500 - 20 \cdot 75T \text{ cal.}$$

Thus:

$$\log K_{p(4.11.6)} = -\frac{67{,}500}{4 \cdot 575T} + \frac{20 \cdot 75}{4 \cdot 575}$$

$$= -3 \cdot 79 \text{ at } 1{,}773°K \ (1{,}500°C)$$

or:

$$K_{p(4.11.6)} = 1 \cdot 62 \times 10^{-4} = \frac{p_{CO} \cdot p_{O_2}^{1/2}}{p_{CO_2}}$$

assuming ideal behaviour of the gases. Substituting the given values of p_{CO} and p_{CO_2}:

$$p_{O_2} = 6 \cdot 62 \times 10^{-5} \text{ atmosphere.}$$

Because the whole system is at equilibrium, the partial pressure of oxygen in equilibrium with the stated values of p_{CO} and p_{CO_2} must necessarily be the same as that in equilibrium with pure nickel and its oxide, reaction *4.11.5*, at this temperature. Hence the partial pressure of oxygen in equilibrium with pure nickel and its oxide at $1{,}773°K$ is $6{\cdot}62 \times 10^{-5}$ atmosphere.

The equilibrium constant for reaction *4.11.5*, the formation reaction for nickel oxide, is:

$$K_{p\,(4.11.5)} = \frac{a_{NiO}}{a_{Ni} \cdot p_{O_2}^{1/2}}$$

$$= \frac{1}{p_{O_2}^{1/2}}$$

since Ni and NiO are both in their standard pure states. Hence, inserting the equilibrium value of p_{O_2}:

$$K_{p\,(4.11.5)} = \frac{1}{\sqrt{(6{\cdot}62 \times 10^{-5})}}$$

$$= 122{\cdot}8.$$

Thus, the standard free-energy change for the formation of NiO at $1{,}773°K$ is:

$$\Delta G^0 = -4{\cdot}575T \log K_p$$

$$= -17{,}000 \text{ cal.}$$

The standard free-energy change could also be obtained from the following considerations. As reaction *4.11.5* is given by the difference between reactions *4.11.3* and *4.11.6*, therefore:

$$\Delta G^0_{(4.11.5)} = \Delta G^0_{(4.11.3)} - \Delta G^0_{(4.11.6)}$$

or:

$$RT \ln K_{p\,(4.11.5)} = RT \ln K_{p\,(4.11.3)} - RT \ln K_{p\,(4.11.6)} = RT \ln \frac{K_{p\,(4.11.3)}}{K_{p\,(4.11.6)}}$$

and:

$$K_{p\,(4.11.5)} = \frac{K_{p\,(4.11.3)}}{K_{p\,(4.11.6)}}.$$

Thus:

$$K_{p\,(4.11.5)} = \frac{1{\cdot}99 \times 10^{-2}}{1{\cdot}62 \times 10^{-4}}$$

$$= 122{\cdot}8.$$

Hence:

$$\Delta G^0_{(4.11.5)} = -4{\cdot}575T \log 122{\cdot}8$$

$$= -17{,}000 \text{ cal at } 1{,}773°K.$$

7

4.12 *Determine whether or not chromic oxide* (Cr_2O_3) *can be reduced by solid carbon at* 1,000°C *without forming the chromium carbide* $Cr_{23}C_6$.

The problem may be considered from the point of view of two possible reactions.

1. Reduction of chromic oxide:

$$Cr_2O_{3(s)} \rightleftharpoons 2Cr_{(s)} + \tfrac{3}{2}O_{2(g)} \qquad \textit{4.12.1}$$

for which:

$$\Delta G^0 = 267{,}750 - 62 \cdot 1T \text{ cal}$$

or at 1,273°K:

$$\Delta G^0 = +188{,}650 \text{ cal}$$
$$= -RT \ln p_{O_2}^{3/2}$$

assuming the condensed phases are pure and the gas is ideal.

Hence:

$$p_{O_2} = \text{antilog} \left[\frac{-188{,}650}{4 \cdot 575 \times 1 \cdot 5 \times 1{,}273} \right]$$
$$= \text{antilog} \, (-21 \cdot 55)$$
$$= 3 \cdot 55 \times 10^{-22} \text{ atmosphere.}$$

2. Carburization of chromic oxide:

$$Cr_2O_{3(s)} + \tfrac{12}{23}C_{(s)} \rightleftharpoons \tfrac{2}{23}Cr_{23}C_{6(s)} + \tfrac{3}{2}O_{2(g)} \qquad \textit{4.12.2}$$

for which the standard free-energy change may be deduced from:

$$\tfrac{23}{6}Cr_{(s)} + C_{(s)} \rightleftharpoons \tfrac{1}{6}Cr_{23}C_{6(s)} : \; \Delta G^0 = -16{,}380 - 1 \cdot 54T \text{ cal}$$

and *4.12.1* as:

$$\Delta G^0_{(4.12.2)} = +259{,}210 - 62 \cdot 9T \text{ cal}$$
$$= +179{,}000 \text{ cal at } 1{,}273°K.$$

Hence:

$$p_{O_2} = \text{antilog} \left[\frac{-179{,}000}{4 \cdot 575 \times 1{,}273 \times 1 \cdot 5} \right]$$
$$= \text{antilog} \, (-20 \cdot 47)$$
$$= 2 \cdot 95 \times 10^{-21} \text{ atmosphere.}$$

It is evident, therefore, that the chromium carbide $Cr_{23}C_6$ is formed from the oxide at a higher partial pressure of oxygen (i.e. has a higher 'oxygen potential') than that required for the reduction of the oxide to the metal. For these calculations indicate that at 1,000°C, the oxide is more stable than either the metal or the carbide when $p_{O_2} > 2 \cdot 95 \times 10^{-21}$ atmosphere, whereas when $2 \cdot 95 \times 10^{-21} > p_{O_2} > 3 \cdot 55 \times 10^{-22}$ atmosphere, the carbide is most stable, and the metal is stable only when $p_{O_2} < 3 \cdot 55 \times 10^{-22}$ atmosphere. Obviously, these pressures are all so small that they are unmeasurable. However, as there is solid carbon in the system, carbon dioxide and carbon monoxide will be formed, and the partial pressure of oxygen in the system will be related to the partial pressures of these gases through the equilibrium constant for the reaction:

$$2CO_{(g)} + O_{2(g)} \rightleftharpoons 2CO_{2(g)}. \qquad 4.12.3$$

In the presence of solid carbon, the partial pressures of the oxides of carbon are further related through the equilibrium constant for the reaction:

$$2CO_{(g)} \rightleftharpoons CO_{2(g)} + C_{(s)}. \qquad 4.12.4$$

The calculated value of the partial pressure of oxygen at equilibrium with chromium oxide and chromium metal and that at equilibrium with chromium oxide and chromium carbide will correspond to unique values of p_{CO} and p_{CO_2}, which may be calculated by the conventional procedure. Thus for reaction 4.12.3:

$$\Delta G^0 = -135,000 + 41 \cdot 5T \text{ cal}$$
$$= -82,100 \text{ cal at } 1,273°K.$$

Hence:

$$\frac{p_{CO_2}^2}{p_{CO}^2 \cdot p_{O_2}} = \text{antilog} \left[\frac{82,100}{4 \cdot 575 \times 1,273} \right]$$
$$= 1 \cdot 26 \times 10^{14}. \qquad 4.12.5$$

But for reaction 4.12.4:

$$\Delta G^0 = +40,800 - 41 \cdot 7T \text{ cal}$$
$$= -12,300 \text{ cal at } 1,273°K.$$

Hence:

$$\frac{p_{CO}^2}{p_{CO_2}} = \text{antilog} \left[\frac{12,300}{1,273 \times 4 \cdot 575} \right]$$
$$= 129. \qquad 4.12.6$$

The partial pressures of CO_2, CO and O_2 in the system must simultaneously satisfy the relations 4.12.5 and 4.12.6. Therefore, by successive substitution of the two oxygen potentials °or reactions 4.12.1 (the reduction reaction) and 4.12.2 (the carburization reaction), the conditions will be found, in terms of the partial pressures of CO_2 and CO, under which these reactions will be at equilibrium.

Substituting the value of p_{O_2} for reaction *4.12.1* into *4.12.5* yields:

$$\frac{p_{CO_2}}{p_{CO}} = 2 \cdot 12 \times 10^{-4}.$$

Combining this ratio with *4.12.6* yields:

$$\left.\begin{array}{l} p_{CO} = 2 \cdot 74 \times 10^{-2}\ \text{atm} \\ p_{CO_2} = 5 \cdot 80 \times 10^{-6}\ \text{atm} \\ (p_{O_2} = 3 \cdot 55 \times 10^{-22}\ \text{atm}) \end{array}\right\}$$ Equilibrium for reduction of Cr_2O_3 to Cr metal.

Similarly, substituting the value of p_{O_2} for reaction *4.12.2* into *4.12.5* yields:

$$\frac{p_{CO_2}}{p_{CO}} = 6 \cdot 09 \times 10^{-4}.$$

Combining this ratio with *4.12.6* yields:

$$\left.\begin{array}{l} p_{CO} = 7 \cdot 85 \times 10^{-2}\ \text{atm} \\ p_{CO_2} = 4 \cdot 78 \times 10^{-5}\ \text{atm} \\ (p_{O_2} = 2 \cdot 95 \times 10^{-21}\ \text{atm}) \end{array}\right\}$$ Equilibrium for carburization of Cr_2O_3 to $Cr_{23}C_6$.

These conditions for equilibrium between chromium oxide and metal and chromium oxide and the carbide indicate immediately that the formation of one or other of these products is a sensitive function of the imposed conditions. For at reduced pressures of oxides of carbon greater than $7 \cdot 85 \times 10^{-2}$ atm the chromium oxide is stable in the presence of solid carbon, whereas in the pressure range $7 \cdot 85 \times 10^{-2}$ atm to $2 \cdot 74 \times 10^{-2}$ atm (about 60–20 mm Hg) the oxide is reduced directly to the carbide $Cr_{23}C_6$. At lower pressures than this, the chromium metal is formed.

This example again illustrates one of the most important principles of thermodynamic equilibrium, namely, that all parts of a heterogeneous system in complete equilibrium must themselves be at equilibrium with each other. In this example the equilibrium conditions for carbide or metal formation from chromium oxide and solid carbon are also the conditions for equilibrium between oxygen and carbon and the oxides of the latter. By calculation of these conditions, the practical realization of carbide or metal formation becomes a possibility.

Exercises

4.A   Calculate the ratio p_{CO}/p_{CO_2} in equilibrium with pure iron and pure ferrous oxide at 1,027°C.

4.B When a gas consisting of eight parts by volume of hydrogen and two parts by volume of an inert diluent, at a total pressure of 1 atmosphere, is passed over a solid mixture of nickel and nickel chloride at 400°C, the partial pressures of H_2, HCl and the inert gas are found to be 0·240, 0·560 and 0·200 respectively at the exit to the reaction chamber. Determine whether or not equilibrium between the gas and the solid is attained during the passage of the gas through the chamber.

4.C Solid magnesium oxide is mixed intimately with solid silicon and heated to 1,400°C, when the following reaction occurs:

$$4MgO_{(s)} + Si_{(s)} \rightleftharpoons 2Mg_{(g)} + Mg_2SiO_{4(s)}.$$

Determine the vapour pressure of magnesium in equilibrium with the solid mixture.

4.D In one process for the separation of zirconium from hafnium, the gaseous tetra-chlorides of these metals are allowed to react at 800°C with a gas containing 67 per cent oxygen and 33 per cent chlorine by volume. If the standard free-energy changes at this temperature for the oxidation of the hafnium and zirconium chlorides to give the (di) oxides and chlorine gas are $+48·85$ and $-34·30$ kcal mole^{-1} of the chloride respectively, determine the end products of the separation process.

4.E On oxidation of most Fe–Ni alloys at 840°C, pure FeO is formed which is insoluble in the alloy. Calculate the activity of iron in an alloy which has been equilibrated with a gas mixture of 57·5 per cent hydrogen and 42·5 per cent water vapour at this temperature.

4.F At 850°C, the activity of nickel in a solid gold–nickel alloy containing 0·40 N_{Ni} is 0·82, relative to pure nickel as the standard state. Find the minimum ratio p_{CO}/p_{CO_2} in which this alloy can be heated without oxidation at this temperature.

4.G Calculate the standard molar free energy of formation of liquid KCl from the liquid metal and chlorine gas at 1,000°K, given that the ratio p_{HCl}/p_{H_2} in equilibrium with the metal and the chloride is $4·0 \times 10^{-13}$ when the total pressure $(p_{HCl} + p_{H_2}) = 1$ atm at the stated temperature.

4.H Calculate the ratio p_{H_2S}/p_{H_2} in equilibrium with pure copper and copper sulphide at 500°C. If the value of the ratio in equilibrium with a gold–copper alloy ($N_{Cu} = 0·85$) is $2·88 \times 10^{-4}$ at the same temperature, calculate the activity coefficient (γ) of copper in the alloy.

4.I Using only the following data, calculate the ratio p_{H_2S}/p_{H_2} in equilibrium with silver and silver sulphide at 600°C.

$$4Ag_{(s)} + S_{2(g)} \rightleftharpoons 2Ag_2S_{(s)} : \Delta G^0_{873°K} = -30,570 \text{ cal}$$

	$H_{2(g)}$	$S_{2(g)}$	$H_2S_{(g)}$	
S^0_{298}	31·21	54·4	49·1	cal deg^{-1} mole^{-1}
ΔH^0_{298}	0	+31,000	−4,800	cal mole^{-1}

Assume that the gases behave ideally and that the heats of reaction are independent of temperature.

4.J Can pure copper sheet be bright annealed (i.e. without forming a surface oxide layer) at 750°C in an atmosphere of high purity nitrogen gas containing 10^{-6} volume-per cent of oxygen?

4.K Determine the minimum temperature at which calcium carbonate $(CaCO_3)$ will dissociate when heated in air containing 0·15 volume-per cent of carbon dioxide.

4.L Pure iron can exist in equilibrium with either pure solid wüstite (FeO) or pure solid magnetite (Fe_3O_4), depending upon the temperature. Determine which of these oxides would be in equilibrium with pure iron at room temperature and the maximum temperature at which this oxide is in equilibrium with iron.

4.M Repeat the calculation given in the previous exercise, evaluating the free-energy–temperature relations from standard enthalpy and entropy data, assuming the latter are independent of temperature. Comment on the difference between the maximum temperature obtained by the two methods of calculation.

4.N Determine the maximum temperature to which molybdenum can be heated without formation of the oxide MoO_2 in an atmosphere of 69 per cent hydrogen and 31 per cent by volume of steam.

4.O Calculate the minimum temperature at which pure solid calcium orthosilicate $(2CaO . SiO_2)$ can be reduced by solid carbon to form pure silicon metal, the partial pressure of carbon monoxide in equilibrium with the solids being (a) 0·03mm Hg (b) 0·001mm Hg.

4.P A steam–hydrogen gas mixture $(p_{H_2O}/p_{H_2} = 0.462)$ is equilibrated at 1,361°C with pure solid iron and a molten slag containing ferrous oxide (FeO). When equilibrium is attained the slag is found to contain 0·376 mole fraction of FeO. Find the activity of the FeO, given that for the reaction:

$$FeO_{(l,\ pure)} + CO_{(g)} \rightleftharpoons Fe_{(s)} + CO_{2(g)} : \Delta G^0 = -12,080 + 9·868T \text{ cal.}$$

4.Q A gas mixture consisting of methane, carbon monoxide, water vapour and hydrogen is circulated continuously over a specimen of pure iron held at 1,050°C. The partial pressure of the water vapour in the mixture is maintained constant at a small value by passing the gas over a desiccant. When equilibrium is established, the iron contains 0·842 weight-per cent carbon and the sum of the partial pressures of methane and carbon monoxide is 0·0081 atm when the total gas pressure is 1·0 atm. In a further series of experiments it is found that a gas consisting of $p_{CO} + p_{CH_4} = 0·0190$ and the same partial pressure of water vapour is in equilibrium with graphite when the total gas pressure is 1 atmosphere. Find the activity of carbon in the metal sample, relative to graphite as the standard state.

4.R A mixture of ferric oxide (Fe_2O_3) and cuprous oxide (CuO) is heated to 600°C in an atmosphere containing SO_3 gas with the intention of converting the copper into a soluble copper sulphate ($CuSO_4$) and leaving the ferric oxide unchanged. Given the following data and using the appropriate standard free-energy relations of appendix 3, determine the range of values of p_{SO_3} in the atmosphere which will allow this to be accomplished at this temperature, assuming that the oxides and sulphates do not form solid solutions.

$$Cu_{(s)} + \tfrac{1}{2}O_{2(g)} + SO_{3(g)} \rightleftharpoons CuSO_{4(s)} \quad : \Delta G^0 = -94,375 - 5·01T \log T \\ + 86·9T \text{ cal}$$

$$2Fe_{(s)} + 1\tfrac{1}{2}O_{2(g)} + 3SO_{3(g)} \rightleftharpoons Fe_2(SO_4)_{3(s)} : \Delta G^0 = -223,370 \\ + 111·04T \text{ cal.}$$

4.S It has been proposed that aluminium could be refined by first forming AlCl gas which could then be dissociated to give $AlCl_3$ gas and pure aluminium. Deduce the feasibility of this process by calculating the approximate values of the equilibrium partial pressures of AlCl at 1,000 and 2,000°K, if the various equilibria are allowed to establish themselves at 1 atmosphere total pressure.

4.T A stream of nitrogen gas is passed over a series of crucibles in a furnace, the latter having been designed to give a negative temperature gradient from the gas entry end. The crucibles contain various zinc-aluminium alloys which, after equilibrium has been achieved, are analysed, their compositions and corresponding temperatures in the furnace being given in the table. In an independent experiment, the weights of zinc vapour condensed from equal volumes of nitrogen passed over pure zinc and the first of the alloys at the same temperature of 1,030°C are 8·20 g and 6·15 g respectively. Show that this alloy system conforms to a relation:

$$RT \ln \gamma_{Zn} = \alpha N_{Al}^2$$

where γ_{Zn} is the activity coefficient of zinc and α is a constant. Calculate the value of this constant.

$T °C$	1,030	860	710	580	530
N_{Zn}	0·706	0·699	0·686	0·670	0·661

4.U On heating, sulphur vapour dissociates from its low temperature molecular form S_8 to molecules containing six, four, two and one atoms of sulphur. If the equilibrium vapour pressure of sulphur is 2·04 atm at 800°K, calculate the pressures of the various molecular species at that temperature. (A graphical solution of the quartic equation in this exercise should be used.)

4.V A producer gas containing 2·5 per cent CO_2, 28 per cent CO, 11 per cent H_2, 4 per cent H_2O by volume, remainder nitrogen, is passed through a regenerator at 1,100°C. Assuming that the gases behave ideally and equilibrium is attained, calculate the composition of the gas at the regenerator outlet.

CHAPTER 5

Solutions

Most of the examples presented in earlier chapters have been concerned with the thermodynamic properties of elements and compounds and mechanical mixtures of these. However, a very profitable field for the application of thermodynamic concepts is the study of liquid and solid solutions. Apart from the obvious use of this approach to determine equilibrium conditions in systems containing solutions, thermodynamics can sometimes be applied to indicate the physical and chemical factors which determine the behaviour of the various components of a solution. One of the simplest ways of expressing such behaviour is through a comparison of the thermodynamic properties of the solution with those for a hypothetical 'ideal' solution of the same composition. Alternatively, as this ideal solution concept is of limited usefulness, the regular solution of Hildebrand [1] is often a better basis for describing the thermodynamic behaviour of real solutions. The use of these models involving the relations between activity, activity coefficient and the partial molar quantities for the components of solutions is illustrated in this and successive chapters.

Ideal and regular solutions

5.1 *If a liquid gold–copper alloy containing 45 atom-per cent of copper is assumed to behave ideally at 1,050°C, calculate the heat absorbed and the entropy change in the system when 1 gram of solid copper is dissolved isothermally at this temperature in a large bath of the alloy of this composition.*

This example concerns the addition of a solute to a solution which is assumed to be ideal. Thus, by definition, the activity of any component of the solution is equal to its mole fraction, relative to the pure component (in the same physical form) as the standard state. Consequent upon this, the partial molar heat of mixing of the component is zero; i.e. from *1.68*:

$$\bar{H}_i - H_i^0 = \bar{H}_i^M = 0 \quad \text{for an ideal solution.}$$

Further, from *1.72*:

$$\bar{S}_i - S_i^0 = S_i^M = -R \ln N_i \quad \text{for an ideal solution.}$$

As on solution in the ideal liquid gold–copper alloy the heat of mixing of 1 gram of liquid copper is zero, the only heat involved in the process is the heat necessary to convert the copper from the solid to the liquid state at 1,050°C. As the equilibrium melting point of copper is 1,083°C, negligible error is introduced by assuming that this heat value is equal to the latent heat of fusion of copper, which is 3,100 cal mole^{-1} or 49 cal g^{-1}. (This is obvious from example 2.5.) The latter quantity will be the heat absorbed when 1 gram of copper is dissolved in the ideal gold–copper alloy at 1,050°C.

The entropy change in the solution process will be the sum of two terms; the entropy change on mixing of the copper:

$$\bar{S}_{Cu}^{M} = -R \ln N_{Cu}$$

and the entropy change on fusion of the copper at 1,050°C (1,323°K):

$$S_{f(Cu)} = \frac{H_{f(Cu)}}{1,323} \simeq \frac{L_{f(Cu)}}{1,323}$$

where $L_{f(Cu)}$ is the latent heat of fusion of copper at the equilibrium melting point.
Thus:

$$\bar{S}_{Cu}^{M} = -4.575 \log 0.45$$

$$= +1.59 \text{ cal deg}^{-1} \text{ mole}^{-1}$$

$$= 0.0250 \text{ cal deg}^{-1} \text{ g}^{-1}$$

and:

$$S_{f(Cu)} = \frac{49}{1,323}$$

$$= 0.0370 \text{ cal deg}^{-1} \text{ g}^{-1}.$$

Thus the entropy change on dissolving 1 gram of solid copper in a 45 atom-per cent copper ideal solution in gold is 0.0620 cal deg^{-1} at 1,050°C. If the copper was, say, at room temperature when added to the liquid bath, the enthalpy and entropy changes would, of course, be increased by the change in these properties on heating solid copper from room temperature to 1,050°C (cf. examples 2.5 and 3.2).

5.2 *Calculate the heat evolved per gram of copper oxidized when pure oxygen is blown through the bath described in the previous example.*

When oxygen is blown through the liquid gold–copper alloy at 1,050°C, the copper alone will be oxidized. As it is assumed that the solution of copper in gold is ideal at this concentration, the reaction of the dissolved copper with the oxygen will be identical, as far as the heat evolved is concerned, with that taking place when oxygen is blown through pure liquid copper supercooled from the melting point of 1,083°C to 1,050°C. This identity follows from the zero heat of mixing of the copper in the ideal gold–copper alloy.

The oxidation of pure liquid copper can be described by:

$$2Cu_{(l)} + \tfrac{1}{2}O_{2(g)} \rightleftharpoons Cu_2O_{(s)}$$

and the heat of reaction is given by:

$$\Delta H_T = -43,700 - 3.68T + 2.60 \times 10^{-3}T^2 - 0.20 \times 10^5 T^{-1} \text{ cal.} \quad 5.2.1$$

The latter equation is calculated by use of the Kirchhoff equation, 1.20, in the manner demonstrated in example 2.6. Values of the heat of reaction at 298°K of solid copper with oxygen to form the solid oxide (-40 kcal mole^{-1}), the latent heat of fusion of copper (3,100 cal mole^{-1}) at the melting point (1,356°K) are required, together with the appropriate heat-capacity-change relations for the oxidation of both solid copper:

$$\Delta C_p = 0.50 + 2.2 \times 10^{-3}T + 0.20 \times 10^5 T^{-2} \text{ cal deg}^{-1} \text{ mole}^{-1}$$

and liquid copper:

$$\Delta C_p = -3.68 + 5.20 \times 10^{-3}T + 0.20 \times 10^5 T^{-2} \text{ cal deg}^{-1} \text{ mole}^{-1}.$$

Equation 5.2.1 is strictly applicable only at temperatures above the melting point of pure copper and the calculation of $\Delta H_{1,323}$ involves the assumption that the C_p data for $Cu_{(l)}$ are valid down to 1,323°K. However, as the temperature range of the extrapolation is small, it is reasonable to assume that the error incurred is not large. Inserting $T = 1,323$°K in equation 5.2.1 yields:

$$\Delta H_{1,323} = -43,830 \text{ cal.}$$

Two mole of liquid copper are oxidized in the reaction, so the heat evolved by blowing oxygen through an *ideal* gold–copper alloy at 1,050°C is:

$$43,830 \text{ cal (2 mole)}^{-1} \text{ of copper} = \frac{43,830}{2 \times 63.54}$$

$$= 345 \text{ cal g}^{-1} \text{ of copper.}$$

5.3   *If the liquid gold–copper alloy discussed in the previous examples is assumed to behave regularly rather than ideally, the activity coefficient of copper in the alloy being equal to 0.41 at 1,050°C, calculate the same quantity as calculated in example 5.2.*

When it is assumed that the liquid gold–copper alloy is a regular solution, the heat of mixing of copper is not zero (as for an ideal solution) but is given, from *1.82*, by:

$$\bar{H}_{Cu}^M = RT \ln \gamma_{Cu}.$$

Substitution of the values given for T and γ_{Cu} yields:

$$\bar{H}_{Cu}^M = -2{,}350 \text{ cal mole}^{-1}.$$

(As the solution is regular this heat of mixing, equal to the excess partial molar free energy of copper, is independent of temperature (see p. 15).)

Thus, compared to the previous example, when 1 mole of copper is oxidized by blowing oxygen through the alloy bath, an additional heat effect arises from the removal of copper from the solution. This heat effect is the reverse of that occurring on solution of 1 mole of copper in the alloy, i.e. the reverse of the partial molar heat of mixing of copper at the temperature of oxidation. Thus a quantity of heat:

$$+2{,}350 \text{ cal mole}^{-1}$$

or:

$$+37 \text{ cal g}^{-1} \text{ of copper (positive heat-endothermic)}$$

must be added to the value of the heat of the oxidation reaction for pure copper as calculated in example 5.2. As this heat of oxidation is (-345 cal g^{-1}), the total heat *evolved* by blowing oxygen through the regular gold–copper alloy at 1,050°C is therefore:

$$+345 - 37 = 308 \text{ cal g}^{-1} \text{ of copper.}$$

The Gibbs–Duhem relation

In the thermodynamic analysis of solutions, it is very commonly the situation that data are more readily measurable for one component than for the other components. Because of this, the Gibbs–Duhem relation, derived in terms of the partial molar free energy in *1.43*, is of great importance, for it relates the thermodynamic quantities for the various components in the solution. It will be recalled that this relation may be written in terms of any of the partial molar state variables of the system. As will be shown, however, its use in the form of *1.43* is rather inconvenient and inaccurate, and modified versions are more commonly used to obtained values for components other than the one for which experiment has yielded data. The following examples illustrate the application of various forms of the Gibbs–Duhem equation to binary solutions. The extension of these principles to three-component (ternary) solutions is discussed in chapter 8.

5.4 *From measurement of the temperature coefficient of the e.m.f. of galvanic cells containing liquid gold–lead alloy electrodes, the following values of the partial molar entropy of mixing of lead have been determined at 830°C for various compositions.*

Mole fraction of lead, N_{Pb}	0·10	0·20	0·30	0·40	0·50
Partial molar entropy of mixing of lead, $\bar{S}_{Pb}^{M}$ (cal mole^{-1} deg^{-1})	8·50	5·00	3·28	2·20	1·60

Mole fraction of lead, N_{Pb}	0·60	0·70	0·80	0·90
Partial molar entropy of mixing of lead, $\bar{S}_{Pb}^{M}$ (cal mole^{-1} deg^{-1})	1·08	0·71	0·42	0·18

Calculate the partial molar entropy of gold ($\bar{S}_{Au}$) in a 40 atom-per cent Au *alloy at this temperature.*

The appropriate Gibbs–Duhem relation is:

$$N_{Pb} \, d\bar{S}_{Pb}^{M} + N_{Au} \, d\bar{S}_{Au}^{M} = 0$$

or, expressed as an indefinite integral:

$$\int d\bar{S}_{Au}^{M} = - \int \frac{N_{Pb}}{N_{Au}} d\bar{S}_{Pb}^{M}. \qquad 5.4.1$$

The limits of integration may be chosen as desired. The upper limit will obviously be that corresponding to the 40 atom-per cent Au alloy. The lower limit may in theory be chosen as any value, but to be of use, this limit must be such as to yield a known value of the entropy of mixing of gold on integration of the left-hand side of *5.4.1*. Thus the most convenient lower integration limit will correspond to pure gold ($N_{Au} = 1$). For then *5.4.1* becomes:

$$\bar{S}_{Au\,(N_{Au}=0.40)}^{M} - \bar{S}_{Au\,(pure)}^{M} = \bar{S}_{Au\,(N_{Au}=0.40)}^{M} = - \int_{N_{Au}=1}^{N_{Au}=0.40} \frac{N_{Pb}}{N_{Au}} d\bar{S}_{Pb}^{M} \quad 5.4.2$$

as $\bar{S}_{Au\,(pure)}^{M} = 0$.

The integral in *5.4.2* can be solved graphically as the area under a curve of N_{Pb}/N_{Au} versus $\bar{S}_{Pb}^{M}$ between the values of $\bar{S}_{Pb}^{M}$ corresponding to $N_{Au} = 0.40(N_{Pb}/N_{Au} = 1.50)$ and $N_{Au} = 1(N_{Pb}/N_{Au} = 0)$. The curve derived from the given data, Fig. 5.4a, is asymptotic to both axes and evaluation of the integral will involve quite serious error. However, the shaded area in Fig. 5.4a, which corresponds to the required integration limits, yields a value of the partial molar entropy of mixing of gold $\bar{S}_{Au}^{M} = (\bar{S}_{Au} - S_{Au}^{0}) = 3.58$ cal deg^{-1} mole^{-1} (using the Trapezoidal rule* with a chord width of $\Delta \bar{S}_{Au}^{M} = 0.5$). This value will, of course, be too small, but is that given by the only reasonable extrapolation of the curve from the available data.

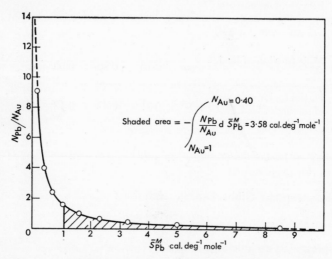

$$\text{Shaded area} = -\int_{N_{Au}=1}^{N_{Au}=0.40} \frac{N_{Pb}}{N_{Au}} \, d\, \bar{S}_{Pb}^{M} = 3.58 \text{ cal.deg}^{-1}\text{mole}^{-1}$$

Fig. 5.4a. Graphical solution of binary Gibbs–Duhem equation. Solution of integral in equation (5.4.2).

The molar entropy of pure gold (S_{Au}^{0}) at 830°C will be given by the integrated form of *1.26*. The required heat capacity data and the standard molar entropy of gold are:

$$C_{p_{Au(s)}} = 5.66 + 1.24 \times 10^{-3}\, T \text{ cal deg}^{-1}\text{ mole}^{-1}$$

$$S_{Au,298}^{0} = 11.32 \text{ cal. deg}^{-1}\text{ mole}^{-1}.$$

However, as the 40 atom-per cent gold–lead alloy for which $\bar{S}_{Au}$ is required, is liquid at 830°C, the value of S_{Au}^{0} to be calculated must be that for pure liquid gold, supercooled from 1,063°C (1,336°K) to 830°C (1,103°K). Thus, following *1.27*:

$$S_{Au(l, 830°C)}^{0} = S_{Au\,298}^{0} + \int_{298}^{1,336} \frac{C_{p_{Au(s)}}}{T} \, dT + \frac{L_f}{T_f} + \int_{1,336}^{1,103} \frac{C_{p_{Au(l)}}}{T} \, dT$$

* See appendix 5.

where L_f, the latent heat of fusion of gold at T_f (1,063°C), = 3,050 cal mole^{-1} and $C_{p_{Au(l)}} = 7.00$ cal deg^{-1} mole^{-1}.

Substituting these values:

$$S^0_{Au(l, 830°C)} = 11.32 + \int_{298}^{1,336} \left[\frac{5.66}{T} + 1.24 \times 10^{-3}\right] dT + \frac{3,050}{1,336} + \int_{1,336}^{1,103} \frac{7.0}{T} dT$$

$$= 11.32 + 9.79 + 2.28 - 1.35$$

$$= 22.04 \text{ cal deg}^{-1} \text{ mole}^{-1}.$$

Hence $\bar{S}_{Au}$, the partial molar entropy of gold in solution in a 40 atom per cent gold–lead alloy at 830°C = $22.04 + 3.58 = 25.62$ cal deg^{-1} mole^{-1}.

The graphical integration of this form of the Gibb–Duhem relation is rather unsatisfactory and, as will be shown presently, it is preferable to use other forms for which, on integration, it is not necessary to evaluate the area under an asymptotic curve.

5.5 *From vapour pressure measurements, the following values have been determined for the activity of mercury in liquid mercury–bismuth alloys at 320°C. Calculate the activity of bismuth in a 20 atom-per cent Bi alloy at this temperature.*

N_{Hg}	0·949	0·893	0·851	0·753	0·653	0·537	0·437	0·330	0·207	0·063
a_{Hg}	0·961	0·929	0·908	0·840	0·765	0·650	0·542	0·432	0·278	0·092

Experimental measurements very commonly yield the activity of a component in a solution directly (e.g. vapour pressure measurements, equilibrium data). The Gibbs–Duhem relation, *1.43*, may readily be expressed in terms of the activities of the components by substitution of the relation:

$$d\bar{G}_i = RT d \ln a_i$$

obtained by differentiation of *1.54*.

On this substitution, it is obtained that:

$$\sum N_i d \ln a_i = 0.$$

Applied to the binary Hg–Bi system, this becomes:

$$N_{Hg} d \ln a_{Hg} + N_{Bi} d \ln a_{Bi} = 0 \qquad 5.5.1$$

or, as an indefinite integral:

$$\int d \ln a_{Bi} = - \int \frac{N_{Hg}}{N_{Bi}} d \ln a_{Hg}. \qquad 5.5.2$$

The upper integration limit will be $N_{Bi} = 0.20$, while the lower limit is chosen so as to yield a known value of a_{Bi} on the left-hand side of 5.5.2. Since by definition, $a_{Bi} \rightarrow 1$ as $N_{Bi} \rightarrow 1$, a lower integration limit of $N_{Bi} = 1$ will yield:

$$\ln a_{Bi\,(N_{Bi}=0.20)} = - \int_{N_{Bi}=1}^{N_{Bi}=0.20} \frac{N_{Hg}}{N_{Bi}} \, d \ln a_{Hg}$$

or:

$$\log a_{Bi\,(N_{Bi}=0.20)} = + \int_{N_{Bi}=0.20}^{N_{Bi}=1} \frac{N_{Hg}}{N_{Bi}} \, d \log a_{Hg}.$$

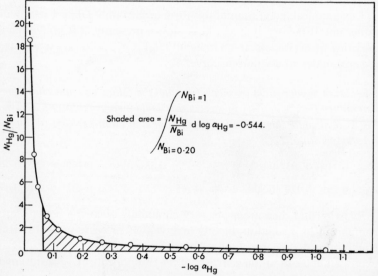

Fig. 5.5a. Graphical solution of binary Gibbs–Duhem equation. Solution of integral in equation (5.5.2).

The activity of bismuth in the 20 atom per cent alloy is given, therefore, as the antilog of the area under a curve of N_{Hg}/N_{Bi} versus $\log a_{Hg}$ between the limits $N_{Bi} = 1$, $(N_{Hg}/N_{Bi} = 0)$, and $N_{Bi} = 0.20$, $(N_{Hg}/N_{Bi} = 4)$. As in the previous example, the area to be measured is under a curve tending to infinity, as shown in Fig. 5.5a. Bearing the inherent errors in mind, the shaded portion shown is of area -0.544 units (using the Trapezoidal rule, $\Delta \log a_{Hg}$ chord width 0.05). This yields a value of:

$$a_{Bi\,(N_{Bi}=0.20)} = \text{antilog } \overline{1}.456$$

$$= 0.286.$$

It is apparent, as in the previous example, that the area measured is too small, and this activity value is too large (the area being a negative quantity). A better result is obtained if the data are expressed in terms of the activity coefficient instead of the activity, using a further version of the Gibbs–Duhem relation.

For a binary system AB, $N_A + N_B = 1$ or $dN_A + dN_B = 0$. Multiplying throughout by:

$$\frac{N_A}{N_A} = \frac{N_B}{N_B} = 1,$$

then:

$$N_A \cdot \frac{dN_A}{N_A} + N_B \cdot \frac{dN_B}{N_B} = 0$$

or:

$$N_A \, d \ln N_A + N_B \, d \ln N_B = 0.$$

Subtraction of this relation from the binary Gibbs–Duhem relation 5.5.1 yields:

$$N_A \, d \ln \gamma_A + N_B \, d \ln \gamma_B = 0 \qquad 5.5.3$$

from the definition of the activity coefficient, $\gamma_i = a_i/N_i$. As an indefinite integral, this form of the Gibbs–Duhem equation yields, for the present system,

$$\int d \ln \gamma_{Bi} = - \int \frac{N_{Hg}}{N_{Bi}} \cdot d \ln \gamma_{Hg}$$

or, integrating between $N_{Bi} = 1$ (where $\gamma_{Bi} = 1$) and $N_{Bi} = 0.20$:

$$\ln \gamma_{Bi\,(N_{Bi}=0.20)} = - \int\limits_{N_{Bi}=1}^{N_{Bi}=0.20} \frac{N_{Hg}}{N_{Bi}} d \ln \gamma_{Hg}$$

or:

$$\log \gamma_{Bi\,(N_{Bi}=0.20)} = + \int\limits_{N_{Bi}=0.20}^{N_{Bi}=1} \frac{N_{Hg}}{N_{Bi}} d \log \gamma_{Hg}.$$

The activity coefficient of bismuth is obtained, therefore, as the antilog of the area under a curve of N_{Hg}/N_{Bi} versus $\log \gamma_{Hg}$ between the limits $N_{Bi} = 1$ ($N_{Hg}/N_{Bi} = 0$) and $N_{Bi} = 0.20$ ($N_{Hg}/N_{Bi} = 4$).

Values of γ_{Bi} are calculated from the table given, by use of the definition $\gamma_i = a_i/N_i$. The area to be integrated is shown shaded in Fig. 5.5b. It should be noted that the curve is *not* asymptotic to the abscissa as $\log \gamma_{Hg}$ is finite when $N_{Bi} = 1$ or $N_{Hg}/N_{Bi} = 0$. Thus the shaded portion

8

of Fig. 5.5b is of area $+0\cdot134$ units (using the Trapezoidal rule, $\Delta \log \gamma_{Hg}$ chord width $0\cdot01$), which yields a value of:

$$\gamma_{Bi\,(N_{Bi}=0\cdot20)} = \text{antilog}\, 0\cdot134$$

$$= 1\cdot36.$$

Hence:

$$a_{Bi} = \gamma_{Bi} \cdot N_{Bi}$$

$$= 1\cdot36 \times 0\cdot20$$

$$= 0\cdot272.$$

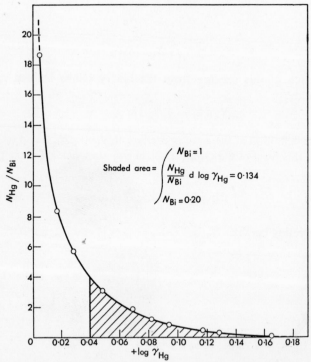

Fig. 5.5b. Graphical solution of binary Gibbs–Duhem equation.

This value is, of course, smaller than that obtained in the first part of this example, but is closer to the true value of the activity of bismuth. The only errors in the value of $a_{Bi} = 0\cdot272$ arise from curve drawing and the use of the Trapezoidal rule, whereas previously a large error arose from the impracticability of area measurement under an asymptotic curve.

5.6 *Calculate the activity of bismuth in a 3 atom-per cent bismuth–mercury alloy at 320°C, using the data given in example 5.5.*

As demonstrated, the use of the Gibbs–Duhem relation expressed in terms of activity coefficient is quite satisfactory when values of the activity of the unknown component are required for solutions containing appreciable amounts of that component. However, when values of the activity are required in dilute solutions of the unknown component, difficulties are encountered due to the asymptotic nature of the curve (as in Fig. 5.5b) with respect to the ordinate. For example, the required evaluation of the activity of bismuth in a Bi–Hg solution at $N_{Bi} = 0.03$ would be difficult using equation 5.5.3 as the area to be measured under the curve would be to a value of $N_{Hg}/N_{Bi} = 32.3$. Activity values in dilute solutions are very important, and this difficulty is a severe limitation on the usefulness of 5.5.3. Fortunately, a modification of this equation has been devised by Wagner [2], which removes the necessity of integrating to a steeply rising curve.

Division of 5.5.3 by dN_B yields:

$$N_A \cdot \frac{d \ln \gamma_A}{dN_B} + N_B \cdot \frac{d \ln \gamma_B}{dN_B} = 0$$

or, as an indefinite integral:

$$\int d \ln \gamma_A = - \int \frac{N_B}{N_A} \cdot \frac{d \ln \gamma_B}{dN_B} \cdot dN_B.$$

On integration by parts, this yields:

$$\int d \ln \gamma_A = - \frac{N_B}{N_A} \ln \gamma_B + \int \frac{\ln \gamma_B}{N_A^2} \cdot dN_B. \qquad 5.6.1$$

To yield the activity of bismuth in the 3 atom per cent bismuth alloy, relation 5.6.1 becomes:

$$\log \gamma_{Bi\,(N_{Bi}=0.03)} = - \left[\frac{N_{Hg}}{N_{Bi}} \log \gamma_{Hg} \right]_{N_{Bi}=1}^{N_{Bi}=0.03} + \int_{N_{Bi}=1}^{N_{Bi}=0.03} \frac{\log \gamma_{Hg}}{N_{Bi}^2} dN_{Hg}. \qquad 5.6.2$$

The integral in this equation is given by the area under a curve of $\log \gamma_{Hg}/N_{Bi}^2$ versus N_{Hg} which, as shown in Fig. 5.6a, is not asymptotic to either of the coordinates. The shaded portion between the limits $N_{Bi} = 0.03$ ($N_{Hg} = 0.97$) and $N_{Bi} = 1$ ($N_{Hg} = 0$) is of area 0.539 units (measured using the Trapezoidal rule, ΔN_{Hg} chord width 0.05). The other term in *5.6.2* requires the value of $\log \gamma_{Hg}$ at $N_{Bi} = 0.03$, which value is read off from the curve of Fig. 5.6a. Thus:

$$\left(\frac{\log \gamma_{Hg}}{N_{Bi}^2}\right)_{N_{Bi}=0.03} = 2.20$$

or:

$$\left(\frac{N_{Hg}}{N_{Bi}} \log \gamma_{Hg}\right)_{N_{Bi}=0.03} = 0.064$$

and:

$$\left(\frac{N_{Hg}}{N_{Bi}} \log \gamma_{Hg}\right)_{N_{Bi}=1} = 0.$$

Hence:

$$\log \gamma_{Bi\,(N_{Bi}=0.03)} = -0.064 + 0.539$$
$$= 0.475$$

or:

$$\gamma_{Bi\,(N_{Bi}=0.03)} = 2.99.$$

Hence:

$$a_{Bi\,(N_{Bi}=0.03)} = 2.99 \times 0.03$$
$$= 0.0897 \text{ as required.}$$

It will be noted that this value is not particularly sensitive to the exact position of the curve of Fig. 5.6a in the region $0.9 < N_{Hg} < 1$, where the scatter of the experimental points necessitates a rather arbitrary fixing of the position of the curve.

Using this analysis, but integrating *5.6.1* up to $N_{Bi} = 0.20$ only, yields:

$$\log \gamma_{Bi\,(N_{Bi}=0.20)} = -0.163 + 0.282$$
$$= 0.119$$

or:

$$\gamma_{Bi\,(N_{Bi}=0.20)} = 1.315.$$

Hence:

$$a_{Bi\,(N_{Bi}=0.20)} = 0.263$$

which compares well with the value of $a_{Bi\,(N_{Bi}=0.20)} = 0.272$, previously obtained.

If the experimental data are adequate, it is sometimes possible to express the thermodynamic behaviour of a solution in terms of empirical equations relating the various thermodynamic parameters with composition. Most commonly, the activity coefficient of a component of a solution is expressed as a function of composition and temperature by an equation valid for a specified temperature range, which is usually, though not always, the range in which the experimental data have been obtained. In such cases, the Gibbs–Duhem relation may be integrated analytically instead of graphically. This is illustrated in the following example.

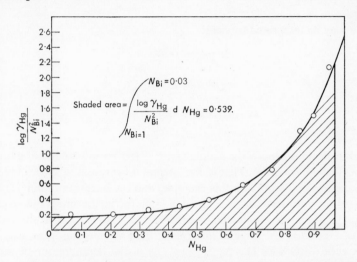

Fig. 5.6a. Graphical solution of binary Gibbs–Duhem equation. Solution of the integral in equation (5.6.2).

5.7   *From e.m.f. measurements, the activity coefficient of zinc in liquid cadmium–zinc alloys at 435°C has been shown to conform to the relation:*

$$\ln \gamma_{Zn} = 0.87\, N_{Cd}^2 - 0.30 N_{Cd}^3.$$

Calculate the activity of cadmium in a 30 atom-per cent Cd alloy at this temperature.

The appropriate form of the Gibbs–Duhem relation is:

$$N_{Zn}\, d \ln \gamma_{Zn} + N_{Cd}\, d \ln \gamma_{Cd} = 0$$

or, as a definite integral:

$N_{Cd} = 0.30$

$$\ln \gamma_{Cd} = -\int_{N_{Zn}=0}^{N_{Zn}=0.7} \frac{N_{Zn}}{N_{Cd}} d \ln \gamma_{Zn} \qquad 5.7.1$$

From the relation given: $N_{Cd} = 0$

$$\ln \gamma_{Zn} = 0.87 N_{Cd}^2 - 0.30 N_{Cd}^3$$

then:

$$d \ln \gamma_{Zn} = [1.74 N_{Cd} - 0.90 N_{Cd}^2]\, d N_{Cd}.$$

Substituting in *5.7.1* and replacing N_{Zn} by $(1 - N_{Cd})$, cancelling where possible and expressing the integration limits in terms of the component Cd gives:

$$\ln \gamma_{Cd} = - \int_{N_{Cd}=1}^{N_{Cd}=0.3} (1.74 - 2.64 N_{Cd} + 0.90 N_{Cd}^2) \, dN_{Cd} \qquad 5.7.2$$

which may be integrated to yield:

$$\ln \gamma_{Cd} = 0.310$$

or:

$$\gamma_{Cd} = 1.363.$$

Thus:

$$a_{Cd \, (N_{Cd}=0.3)} = 1.363 \times 0.3$$
$$= 0.409.$$

This method is usually the simplest way of analytically integrating the Gibbs–Duhem equation. That is, the integral is expressed in terms of the *unknown* component (Cd in this example) and the integration limits are changed accordingly; for then the denominator in the integrand (e.g. N_{Cd} in *5.7.1*) may be eliminated by cancellation, as in *5.7.2*. The alternative, of expressing the integral in terms of the known component, leads to an expression with $(1 - N_{\text{known component}})$ in the denominator of the integrand which, in general, then has to be integrated by parts.

It is commonly found that activity coefficient data for a solution are expressed by a relation of the form:

$$RT \ln \gamma_A = \alpha N_B^2$$

where α is a constant. Such a relation leads to a similar expression for the activity coefficient of component B of the binary solution. For, from this relation:

$$RT \, d \ln \gamma_A = -2\alpha(1 - N_A) \, dN_A$$

which on substitution in the integrated form of *5.5.3*:

$$\ln \gamma_B = - \int \frac{N_A}{N_B} d \ln \gamma_A$$

yields:

$$\ln \gamma_B = \frac{2\alpha}{RT} \int \frac{N_A(1 - N_A)}{N_B} \cdot dN_A$$

$$= \frac{2\alpha}{RT} \cdot \frac{N_A^2}{2}$$

or:

$$RT \ln \gamma_B = \alpha N_A^2.$$

Hence, for a binary solution described by a relation for component A of this type, there is no need to use the Gibbs–Duhem equation to obtain data for component B.

As noted in chapter 1, p. 15, it may be shown that for a binary regular solution, defined by *1.80*, the functions

$$\alpha_A\left(= RT\frac{\ln\gamma_A}{N_B^2}\right) \quad \text{and} \quad \alpha_B\left(= RT\frac{\ln\gamma_B}{N_A^2}\right)$$

are equal and constant and that the quantity $RT\ln\gamma_i$ is independent of temperature. Thus activity coefficient data for regular solutions are expressible by relations of the form of *1.84* and the observations just made will be applicable to such solutions. However, it should be emphasized again that the existence of such a functional relation for activity coefficient data for a solution does not, of itself, imply that the solution is regular.

The following example demonstrates the ease with which data for the unknown component may be deduced when the known activity coefficient data conforms to this functional relation.

5.8 *From extrapolated data for the solid alloys, the activity coefficient of aluminium in liquid Al–Zn alloys, relative to liquid aluminium as the standard state, is given by:*

$$RT\ln\gamma_{Al(l)} = 1,750(1 - N_{Al})^2.$$

Calculate the activity of zinc at 550°C (i.e. just above the liquidus) in the equi-atomic solution.

From the relation given, it is apparent that it is unnecessary to use the Gibbs–Duhem relation. Thus:

$$\frac{RT\ln\gamma_{Al}}{N_{Zn}^2} = \frac{RT\ln\gamma_{Zn}}{N_{Al}^2} = 1,750.$$

Hence:

$$\gamma_{Zn\,(N_{Zn}=0\cdot5)} = 1\cdot308$$

and:

$$a_{Zn\,(N_{Zn}=0\cdot5)} = 0\cdot654.$$

Excess thermodynamic quantities

5.9 *From e.m.f. measurements, the partial molar free energy of mixing of silver in a liquid gold–silver alloy containing 80 atom-per cent Ag is calculated to be −700 cal mole⁻¹ at 1,085°C, relative to liquid silver as the standard state. Assuming that gold–silver alloys behave regularly at this temperature, calculate the excess integral molar free energy of the solution of this composition*

In addition to involving the use of excess quantities, this example further illustrates the considerable simplification of thermodynamic calculations in systems which adhere to regular solution behaviour. In particular, such behaviour enables quantities to be calculated from much more limited experimental data than is possible for a non-regular (non-ideal) solution. The single quantity $\bar{G}_{Ag}^{M} = -700$ cal mole^{-1} in a binary solution $N_{Ag} = 0.80$, would in general be inadequate as a basis for the calculation of any integral quantity, since the latter requires thermodynamic data for both components of a binary system. However, with the assumption of regular solution behaviour, this single quantity for one component may be used to calculate data for the other component. For, from *1.75*, the excess partial molar free energy of a component i of a solution is given by:

$$\bar{G}_i^E = \bar{G}_i - \bar{G}_i^{ideal}.$$

From the definition of quantities of mixing, this is equivalent to:

$$\bar{G}_i^E = (\bar{G}_i^M + G_i^0) - (\bar{G}_i^M + G_i^0)^{ideal}.$$

Hence:

$$\bar{G}_i^E = \bar{G}_i^M - \bar{G}_i^{M\,ideal}$$

$$= \bar{G}_i^M - RT \ln N_i \quad \text{from } 1.67.$$

This relation is completely general and applicable to a component of any solution.

From the data given for the Au–Ag system at $1,085°C$ $(1,358°K)$:

$$\bar{G}_{Ag\,(N_{Ag}=0.8)}^E = -700 - RT \ln N_{Ag}$$

$$= -700 + 603$$

$$= -97 \text{ cal mole}^{-1}.$$

However, if a system is assumed to behave regularly, the function α, defined in *1.84* as:

$$\alpha_i = \frac{RT \ln \gamma_i}{(1 - N_i)^2}$$

may be assumed to be a constant for the components of the solution (cf. previous example). Thus, for a regular Au–Ag alloy:

$$\frac{RT \ln \gamma_{Au}}{N_{Ag}^2} = \frac{RT \ln \gamma_{Ag}}{N_{Au}^2}$$

or, from *1.79*:

$$\frac{\bar{G}_{Au}^E}{N_{Ag}^2} = \frac{\bar{G}_{Ag}^E}{N_{Au}^2}.$$

Substituting the given values:

$$\bar{G}_{Au}^E = -97 \times \left(\frac{0 \cdot 80}{0 \cdot 20}\right)^2$$

$$= -1,552 \text{ cal mole}^{-1}.$$

From *1.42* applied to excess free energies in the Au–Ag system, the excess integral molar free energy of the solution is given by:

$$G^E = N_{Au}\, \bar{G}_{Au}^E + N_{Ag}\, \bar{G}_{Ag}^E$$

or:

$$G_{(N_{Ag}=0 \cdot 8)}^E = 0 \cdot 2 \times (-1,552) + 0 \cdot 8(-97)$$

$$= -388 \text{ cal mole}^{-1} \text{ of solution.} \quad \checkmark$$

5.10 *At 705°K, the available experimental data for integral heats and entropies of mixing of the non-ideal, non-regular liquid systems* Cd–Pb, Cd–Sn *and* Cd–Zn *(designated 1–2), may be described by empirical equations of the form:*

$$H^M = AN_1 N_2 + BN_2 \log N_2$$

$$S^M = -C(N_1 \log N_1 + N_2 \log N_2)$$

where the values for the constants A, B *and* C *for the three alloy systems are listed below. Compare the deviations of these systems from ideal behaviour in terms of the values of the excess partial molar free energy of cadmium in the equi-atomic solutions.*

System	A	B	C
Cd–Pb	+1,430	−1,660	+4·8
Cd–Sn	+880	−1,290	+5·3
Cd–Zn	+1,600	−830	+4·6

This example demonstrates how experimental thermodynamic data, expressed in this instance by means of empirical functions of composition, may be used to derive the quantities most commonly employed to describe the behaviour of non-ideal, non-regular solutions.

Using *1.63* applied to integral quantities of mixing:

$$G^M = H^M - TS^M$$

the integral free energy of mixing of the alloy systems at 705°K may be deduced, as a function of composition, from the relations given for the enthalpy and entropy. Thus:

$$G^M = AN_1 N_2 + 705CN_1 \log N_1 + (B + 705C) N_2 \log N_2. \quad \textit{5.10.1}$$

The partial molar free energy of mixing ($\bar{G}_1^M$) for component 1 can be obtained from this, using *1.47* applied to free energies of mixing:

$$\bar{G}_1^M = G^M + (1 - N_1)\frac{\mathrm{d}G^M}{\mathrm{d}N_1}. \qquad 5.10.2$$

Differentiating *5.10.1* with respect to N_1:

$$\frac{\mathrm{d}G^M}{\mathrm{d}N_1} = A(1 - 2N_1) + 705C(0\cdot434 + \log N_1)$$
$$- (B + 705C)(0\cdot434 + \log N_2). \qquad 5.10.3$$

Substituting *5.10.1* and *5.10.3* into *5.10.2* yields:

$$\bar{G}_1^M = AN_2^2 + 705C\log N_1 - 0\cdot434BN_2.$$

Thus for $N_1 = N_2 = 0\cdot5$,

$$\bar{G}_{\mathrm{Cd}}^M = 0\cdot25A - 212\cdot1C - 0\cdot217B$$

$$= -300 \text{ cal mole}^{-1} \text{ for Cd–Pb system}$$
$$= -625 \text{ cal mole}^{-1} \text{ for Cd–Sn system} \left.\right\} \text{ at } N_{\mathrm{Cd}} = 0\cdot5.$$
$$= -395 \text{ cal mole}^{-1} \text{ for Cd–Zn system}$$

From *1.54*:

$$\bar{G}_i^M = RT\ln a_i$$

and hence:

$$a_{\mathrm{Cd}} = 0\cdot806 \text{ for Cd–Pb}$$
$$= 0\cdot640 \text{ for Cd–Sn} \left.\right\} \text{ at } N_{\mathrm{Cd}} = 0\cdot5$$
$$= 0\cdot755 \text{ for Cd–Zn}$$

and:

$$\gamma_{\mathrm{Cd}} = 1\cdot61 \text{ for Cd–Pb}$$
$$= 1\cdot28 \text{ for Cd–Sn} \left.\right\} \text{ at } N_{\mathrm{Cd}} = 0\cdot5.$$
$$= 1\cdot51 \text{ for Cd–Zn}$$

However, from *1.79*:

$$\bar{G}_i^E = RT\ln \gamma_i.$$

Hence:

$$\bar{G}_{\mathrm{Cd}}^E = +667 \text{ cal mole}^{-1} \text{ for Cd–Pb}$$
$$= +346 \text{ cal mole}^{-1} \text{ for Cd–Sn} \left.\right\} \text{ at } N_{\mathrm{Cd}} = 0\cdot5.$$
$$= +578 \text{ cal mole}^{-1} \text{ for Cd–Zn}$$

The magnitudes of these positive excess partial molar free energies show immediately the extent of the positive deviations of the solutions from ideal behaviour. Thus the Cd–Sn system is more ideal than the Cd–Zn, which in turn deviates less from ideal behaviour than does the Cd–Pb system.

As would be expected from *1.79*, the activity coefficients have values which also indicate the respective order of the deviations of these systems from ideality. However, because of the logarithmic relation of *1.79*, the relative magnitudes of the deviations from ideality, as indicated by the activity coefficients and the excess partial molar free energies of cadmium, are markedly different. Although the activity coefficient is the quantity employed as a measure of the deviation from ideality in, for example, equilibrium calculations, the excess partial molar free energy is the more useful criterion when considering the causes for the non-ideal behaviour of a system.

The interrelation of quantities in solution thermodynamics

Several of the previous examples in this chapter have illustrated the use of the various quantities which describe the thermodynamic behaviour of ideal, regular and general solutions. However, when teaching thermodynamics, it has been the experience of the authors that students commonly confuse the various quantities involved in problems of this type. For example, some students find difficulty in distinguishing between excess and relative molar quantities. With this in mind, it has been found useful for the student to consider problems of an algebraic nature involving these quantities. By this means, he must understand and interrelate the quantities without the 'distracting' requirement of slide-rule manipulation. The last two examples in this chapter are of this algebraic type, illustrating the relations between the functions involved in the description of the thermodynamics of solutions.

5.11   *Describe how to calculate the value of the integral molar entropy of a non-ideal, non-regular solution* AB *(containing n_A mole of A and n_B mole of B), assuming that the following data have been determined at a constant temperature T:*

    (a) *The partial molar enthalpy of component A over a range of composition from pure B up to and including the composition of the solution.*

    (b) *The activity of component A over the same range of composition.*

    (c) *The standard molar free energies of components A and B and the standard molar enthalpy of component B.*

If these data were not available, but it could be assumed that the solution behaved regularly, what single state variable of the pure components would be needed to deduce the integral molar entropy?

It should be noted that the integral molar entropy and *not* the integral molar entropy of mixing of the solution is required. The activity data for component A yield values of the partial molar free energy of mixing, which must then be combined with the available standard free energy of A to obtain the partial molar free energy of component A as a function of composition in the solution. These data can then be used to calculate corresponding data for component B and hence the integral molar free energy of the solution. Similar manipulation of the partial molar enthalpy data yields the integral molar enthalpy. The integral molar entropy can then be obtained by use of the definitional relation, *1.31*.

In addition to the known quantities, G_A^0, G_B^0 and H_B^0, the available data may be expressed by:

$$\bar{H}_A = f_1(N_A) \qquad\qquad 5.11.1$$

$$a_A = f_2(N_A) \qquad\qquad 5.11.2$$

these relations being known over the range of composition $0 \leqslant N_A \leqslant X_A$, where:

$$X_A = \frac{n_A}{n_A + n_B}.$$

From *1.54*:

$$\bar{G}_A - G_A^0 = RT \ln a_A,$$

and, from the known value of G_A^0 and *5.11.2*, the partial molar free energy of A may be calculated. That is:

$$\bar{G}_A = f_3(N_A). \qquad\qquad 5.11.3$$

However, from the Gibbs–Duhem relation *1.43*:

$$N_A \, d\bar{G}_A + N_B \, d\bar{G}_B = 0$$

or:

$$\bar{G}_B - G_B^0 = - \int_0^{X_A} \frac{N_A}{N_B} d\bar{G}_A$$

and by insertion of the differential of *5.11.3* and the value of G_B^0, $\bar{G}_B$ may be calculated at the composition X_A of the solution. The integral molar free energy G of the solution is then derived using *1.42*:

$$G = N_A \bar{G}_A + N_B \bar{G}_B.$$

Similarly, from *5.11.1* and the known value of H_B^0 in conjunction with the Gibbs–Duhem relation applied to partial molar enthalpies:

$$\bar{H}_B - H_B^0 = -\int\limits_0^{X_A} \frac{N_A}{N_B} \, d\bar{H}_A$$

the partial molar enthalpy of B at the composition X_A of the solution may be calculated. The integral molar enthalpy H of the solution is derived from *1.42* applied to enthalpies:

$$H = N_A \bar{H}_A + N_B \bar{H}_B.$$

The required quantity, the integral molar entropy of the solution, is then obtained from:

$$S = \frac{H - G}{T}.$$

If the solution is regular (and none of the previous data is available), then, from *1.80* for a regular solution AB, the partial molar entropies of mixing are given by:

and:
$$\left.\begin{aligned}
\bar{S}_A^M &= \bar{S}_A - S_A^0 = -R\ln N_A \\
\bar{S}_B^M &= \bar{S}_B - S_B^0 = -R\ln N_B
\end{aligned}\right\} \qquad 5.11.4$$

where S_A^0 and S_B^0 are the standard molar entropies of the pure components A and B at the temperature T. Hence if these latter quantities are known, the partial molar entropies of A and B in the solution may be calculated from *5.11.4*. Using these values the required quantity, the integral molar entropy of the solution, may be calculated from *1.42* applied to entropies:

$$S = N_A \bar{S}_A + N_B \bar{S}_B.$$

5.12 *The integral molar entropy of a non-ideal, non-regular liquid solution A–B is known as a complete function of composition* $(0 \leqslant N_A \leqslant 1)$ *at a temperature T, together with the free energy of the pure component A and the activity of A in a solution containing X_A atom fraction of that component. Show how to calculate the partial molar enthalpy of A and the excess partial molar entropy of B in the solution X_A at the temperature T.*

The available data may be represented by:

$$S = f_1(N_A) \qquad\qquad 5.12.1$$

with G_A^0 and a_A in the solution X_A.

The first step is to calculate the partial molar entropies of the components in the solution X_A. From *1.46* and *1.47*, partial molar quantities may be found for any solution (either graphically or analytically) if the integral quantity is known as a function of composition. Thus for the partial molar entropies:

$$\left[\bar{S}_A = S + N_A \frac{\partial S}{\partial N_A}\right]_{N_A = X_A}$$

$$\left[\bar{S}_B = S - (1 - N_A)\frac{\partial S}{\partial N_A}\right]_{N_A = X_A}$$

by means of which $\bar{S}_A$ and $\bar{S}_B$ in the present example may be calculated analytically.

From *1.54*:

$$\bar{G}_A = G_A^0 + RT \ln a_A$$

and hence, from the available values of G_A^0 and a_A (in the solution of composition X_A), the partial molar free energy of component A in the solution X_A may be calculated.

Then, from *1.31* applied to partial molar quantities:

$$\bar{H}_A = \bar{G}_A + T\bar{S}_A$$

the partial molar enthalpy of component A in the solution X_A is found, as required.

The excess partial molar entropy of component B in the solution X_A is given, following *1.75*, by:

$$\bar{S}_B^E = \bar{S}_B - \bar{S}_B^{\text{ideal}}$$
$$= \bar{S}_B - (\bar{S}_B^M + S_B^0)^{\text{ideal}} \qquad \qquad 5.12.2$$

where $\bar{S}_B^{M\,\text{ideal}}$ is the partial molar entropy of mixing of component B in a hypothetical ideal solution of composition X_A.

But from *1.72*:

$$\bar{S}_B^{M\,\text{ideal}} = -R \ln N_B$$
$$= -R \ln(1 - X_A)$$

and this quantity may be calculated directly. In addition, S_B^0, the molar entropy of pure component B is given by *5.12.1* when $N_A = 0$ (i.e. at pure B) and may also be calculated.

Hence, with the value of $\bar{S}_B$ deduced previously, all the quantities on the right-hand side of *5.12.2* are known and the value of the excess partial molar entropy of component B in the solution X_A may be calculated.

Exercises

5.A Liquid tin–bismuth alloys are approximately ideal at 1,000°C, at which temperature the vapour pressures of the pure components are $1 \cdot 66 \times 10^{-4}$ and $1 \cdot 910$ mm Hg respectively. If the latent heats of vaporization of pure tin and bismuth are taken to be $68 \cdot 20$ and $44 \cdot 53$ kcal mole^{-1} respectively at this temperature, calculate the latent heat of vaporization of an alloy containing 3 atom-per cent bismuth at the same temperature.

weighed

5.B An inert gas containing $0 \cdot 3$ per cent by volume of sulphur vapour (S$_2$) is pumped at 2 atmosphere pressure through a liquid iron–manganese alloy containing 30 atom-per cent manganese at 1,600°C. Under these conditions, the sulphur reacts only with the manganese, with a heat of reaction of $-63 \cdot 1$ kcal mole^{-1} of MnS formed. If it is assumed that Fe–Mn alloys behave ideally at this temperature, calculate the heat evolved in the bath per thousand litres of gas blown through. What is the heat effect if the alloy is assumed to behave regularly, rather than ideally, the activity coefficient of manganese being taken as $1 \cdot 14$?

5.C The latent heat of vaporization of manganese is $53 \cdot 7$ kcal mole^{-1} at the boiling point, 2,095°C. Assuming that this value does not change significantly with temperature, determine the vapour pressure of manganese at 1,600°C.

Assuming that manganese behaves ideally when dissolved in a liquid steel, determine whether or not a steel containing $1 \cdot 0$ weight-per cent manganese would lose any of this element when exposed to a vacuum of $0 \cdot 1$ mm Hg pressure at 1,600°C.

5.D An addition of 40 g of pure chromium is added to a bath of 1 kg of pure iron at 1,600°C. If the densities of Cr and Fe are $6 \cdot 1$ and $6 \cdot 9$ g cc^{-1} respectively at this temperature, and liquid ferrochrome is assumed to behave ideally, what is the density of the resulting alloy?

5.E From measurements of the e.m.f. and its temperature variation for galvanic cells with liquid aluminium anodes and liquid aluminium–bismuth alloy cathodes, the following smoothed values of the partial molar enthalpy of mixing of aluminium have been determined at 900°C for alloys containing up to 26 atom-per cent aluminium:

Atom-per cent Al	1	2	4	6	8	10	12
$\bar{H}_{Al}^{M}$, kcal mole^{-1}	5·76	5·53	5·23	5·00	4·80	4·63	4·47

Atom-per cent Al	14	16	18	20	22	24	26
$\bar{H}_{Al}^{M}$, kcal mole^{-1}	4·30	4·14	3·98	3·81	3·65	3·48	3·32

Calculate the partial molar heat of mixing of bismuth in the 80 atom-per cent Bi alloy at this temperature.

5.F From measurements of the equilibrium distribution of aluminium between liquid iron and silver, the activity coefficient of aluminium in Fe–Al alloys ($0 < N_{Al} < 0.25$) is given at 1,600°C by:

$$\log \gamma_{Al} = 2.60 N_{Al} - 1.51.$$

Calculate the activity of iron in the 80 atom-per cent Fe alloy at this temperature.

5.G The activity coefficient of sodium in liquid Hg–Na alloys at 25°C conforms to the relation:

$$\log \gamma_{Na} = -12.81 + 15.61 N_{Na} + 7.53 N_{Na}^{2}$$

referred to pure liquid sodium as the standard state. Calculate the activity of mercury in a 90 atom-per cent Hg alloy.

5.H From e.m.f. measurements, the partial molar free energy of mixing of magnesium in liquid Mg–Pb alloys at 560°C has been calculated at various compositions, as shown in the table.

N_{Pb}	0·2	0·3	0·4	0·5	0·6	0·7	0·8	0·9
$\bar{G}_{Mg}^{M}$, kcal mole^{-1}	−0·8	−1·53	−2·75	−3·75	−4·52	−5·50	−6·70	−8·10

Calculate the excess integral molar free energy of the equi-atomic solution.

5.I The volume changes on alloying liquid zinc and liquid tin to form liquid alloys at 420°C are given in the table. From these data, calculate the partial molar volume of mixing of tin in an alloy containing 40 atom-per cent zinc at the same temperature.

N_{Zn}	0·10	0·20	0·30	0·40	0·50
V^{M}, cc mole^{-1}	+0·0539	0·0964	0·1274	0·1542	0·1763

N_{Zn}	0·60	0·70	0·80	0·90
V^{M}, cc mole^{-1}	0·1888	0·1779	0·1441	0·0890

5.J From e.m.f. measurements, the partial molar entropy of mixing of zinc in liquid Zn–Ga alloys (relative to liquid zinc as the standard state) has been determined at 490°C over the complete composition range. From these data, given in the table, calculate the integral molar entropy of mixing of the solution containing 70 atom-per cent gallium.

N_{Ga}	0·1	0·2	0·3	0·4	0·5	0·6	0·7	0·8	0·9
$\bar{S}_{Zn}^{M}$, cal mole^{-1} deg^{-1}	0·32	0·645	1·00	1·42	1·88	2·42	3·09	4·00	5·50

5.K From vapour pressure measurements at 324°C, the following values of the activity coefficient of mercury in mercury–tin amalgams may be calculated:

N_{Hg}	0·2	0·3	0·4	0·5
γ_{Hg}	1·58	1·50	1·44	1·38

Assuming that this system is regular, calculate the integral free energy of mixing of the 30 atom-per cent Hg solution.

5.L If liquid Fe–Al alloys at 1,600°C conform to the relation:

$$\bar{G}_{Al}^{E} = -12,900 + 22,250 N_{Al}, \text{ cal mole}^{-1},$$

and the vapour pressure (in mm Hg) of pure molten iron is given by:

$$\log p_{Fe} = -\frac{20,150}{T} - 1·27 \log T + 13·98$$

calculate the vapour pressure of iron over an alloy containing 80 atom-per cent Fe at 1,600°C.

5.M Liquid brasses conform to the relation:

$$RT \ln \gamma_{Zn} = -5,000 N_{Cu}^{2}$$

and the vapour pressure of pure copper is given by:

$$\log p(\text{mm Hg}) = -\frac{17,520}{T} - 1·21 \log T + 13·21.$$

Calculate the vapour pressure of copper over a 60:40 brass at 1,200°C.

5.N Liquid copper–silver alloys are found to be regular at 1,150°C, at which temperature the partial molar heat of mixing of copper is as given, for various compositions, in the table. Derive an expression for the

9

variation of the activity coefficient of silver with composition at this temperature.

N_{Ag}	0·1	0·2	0·3	0·4	0·5	0·6	0·7
$\bar{H}_{Cu}^{M}$, cal mole^{-1}	40	145	325	560	825	1,160	1,590

5.O The thermodynamic behaviour of α brasses at 298°K may be described by the relations:

$$\bar{H}_{Zn}^{M} = -5,350N_{Cu}^{2} - 2,830N_{Cu}, \text{ cal mole}^{-1}$$

$$\bar{S}_{Zn}^{M} = -3·7\log N_{Zn}, \text{ cal mole}^{-1} \text{ deg}^{-1}.$$

Derive a relation between the composition and the excess integral molar free energy of the solution.

5.P At 930°C, Fe–Ni austenites are found to behave regularly, the integral enthalpy of mixing being given by:

$$H^{M} = -1,300N_{Fe} N_{Ni}, \text{ cal mole}^{-1}.$$

Calculate the excess partial molar free energy of iron in the 30 atom-per cent Ni solution.

5.Q Impure liquid lead, containing copper in solution, is refined by adding lead sulphide to the bath. The reaction which occurs may be represented by:

$$PbS_{(l)} + 2Cu_{(l)} \rightleftharpoons Cu_2S_{(l)} + Pb_{(l)},$$

the standard free-energy change being $-17·5$ kcal at 1,550°C. Assuming that the sulphides are immiscible and that at low concentrations, copper forms a regular solution in lead, described by:

$$\bar{H}_{Cu}^{M} = 2,700N_{Pb}^{2}, \text{ cal mole}^{-1},$$

calculate the extent to which the lead can be purified at 1,550°C.

5.R When more than about 2 weight-per cent of nickel is dissolved in iron, a continuous series of solid solutions is formed at 840°C. The dissolved iron is more readily oxidized than the nickel, and the FeO formed is insoluble in the alloy. An atmosphere of 57·5 per cent H_2 and 42·5 per cent H_2O by volume is in equilibrium at 1 atmosphere pressure with an Fe–Ni alloy containing 85·4 atom-per cent Fe at this temperature. What is the value of the excess partial molar free energy of iron in the alloy?

5.s   At 700°C, the integral heats of mixing of the liquid Cu–Cd system are found to conform to the relation:

$$H^M = 200 N_{Cu} N_{Cd}, \text{ cal mole}^{-1},$$

the partial molar entropy of mixing of cadmium being $1 \cdot 142$ cal mole^{-1} deg^{-1} in the equi-atomic solution and the free energy of pure liquid cadmium being $-15 \cdot 3$ kcal mole^{-1} at this temperature. Calculate the activity coefficient and the partial molar free energy of cadmium in the equi-atomic solution.

5.t   The system AB behaves regularly, the activity of component A in a solution containing X_A mole fraction of A being $(a_A)_1$ at a temperature T_1. Show how the integral heat of formation of the solution at a temperature $T_2 (\neq T_1)$ may be calculated.

5.u   At a temperature T, a volatile component B forms an extensive terminal solid solution with component A. Measurements of the vapour pressure of pure B and over solutions of various compositions are readily made. Indicate how the non-regular behaviour of these solutions may be deduced from such measurements, and how to calculate the composition dependence of the excess integral free energy of the solution AB at the temperature T.

References

1. J. H. HILDEBRAND, J. Am. Chem. Soc., 51, 1929, p. 66.
2. C. WAGNER, Thermodynamics of Alloys, Addison Wesley, 1952.

CHAPTER 6

Dilute Solutions and Alternative Standard States

As indicated in chapter 1, when a solute is present in a solution at relatively low concentration it is sometimes more convenient to refer the activity of the solute to an infinitely dilute standard state, in preference to the pure substance standard state. For example, in many solutions of interest, the pure solute exists in a different physical state to that in which it appears in the solution. In such cases, it is obviously more physically realistic to refer the solute to an infinitely dilute solution rather than to the pure solute as the standard state. From the use of such alternative standard states, the determination of the activity of a solute in a dilute, multicomponent solution becomes possible by combination of the appropriate interaction parameters measured on simple binary and ternary alloys containing the solute.

The equilibrium constant for a reaction can be expressed in terms of activities referred to a number of standard states, and can then be manipulated in a manner similar to those demonstrated in the examples of chapter 4. The only requirement for such manipulation is that the standard free-energy change for the reaction, with which the equilibrium constant is related through *1.58*, is also expressed in terms of the respective standard states chosen for each of the components of the reaction. The most common method of calculation of the free-energy change accompanying a change of standard state of a solute is demonstrated in example 6.1. The combination of such free-energy changes with that for a reaction in which all the components are referred to their pure states, enabling the equilibrium constant for the reaction to be determined when one or more solutes are referred to an alternative standard state, is illustrated in example 6.4. The usual method for the determination of interaction coefficients from experimental data is illustrated in examples 6.3 and 6.5 and the utilization of interaction coefficients for the solution of an equilibrium problem in a multi-component system is demonstrated in example 6.4.

6.1 *The melting point of pure titanium is 1,660°C and the heat of fusion is 4,500 cal mole^{-1}. The activity coefficient of titanium in iron at infinite dilution, relative to pure solid titanium as the standard state (i.e. γ^0) is 0·011 at 1,623°C. The atomic weights of titanium and iron are respectively 47·90 and 55·85. Calculate the change in the free energy when the standard state is transferred from pure solid titanium to the infinitely dilute, weight-per cent solution of titanium in iron at 1,623°C.*

The free-energy change at 1,623°C (1,900°K) accompanying the change of standard state from pure *liquid* titanium to an infinitely dilute, weight-per cent solution of titanium in liquid iron is obtained by use of equation *1.97*:

$$\text{Ti}_{(l,\ \text{pure})} \rightleftharpoons \text{Ti}_{(\%,\ \text{dilute})} \qquad \textit{6.1.1}$$

$$\Delta G^0 = G^0_{(\%,\ \text{dilute})} - G^0_{(\text{pure})}$$

$$= RT \ln \gamma^0 \cdot \left(\frac{M_{\text{Fe}}}{M_{\text{Ti}} \cdot 100} \right)$$

where M_{Fe} and M_{Ti} are the atomic weights of iron and titanium. Substituting the given values in this relation:

$$\Delta G^0 = 4 \cdot 575 \times 1,900 \log 0 \cdot 011 \left(\frac{55 \cdot 85}{47 \cdot 90 \times 100} \right)$$

$$= -33,830 \text{ cal mole}^{-1}.$$

This free-energy change applies to the dilution of pure liquid titanium. However, pure titanium is solid at 1,623°C and hence the free-energy change accompanying the fusion of titanium must be taken into account. The heat of fusion is given as 4,500 cal mole^{-1} at the melting point (1,933°K), from which the entropy of fusion is obtained by use of *1.100*:

$$S_f = \frac{L_f}{T_f}$$

$$= \frac{4,500}{1,933}$$

$$= 2 \cdot 33 \text{ cal deg}^{-1} \text{ mole}^{-1}.$$

Assuming S_f and L_f are independent of temperature, the free-energy change for the reaction:

$$\text{Ti}_{(s,\ \text{pure})} \rightleftharpoons \text{Ti}_{(l,\ \text{pure})} \qquad \textit{6.1.2}$$

is given by:

$$G_f = +4,500 - 2 \cdot 33 T \text{ cal}$$

$$= +70 \text{ cal at } 1,623°C \ (1,900°K).$$

The free-energy change accompanying the overall change in standard state, that is:

$$Ti_{(s, pure)} \rightleftharpoons Ti_{(wt\%, \, dilute \, in \, Fe)}$$

is then obtained by adding *6.1.1* and *6.1.2*:

$$\Delta G^0 = -33,830 + 70$$

$$= -33,760 \text{ cal mole}^{-1} \text{ at } 1,623°C.$$

6.2 *From experimental measurements of the equilibria between* H_2–H_2O *gas mixtures, pure solid silica and silicon dissolved in liquid iron, the free-energy change accompanying the transfer of standard state from pure liquid silicon to the infinitely dilute, weight-per cent solution of silicon in iron, that is:*

$$Si_{(pure, \, l)} \rightleftharpoons Si_{(wt\%, \, dilute \, in \, Fe}\,\,)$$

has been evaluated as:

$$\Delta G^0 = -28,500 - 5 \cdot 8T \text{ cal mole}^{-1}.$$

At 1,600°C *the activity coefficient of silicon in iron, relative to pure silicon as the standard state, is* 0·0014 *at 1 atom-per cent silicon. Calculate the activity coefficient of silicon, relative to the weight-per cent standard state, at this concentration.*

The first step is to calculate the activity of silicon referred to the dilute standard state, making use of *1.97* and *1.93*.

At 1,600°C (1,873°K) the free-energy change accompanying the transfer of standard state from pure liquid silicon to the dilute, weight-per cent solution is:

$$\Delta G^0 = -28,500 - (5 \cdot 8 \times 1,873)$$

$$= -39,360 \text{ cal mole}^{-1}.$$

The activity coefficient of silicon at infinite dilution (relative to pure silicon as the standard state) can be obtained, therefore, by substituting this value and the atomic weights for silicon (28·09) and iron (55·85) into *1.97*. That is:

$$\Delta G^0 = RT \ln\left(\frac{M_{Fe} \cdot \gamma_{Si}^0}{M_{Si} \cdot 100}\right)$$

or:

$$-39,360 = 4 \cdot 575 \times 1,873 \log\left(\frac{55 \cdot 85 \cdot \gamma_{Si}^0}{28 \cdot 09 \times 100}\right).$$

Hence:

$$\gamma_{Si(1,873)}^0 = 0 \cdot 00128.$$

From the given data, the activity of silicon at 1 atom-per cent silicon, relative to pure silicon as the standard state, is:

$$a_{Si\,(pure)} = N_{Si} \cdot \gamma_{Si}^0$$
$$= 0.01 \times 0.0014$$
$$= 0.000014.$$

The activity of silicon at this concentration, relative to the infinitely dilute, weight-per cent solution of silicon in iron as the standard state, is given, therefore, by *1.98*. That is:

$$\frac{a_{Si\,(pure)}}{a_{Si\,(dilute)}} = \frac{M_{Fe} \cdot \gamma_{Si}^0}{M_{Si} \cdot 100}.$$

Substituting the calculated values of $a_{Si\,(pure)}$, γ_{Si}^0 and the atomic weights:

$$a_{Si\,(dilute)} = 0.55.$$

This is the activity of silicon in the 1 atom-per cent silicon alloy on the infinitely dilute, weight-per cent standard state scale. Thus, from the definitional relation *1.92* the activity coefficient, relative to this scale, is obtained by dividing the activity by the weight-per cent concentration of silicon. However, the concentration of silicon in the alloy is given as the atom fraction, so this must be converted into weight-per cent. At $N_{Si} = 0.01$:

$$0.01 = \frac{\dfrac{wt\%Si}{28.09}}{\dfrac{wt\%Si}{28.09} + \dfrac{(100 - wt\%Si)}{55.85}} \approx \frac{wt\%Si \cdot 55.85}{100 \cdot 28.09}$$

where 28·09 and 55·85 are the atomic weights of silicon and iron respectively. Thus:

$$\text{weight-per cent silicon} = 0.50.$$

The activity coefficient of silicon, relative to the infinitely dilute, weight-per cent standard state, is then given by:

$$f_{Si} = \frac{a_{Si\,(dilute)}}{wt\%Si} = \frac{0.55}{0.50}$$
$$= 1.1.$$

6.3 *A pure iron–manganese alloy containing 0.70 weight-per cent of manganese is brought to equilibrium at 1,335°C with a gas mixture of hydrogen sulphide and hydrogen in the ratio $p_{H_2S}/p_{H_2} = 5.70 \times 10^{-4}$. On* *analysis, the equilibrated alloy specimen is found to contain* 0·0032 *weight-per cent of sulphur. If the activity coefficient of sulphur (relative to the infinitely dilute, weight-per cent standard state) is unity in dilute binary Fe–S alloys, calculate the interaction parameter for the effect of manganese on the activity coefficient of sulphur at* 1,335°C.

For the reaction:

$$H_{2(g)} + S_{(soln. \ in \ Fe)} \rightleftharpoons H_2S_{(g)} \qquad\qquad 6.3.1$$

the standard free-energy change in the relevant temperature range is given by:

$$\Delta G^0 = -9,870 + 9·39T \ cal$$

where the standard state for sulphur dissolved in iron is the infinitely dilute, weight-per cent solution.

From *1.58*, the equilibrium constant for reaction *6.3.1* is given by:

$$\log K_p = +\frac{9,870}{4·575T} - \frac{9·39}{4·575}$$

which at 1,335°C (1,608°K):

$$= -0·718$$

or:

$$K_{p1,608} = 0·191.$$

Assuming that the gases behave ideally, the equilibrium constant for this reaction can be written as:

$$K_p = \frac{p_{H_2S}}{p_{H_2} \times (wt \% S \times f_S)}$$

where f_S is the activity coefficient of sulphur in the ternary Fe–Mn–S alloy. Inserting the given values for p_{H_2S}/p_{H_2} and wt% S, in the ternary alloy:

$$f_S = 0·933.$$

From *1.101* the activity of sulphur in the ternary alloy is equal to the product of f_S^S, the activity coefficient of sulphur in binary Fe–S melts containing the same concentration of sulphur as the ternary alloy, and f_S^{Mn}, the effect of manganese on this activity coefficient. That is:

$$f_S = f_S^S \times f_S^{Mn}.$$

But it is stated that $f_S^S = 1$, therefore:

$$f_S = f_S^{Mn} = 0·933.$$

The interaction parameter e_S^{Mn} is defined by *1.102* as:

$$e_S^{Mn} = \frac{\partial . \log f_S^{Mn}}{\partial . wt \% Mn}.$$

Making the reasonable assumption that $\log f_S^{Mn}$ is a linear function of the manganese content up to at least the concentration present in the ternary alloy, then:

$$e_S^{Mn} = \frac{\log f_S^{Mn}}{wt \% Mn}$$

$$= -\frac{0\cdot0301}{0\cdot70}$$

$$= -0\cdot043.$$

6.4 *Calculate the residual oxygen content of liquid iron containing* 0·10 *weight-per cent silicon in equilibrium with solid silica at* 1,600°C.

The maximum solubility of oxygen in pure liquid iron is 0·23 weight-per cent at 1,600°C, the solubility being lowered when silicon is dissolved in the iron. Because the silicon and oxygen are present as dilute solutions in the liquid iron, it is preferable to solve this problem in terms of the infinitely dilute, weight-per cent standard state. The following interaction parameters, valid at 1,600°C, for the system Fe–Si–O are available:

$$e_{Si}^{Si} = +0\cdot32 \qquad\qquad e_O^O = -0\cdot20$$

$$e_{Si}^O = -0\cdot24 \qquad\qquad e_O^{Si} = -0\cdot14$$

The free energy of formation of pure solid silica from pure liquid silicon and oxygen gas in the temperature range 1,700 to 1,986°K is given by:

$$Si_{(l)} + O_{2(g)} \rightleftharpoons SiO_{2(s)} : \quad \Delta G^0 = -226,500 + 47\cdot50T \text{ cal.} \qquad 6.4.1$$

The reaction required to yield the answer is the formation of pure solid silica from silicon and oxygen dissolved in liquid iron. It is necessary, therefore, to know the free energies of solution of both oxygen and silicon in iron. If the standard state selected for consideration of these solutes is the infinitely dilute, weight-per cent solution, the free-energies of solution are equivalent to those for the transfer of standard state from the pure form, stable at 1,600°C, to the infinitely dilute solution. These are given by:

$$O_{2(g)} \rightleftharpoons 2O_{(\% \text{ in Fe})} : \quad \Delta G^0 = -55,800 - 1\cdot46T \text{ cal} \qquad 6.4.2$$

$$Si_{(l)} \rightleftharpoons Si_{(\% \text{ in Fe})} : \quad \Delta G^0 = -28,500 - 6\cdot1T \text{ cal.} \qquad 6.4.3$$

Subtracting *6.4.2* and *6.4.3* from *6.4.1* yields:

$$\mathrm{Si}_{(\%\ \mathrm{in\ Fe})} + 2\mathrm{O}_{(\%\ \mathrm{in\ Fe})} \rightleftharpoons \mathrm{SiO}_{2(\mathrm{s})} : \quad \Delta G^0 = -142{,}200 + 55 \cdot 06T \text{ cal} \quad 6.4.4$$

or, at $1{,}873°K$ ($1{,}600°C$):

$$\Delta G^0_{1,873} = -39{,}100 \text{ cal.}$$

The equilibrium constant for *6.4.4* is given by:

$$K_p = \frac{a_{\mathrm{SiO_2}}}{a_{\mathrm{Si}} \cdot a_{\mathrm{O}}^2} \cdot$$

But, from *1.58*:

$$\log K_p = -\frac{\Delta G^0}{4 \cdot 575T}$$

$$= +\frac{39{,}100}{4 \cdot 575 \times 1{,}873} \text{ at } 1{,}873°K.$$

Hence:

$$K_{p1,873} = 36{,}560.$$

The liquid iron solution is stated to be in equilibrium with pure solid silica. This is the standard state for silica (i.e. $a_{\mathrm{SiO_2}} = 1$) in reaction *6.4.4* and, therefore:

$$\frac{1}{K_p} = a_{\mathrm{Si}} \cdot a_{\mathrm{O}}^2 = \frac{1}{36{,}560} = 2 \cdot 74 \times 10^{-5}. \qquad 6.4.5$$

To obtain the equilibrium oxygen content of the liquid iron from this relation, the activity coefficients for silicon and oxygen in dilute Fe–Si–O melts containing $0 \cdot 10$ weight-per cent of silicon must be known. Thus, using *1.101* and *1.105*:

$$\log f_{\mathrm{Si}} = \log f_{\mathrm{Si}}^{\mathrm{Si}} + \log f_{\mathrm{Si}}^{\mathrm{O}}$$

$$= \%\mathrm{Si} \cdot e_{\mathrm{Si}}^{\mathrm{Si}} + \%\mathrm{O} \cdot e_{\mathrm{Si}}^{\mathrm{O}}$$

and, inserting the values given for the interaction parameters, at $0 \cdot 1$ weight-per cent silicon:

$$\log f_{\mathrm{Si}} = (0 \cdot 1 \times 0 \cdot 32) + (\%\mathrm{O} \times -0 \cdot 24)$$

$$= 0 \cdot 032 - 0 \cdot 24 \%\mathrm{O}.$$

Similarly:

$$\log f_{\mathrm{O}} = \%\mathrm{O} \cdot e_{\mathrm{O}}^{\mathrm{O}} + \%\mathrm{Si} \cdot e_{\mathrm{O}}^{\mathrm{Si}}$$

$$= (\%\mathrm{O} \times -0 \cdot 20) + (0 \cdot 1 \times -0 \cdot 14)$$

$$= -0 \cdot 20 \%\mathrm{O} - 0 \cdot 014.$$

Equation *6.4.5* can be written as:

$$(f_{Si} \cdot \%Si) \cdot (f_O \cdot \%O)^2 = 2 \cdot 74 \times 10^{-5}$$

or:

$$\log f_{Si} + 2 \log f_O + \log \%Si + 2 \log \%O = \log(2 \cdot 74 \times 10^{-5}).$$

Substituting the relations for $\log f_{Si}$ and $\log f_O$ at $0 \cdot 1$ weight-per cent silicon, this becomes:

$$0 \cdot 032 - 0 \cdot 24 \%O - 0 \cdot 40 \%O - 0 \cdot 028 - 1 \cdot 0 + 2 \log \%O = -4 \cdot 562$$

or:

$$2 \log \%O - 0 \cdot 64 \%O = -3 \cdot 558.$$

This relation can be solved by plotting the expression:

$$(2 \log \%O - 0 \cdot 64 \%O) \text{ versus } \%O$$

and determining the value of $\%O$ at $-3 \cdot 558$ on the graph. The value so obtained is $0 \cdot 017$. Hence $0 \cdot 017$ weight-per cent oxygen is in equilibrium with $0 \cdot 1$ weight-per cent silicon, both dissolved in otherwise pure liquid iron at $1{,}600°C$.

6.5 *The following data have been obtained at* $1{,}600°C$ *for the carbon and oxygen contents of liquid iron in equilibrium with carbon monoxide at 1 atmosphere pressure:*

Carbon wt%	0·05	0·10	0·20	0·40	0·60	0·80
Oxygen wt%	0·0482	0·0245	0·0127	0·0066	0·0047	0·0038

In pure liquid Fe–C *alloys at* $1{,}600°C$ *the activity coefficient of carbon is given by the relation:*

$$\log f_C^C = [\%C \cdot e_C^C] = 0 \cdot 30 \%C.$$

Assuming that in pure liquid Fe–O *alloys the parameter* e_O^O *is zero, determine the values of the interaction parameters* e_O^C *and* e_C^O.

The data given apply for the reaction:

$$C_{(in\,Fe)} + O_{(in\,Fe)} \rightleftharpoons CO_{(g)}$$

for which the equilibrium constant is:

$$K_p = \frac{f_{CO}}{a_C \cdot a_O}$$

$$= \frac{p_{CO}}{wt\%C \cdot wt\%O \cdot f_C \cdot f_O}$$

assuming that CO behaves as an ideal gas. The numerical value of K_p is not given in the example but, because p_{CO} is given as 1 atmosphere, then

$$K_p \cdot f_C \cdot f_O = \frac{1}{\text{wt} \% C . \text{wt} \% O} = K' \qquad 6.5.1$$

where K' is a composition-dependent term, values of which can be calculated from the table given. Taking logarithms and rearranging terms, 6.5.1 becomes:

$$\log K' - \log K_p = \log f_C + \log f_O. \qquad 6.5.2$$

By definition of the infinitely dilute, weight-per cent standard state, $\log f_C$ tends to zero (i.e. $f_C \rightarrow 1$) as weight-per cent carbon tends to zero. Also, $\log f_O$ ($= \% O . e_O^O + \% C . e_O^C$) will tend to zero at 0 per cent carbon if $e_O^O = 0$. Hence extrapolation of a plot of $\log K'$ versus weight-per cent carbon to 0 per cent carbon yields the value of $\log K_p$. Further, at any chosen carbon content (from 6.5.2), the slope of the graph will be equal to:

$$\frac{\log f_C + \log f_O}{\text{wt} \% C}$$

at that particular carbon content.

Plotting the given data in this manner, $\log K'$ is found to be a linear function of the carbon content, the slope of this line being $-0 \cdot 124$. Hence:

$$\log f_C + \log f_O = -0 \cdot 124 \% C. \qquad 6.5.3$$

These activity coefficients, f_C and f_O in the ternary alloys, can be expressed as the products of the respective activity coefficients in the Fe–C or Fe–O binary alloys and the respective interaction coefficients (cf. equation 1.101). That is:

$$f_{C \, (\text{ternary})} = f_C^C \times f_C^O$$

or:

$$\log f_{C \, (\text{ternary})} = \log f_C^C + \log f_C^O.$$

Similarly:

$$\log f_{O \, (\text{ternary})} = \log f_O^O + \log f_O^C.$$

Substitution of these equalities in 6.5.3 yields:

$$\log f_C^C + \log f_C^O + \log f_O^O + \log f_O^C = -0 \cdot 124 \% C$$

or, inserting the given values of $\log f_C^C$ and $\log f_O^O$ ($= \% O . e_O^O = 0$) and rearranging:

$$\log f_C^O + \log f_O^C = -0 \cdot 424 \% C. \qquad 6.5.4$$

Within the concentration range to which Henry's law applies to carbon and oxygen in liquid iron, the terms $\log f_C^O$ and $\log f_O^C$ are linear functions of the concentrations of oxygen and carbon respectively. That is:

$$\log f_C^O = \%O . e_C^O \qquad 6.5.5$$

$$\log f_O^C = \%C . e_O^C \qquad 6.5.6$$

where e_C^O and e_O^C are the interaction parameters which are to be determined. Further, at high dilution, these parameters are related by 1.107:

$$e_O^C = \frac{16}{12} . e_C^O \qquad 6.5.7$$

where 16 and 12 are the approximate atomic weights of oxygen and carbon respectively. Substituting 6.5.5, 6.5.6 and 6.5.7 into 6.5.4, and solving for e_C^O yields:

$$\%O . e_C^O + \frac{16}{12} \%C . e_C^O = -0.424 \%C. \qquad 6.5.8$$

But, from the given data, 0·0127 weight-per cent of oxygen is in equilibrium with 0·20 weight-per cent of carbon at 1,600°C. Thus:

$$0.0127 e_C^O + 0.267 e_C^O = -0.0848$$

or:

$$e_C^O = -0.30$$

and, from 6.5.7:

$$e_O^C = -0.40.$$

The values of e_C^O and e_O^C so calculated are approximately independent of composition in the range 0·2–0·8 weight-per cent carbon, but become significantly larger when the data given for the two lower carbon concentrations are substituted in 6.5.8. This is due primarily to the initial assumption that $e_O^O = 0$. In fact, the experimental value for this parameter is -0.20. At very low carbon concentrations the oxygen content of liquid iron increases markedly and hence the value of $\log f_O^O$ (assumed zero in 6.5.4) becomes increasingly significant. For example, using the data given, $\log f_O^O$ is calculated to be -0.00964 at 0·05 per cent carbon, this value decreasing to -0.00254 at 0·2 per cent carbon and to 0·00076 at 0·8 per cent carbon. Thus the effect of equating $\log f_O^O$ to zero is negligible only at moderate and high carbon contents.

A further probable source of error is the use of equation 6.5.7 to deduce the value of e_O^C. There are as yet relatively few experimental data available with which the validity of this relation can be tested and, whilst the equality is thermodynamically justified at infinite dilution, it is possible that the derived value of e_O^C is not accurate for more concentrated (although still dilute) solutions.

It should be noted that when the actual value of $\log f_O^O$ is taken into account, the intercept of the $\log K'$ versus weight-per cent carbon plot on the zero carbon axis is equal to $\log K_p + \log f_{O\,(0\%\,carbon)}^O$. To obtain a solution by the method described here, it is then necessary to plot $\log K'$ versus $(wt\%C.f_O^O)$, the slope of which is equal to:

$$\frac{\log f_O^C + \log f_C^C + \log f_C^O}{wt\%C}.$$

The procedure for solution is then similar to that shown.

Exercises

6.A   Pure hydrogen is circulated at 1 atmosphere pressure in a closed system over pure zirconium heated to 800°C and then over nickel, heated to the same temperature, to remove dissolved oxygen from the nickel. The solubility of oxygen in nickel in equilibrium with the oxide NiO is 0·019 weight-per cent at this temperature. If oxygen dissolved in nickel conforms to Henry's law at all concentrations below the solubility limit, calculate the oxygen concentration remaining in the nickel when equilibrium is attained.

6.B   In one refining process for lead, copper is removed from the lead by reaction with lead sulphide (PbS) to form copper sulphide (Cu_2S). The sulphides are solid at the reaction temperature of 400°C and the maximum solubility of copper in liquid lead is restricted, being only 0·40 atom-per cent at the reaction temperature. Assuming that, within the composition range of the homogeneous liquid solution, copper in liquid lead conforms to Henry's law, find the atom-per cent concentration of copper in equilibrium with liquid lead, PbS and Cu_2S at the reaction temperature.

6.C   If liquid iron–manganese solutions can be regarded as ideal, determine the change in free energy accompanying the transfer of standard state from pure liquid manganese to the infinitely dilute, weight-per cent solution of manganese in liquid iron.

6.D   At 1,600°C, the activity coefficient of vanadium at infinite dilution in liquid iron, relative to pure solid vanadium as the standard state, is

0·068. Calculate the free-energy change accompanying the transfer of standard state from pure solid vanadium to the infinitely dilute, weight-per cent solution of vanadium in liquid iron.

6.E At 1,100°K the activity of component B in a face-centred-cubic solid solution AB is given as a function of N_B, the atom fraction of B, by:

$$a_B = 0·24N_B \quad (0 < N_B < 0·025)$$

where a_B is referred to pure B as the standard state. The standard free-energy change accompanying the oxidation of pure B is $-74,000$ cal mole^{-1} at 1,100°K. On heating, pure B undergoes an allotropic change from a body-centred-cubic to a face-centred-cubic structure at 1,180°K, accompanied by a latent heat of transformation of 220 cal mole^{-1}. Calculate the equilibrium constant at 1,100°K for the reaction:

$$B_{(2 \text{ atom-per cent in A})} + O_{2(g)} \rightleftharpoons BO_{2 \text{ (pure solid)}}$$

referred to a standard state of the infinitely dilute atom fraction solution of B in A.

6.F The alloy system AB obeys Henry's law up to 3 weight-per cent of component B, the slope of the Henry's law line being 0·17 at 1,000°K, with respect to pure B as the standard state. On oxidation of a molten alloy containing 1·5 weight-per cent B at 1,000°K, the solid oxide film on the surface of the melt is found to be pure BO_2. The standard free-energy change for the oxidation of pure B is $-60·0$ kcal mole^{-1} at 1,000°K and pure B melts at 1,025°K with a latent heat of fusion of 2·6 kcal mole^{-1}. If the atomic weights of A and B are 97 and 73 respectively, calculate the standard free-energy change for the oxidation of B in the 1·5 weight-per cent alloy at 1,000°K with respect to the infinitely dilute, weight-per cent standard state of B in A.

6.G A hydrogen–steam atmosphere containing 16·67 per cent by volume of steam is equilibrated with pure liquid iron at various temperatures. On analysis of quenched samples, the iron is found to contain 0·0472, 0·0597 and 0·0752 weight-per cent oxygen when equilibrated respectively at 1,550, 1,600 and 1,650°C. The activity coefficient of oxygen, relative to the infinitely dilute, weight-per cent standard state, varies with temperature as follows:

Temperature, °C	1,550	1,600	1,650
$\log f_O$	$-0·23[\%O]$	$-0·20[\%O]$	$-0·18[\%O]$

Express as a function of temperature the free-energy change accompanying the transfer of oxygen gas into an infinitely dilute, weight-per cent solution in liquid iron (i.e. the free energy change for the reaction:

$$\tfrac{1}{2}O_{2(g)} \rightleftharpoons O_{(wt\,\%\ in\ Fe)}).$$

6.H   The following values have been determined for the activity of carbon at 925°C in solid iron–carbon (austenitic) alloys, relative to graphite as the standard state for carbon:

N_C	0·005	0·010	0·015	0·020	0·025	0·030
a_C	0·064	0·132	0·205	0·280	0·361	0·445

Determine the activity of carbon at 0·5 weight-per cent concentration, relative to the infinitely dilute, weight-per cent standard state.

6.I   An iron–1 weight-per cent vanadium alloy is equilibrated at 1,623°C with a hydrogen–steam mixture containing 5 per cent by volume of steam. On analysis the metal is found to contain 0·033 weight-per cent oxygen. Assuming that oxygen dissolved in iron obeys Henry's law, find the effect of vanadium on the activity coefficient of oxygen. The free-energy change accompanying the change of standard state from oxygen gas to the infinitely dilute, weight-per cent solution of oxygen in iron is given by:

$$\tfrac{1}{2}O_{2(g)} \rightleftharpoons O_{(wt\,\%\ in\ Fe)} : \Delta G^0 = -27,790 - 0.79T \text{ cal.}$$

6.J   The ratio p_{H_2S}/p_{H_2} in equilibrium with iron containing 0·04 weight-per cent sulphur and 1·2 weight-per cent carbon is $1·40 \times 10^{-4}$ at 1,600°C. In dilute Fe–S alloys the interaction parameter e_S^S is $-0·028$, relative to the infinitely dilute, weight-per cent standard state of sulphur in iron. Find the effect of carbon on the activity coefficient of sulphur (i.e. e_S^C) in the ternary alloy. The free-energy change accompanying the transfer of standard state from sulphur gas to the infinitely dilute, weight-per cent solution in iron is given by:

$$\tfrac{1}{2}S_{2(g)} \rightleftharpoons S_{(wt\,\%\ in\ Fe)} : \Delta G^0 = -31,520 + 5·27T \text{ cal.}$$

6.K   The solubility of oxygen in pure liquid iron is 0·230 weight-per cent at 1,600°C and, within this solubility range, the activity coefficient of the dissolved oxygen is given by:

$$\log f_O = -0·20[\%O]$$

relative to the infinitely dilute, weight-per cent standard state. Determine the oxygen content of liquid iron held in a solid magnesia crucible if equilibrium is established at 1,600°C under a vacuum of (a) 0·001 atmosphere pressure, (b) 0·01 mm Hg pressure. Use the data for the transfer in standard state given in exercise 6.I.

6.L At one stage during the refining of a bath of molten steel, the metal composition was found to be:

Element	C	S	P	Mn
Weight-per cent	0·06	0·028	0·025	0·13

At the time of sampling of the bath the temperature of the latter was 1,570°C and the activity of the P_2O_5 in the slag was $9·6 \times 10^{-19}$, relative to pure liquid P_2O_5 as the standard state. Assuming that the partial pressure of carbon monoxide formed by oxidation of the carbon was 1 atmosphere and given the following data, determine whether or not the carbon and phosphorus oxidation reactions were in equilibrium with respect to the oxygen content of the metal bath.

$$C_{(\% \text{ in Fe})} + O_{(\% \text{ in Fe})} \rightleftharpoons CO_{(g)} \quad : \quad \varDelta G^0 = -3,710 - 10·09T \text{ cal}$$

$$2P_{(\% \text{ in Fe})} + 5O_{(\% \text{ in Fe})} \rightleftharpoons P_2O_{5(l)} : \quad \varDelta G^0 = -164,174 + 138·63T \text{ cal}$$

where the standard state for C, P and O in iron is the infinitely dilute, weight-per cent solution.

	Solute X			
	C	S	P	Mn
e_C^X	0·23	0·045	0·047	−0·002
e_P^X	0·12	0·041	0	−0·012

CHAPTER 7

Evaluation of Experimental Data

A variety of experimental methods are used to obtain data from which the thermodynamic properties of a system, or a component or phase in a system, can be determined. Several detailed reviews of these experimental methods have been published [1, 2, 3] and a comprehensive assessment of the accuracies and limitations of the various techniques has been given [3]. These aspects of experimental thermodynamics are not, therefore, considered here. However, having obtained the experimental data, the problem remains as to how these can best be used to obtain the required thermodynamic properties.

Many of the worked examples presented in the earlier chapters are, in reality, calculations starting with experimental data. For example, the heat capacity/temperature relations which form the basis of most of the problems presented in chapters 2 and 3 have been evaluated from calorimetric experiments. The use of experimental data to evaluate the equilibrium constant for a reaction, which in turn is used to obtain other thermodynamic quantities, is demonstrated in chapters 4, 5 and 6. Evaluations of the thermodynamic properties of a component of a solution, from experimental measurements of properties of another component, are described in chapter 5.

The thermodynamic relations upon which these evaluations are based are all presented in outline in chapter 1, and the examples can be solved by application of the appropriate basic relations. However, there are two additional techniques which are commonly in use for obtaining thermodynamic information from experimental data, the treatments involved being somewhat less obvious from the relations given in chapter 1. These techniques are:

1. Measurement of equilibrium e.m.f.s of galvanic (electrochemical) cells.
2. Calculations using data directly derivable from phase equilibrium diagrams.

This chapter contains a brief review of the thermodynamic principles involved in these methods and worked examples to illustrate their application.

Calculation of thermodynamic quantities from measured e.m.f.s of galvanic cells

Measurement of the e.m.f. generated when a reaction occurs in a galvanic cell is, in theory, one of the most direct and simple methods for obtaining free energy and other thermodynamic data for the reaction and the components in the reaction. From the combined First and Second Laws of Thermodynamics, the change in the free energy accompanying a reaction which is made to proceed reversibly at constant temperature and pressure is given, following equation *1.33*, by:

$$dG = -\delta W$$

where W is the maximum work, other than mechanical work, which the system is capable of performing. Integration at constant temperature and pressure yields, for a finite reversible process:

$$\Delta G = -W. \qquad\qquad 7.a$$

This work may be available in electrical form if the system comprises a suitable galvanic cell. In this case the maximum work (W) available, following a given amount of reaction, is equivalent to the product of the potential drop across the cell and the quantity of electricity which passes. Thus, for a reaction involving 1 mole of a substance,

$$W = zFE \qquad\qquad 7.b$$

where E (volt) is the potential drop across the cell, z is the number of electrons transferred, per molecule of substance, F is the charge on 1 gram electron (96,494 coulomb g-equiv^{-1}) and 1 gram electron is the number of electrons corresponding to 1 gram mole of univalent ions ($\equiv$ Avogadro's number).

The magnitude of the external work obtained from the cell is dependent upon the value of the e.m.f. generated by the cell, this latter being a maximum when the cell reaction can be regarded as taking place reversibly. Such a condition is realized when an external potential source is connected in opposition to, and adjusted to balance exactly, the cell e.m.f. such that no current flows through the external circuit. Under these conditions the work term (W) in equations *7.a* and *7.b* can be equated and the reversible free-energy change in the reaction is given by:

$$\Delta G = -zFE. \qquad\qquad 7.c$$

Changes in other thermodynamic quantities during a reaction can also be expressed in terms of the e.m.f. generated when the reaction takes place reversibly in a cell. Thus, applying equation *1.33* to the changes of extensive properties in a reaction:

$$d\Delta G = \Delta V dP - \Delta S dT$$

or, at constant pressure:

$$\left(\frac{\partial \Delta G}{\partial T}\right)_P = -\Delta S.$$

But differentiation of equation 7.c with respect to temperature yields:

$$\left(\frac{\partial \Delta G}{\partial T}\right)_P = -zF\left(\frac{\partial E}{\partial T}\right)_P.$$

Hence:

$$\Delta S = zF\left(\frac{\partial E}{\partial T}\right)_P. \qquad 7.d$$

Similarly, substitution of 7.c and 7.d in the definitional relation 1.31 (applied to the property changes in a reaction) gives:

$$\Delta H = -zF\left[E - T\left(\frac{\partial E}{\partial T}\right)_P\right]. \qquad 7.e$$

In practice the cell e.m.f. is measured potentiometrically as the value of the external e.m.f. necessary to balance the cell. When the reaction involves 1 mole of a single species of ion, z is then equal to the valency exhibited by that ion in the solution. Clearly, if z is to be unique, the ions participating in the reaction must exhibit only one valency in the particular reaction under consideration.

It is important to appreciate that the cell e.m.f., E, occurring in the above equations is that measured reversibly; i.e. under conditions in which no energy is being introduced or extracted from the cell. In practice, however, the majority of electrode processes involve the passage of a net current across the electrode/solution interface; the cell reaction thus proceeds at a finite speed, is therefore irreversible and cannot be treated directly by thermodynamic methods. The e.m.f. (e_i) of a cell electrode operating at a current density i differs from the reversible value (e_r). This difference, η_i, is called the overpotential (or overvoltage). That is:

$$\eta_i = e_i - e_r.$$

η_i does not arise from a single cause, but is made up of three separate components:

Ohmic overpotential (η_O) (which is zero when no current flows) arises from the ohmic resistance of the solution and electrode.

Concentration overpotential (η_C) results from the concentration gradient in the electrolyte immediately surrounding the electrode which is necessary to enable the ions to diffuse to or from the electrode at a rate equal to their discharge rate.

Activation overpotential (η_A) is directly connected with the activation energy of the rate controlling reaction in the transfer of ions to the final state in the electrode metal surface or gas.

The above description of irreversible electrode processes is brief, since the subject is outside the scope of thermodynamics and has been described in detail elsewhere [4]. However, such effects are of the utmost importance in considering practical problems associated with galvanic cells, such as electrolysis, corrosion, etc. To summarize, when obtaining useful work from a spontaneous cell reaction, the cell e.m.f. is less than the reversible value and conversely, when driving the cell by an external energy source, an e.m.f. greater than the reversible value is required.

In the examples which follow it is assumed that the ions participating in the reaction exhibit only one valency and the recorded e.m.f. is the true potential under reversible conditions for the reaction being considered.

7.1   *The e.m.f. of the galvanic cell*

$$Pb_{(s)} | PbCl_{2(s)} | AgCl_{(s)} | Ag_{(s)}$$

where all components are present as pure solids in contact with HCl *electrolyte, is* 0·490 *volt at* 25°C *and, at that temperature, the temperature coefficient of the e.m.f. is* $-1·84 \times 10^{-4}$ *volt* deg^{-1}. *The standard entropies (i.e at* 25°C) *for* Pb, Ag *and* AgCl *are* 15·5, 10·2 *and* 23·0 cal deg^{-1} mole^{-1} *respectively. Calculate the free-energy and entropy changes for the cell reaction and the standard entropy of* PbCl$_2$ *at* 25°C.

The first step is to determine the cell reaction. In all problems concerned with galvanic cells it is necessary to appreciate the reactions that occur when work is being withdrawn from, or injected into, the cell. Reference to *7.c* shows that a positive cell e.m.f. is associated with a negative value of ΔG (i.e. a spontaneous reaction) and it is necessary, therefore, to specify the direction of spontaneity. For this purpose, the convention adopted is to write the cell such that the spontaneous reaction (associated with a positive e.m.f.) involves the passage of positive ions through the cell from left to right, and of negative ions from right to left. Returning now to the example under consideration, the spontaneous reaction (obtained by shortcircuiting the electrodes) involves the dissolution of the lead electrode:

$$Pb_{(s)} \to Pb^{++} + 2e^-$$

where *e* represents an electron. Simultaneously silver ions are converted to metallic silver:

$$2Ag^+ + 2e^- \to 2Ag_{(s)}.$$

The net spontaneous cell reaction is therefore:

$$Pb_{(s)} + 2AgCl_{(s)} \rightarrow PbCl_{2(s)} + 2Ag_{(s)}.$$

This means that the passage of 2 gram electron charges (i.e. 2 Faraday) through the cell causes the solution of 1 gram atom of lead and the simultaneous precipitation of 2 gram atom of silver.

The components of the reaction are all present in their respective standard states and hence the free-energy change accompanying the reaction, given by equation 7.c, is equal to the standard free-energy change for the reaction at the temperature of the measurements. That is:

$$\Delta G^0 = -zFE^0$$

where E^0 is the e.m.f. of the reaction under the standard conditions.

If ΔG^0 is to be expressed in calories and E^0 is measured in volts, the units of the Faraday must be converted from coulomb g-equiv^{-1} to cal volt^{-1} g-equiv^{-1}. Thus, since 1 cal = 4·184 joule:

$$F = \frac{96,494}{4·184} = 23,066 \text{ cal volt}^{-1} \text{ g-equiv}^{-1}.$$

In the example, the maximum e.m.f. when the cell is operating reversibly (i.e. the balancing external e.m.f.) is 0·490 volt at 25°C. Therefore:

$$\Delta G^0_{298} = -(2 \times 23,066 \times 0·490)$$

$$= -22,600 \text{ cal.}$$

The standard entropy change for the reaction is obtained by use of equation 7.d applied to standard changes:

$$\Delta S^0 = zF\left(\frac{\partial E^0}{\partial T}\right)_P.$$

The temperature coefficient of the e.m.f., $(\partial E^0/\partial T)_P$ is given as $-1·84 \times 10^{-4}$ volt deg^{-1} at 25°C. Therefore:

$$\Delta S^0 = 2 \times 23,066 \times (-1·84 \times 10^{-4})$$

$$= -8·5 \text{ cal deg}^{-1}.$$

The entropy change for the reaction is the difference between the entropies of the products and the reactants:

$$\Delta S^0 = S^0_{PbCl_2} + 2S^0_{Ag} - S^0_{Pb} - 2S^0_{AgCl}.$$

Substituting the given values:

$$S^0_{\text{PbCl}_2} = -8\cdot5 - (2\times10\cdot2) + 15\cdot5 - (2\times23\cdot0)$$
$$= 32\cdot6 \text{ cal deg}^{-1}\text{ mole}^{-1}.$$

7.2 *A galvanic cell is set up with electrodes of solid aluminium and solid aluminium–zinc alloy, and an electrolyte of a fused AlCl$_3$–NaCl mixture. When the mole fraction of aluminium in the alloy electrode is 0·38, the e.m.f. of the cell is 7·43 millivolt at 380°C and the temperature coefficient of the e.m.f. is 2·9 × 10^{-5} volt deg^{-1}. Calculate the activity, and the partial molar free energy and enthalpy of mixing, of aluminium in the alloy at 380°C.*

The cell can be written as:

$$\text{Al}_{(s,\text{ pure})}|\text{AlCl}_3 - \text{NaCl}|\text{Al}_{(s,\text{ in Al–Zn})}{}^*$$

and the cell reaction is:

$$\text{Al}_{(s,\text{ pure})} \rightarrow \text{Al}_{(s,\text{ in Al–Zn})}$$

At the pure aluminium anode, 1 gram atom of aluminium ions (Al^{+++}) is formed by the passage of 3 Faraday of electricity. Simultaneously 1 gram atom of aluminium ions is discharged at the alloy cathode and dissolves in the alloy.

The measured e.m.f. of the cell at equilibrium is therefore related to the transfer of 1 gram atom of aluminium from pure aluminium into the alloy. It follows from the definition of quantities of mixing (p. 11) that the e.m.f. data will yield relative partial molar properties of aluminium in the alloy.

In order to demonstrate the method for solving this example, it is necessary to derive the dependence of the free-energy change for the cell reaction on the activity of the aluminium in the alloy.

In the general case, for a reaction between components X and Y to produce P and Q:

$$bX + cY \rightleftharpoons mP + nQ,$$

the relation between the free-energy change and the activity of the components is obtained by combining *1.55* and *1.56*:

$$\Delta G - \Delta G^0 = RT\ln\left(\frac{a_P^m \cdot a_Q^n}{a_X^b \cdot a_Y^c}\right). \qquad 7.2.1$$

---

* This type of cell, in which the electrochemical difference between the electrodes is the concentration of the transported component, is called a *concentration cell*.

As in example *7.1*, when all the components are present in their standard states in a galvanic cell, the e.m.f. (E^0) of the cell is related to the standard free-energy change for the reaction by the expression:

$$\Delta G^0 = -zFE^0.$$

Similarly when one or more of the components are not in their standard states, the measured e.m.f. (E) is related to the free-energy change by:

$$\Delta G = -zFE. \qquad 7.2.2$$

Substituting these equalities in *7.2.1* yields:

$$E - E^0 = -\frac{RT}{zF} . \ln\left(\frac{a_P^m . a_Q^n}{a_X^b . a_Y^c}\right). \qquad 7.2.3$$

It will be noted that the activity term has the same form as the equilibrium constant for the reaction. However, in a galvanic cell reaction, the concentrations and hence the activities of the components of the two electrodes differ from the equilibrium values; otherwise ΔG (and hence E) would be equal to zero. In practice the cell reaction is prevented from reaching equilibrium by applying a back e.m.f. equal to E. Provided this condition is achieved and no chemical reaction occurs in the cell, the activities of the components, at the concentrations at which they are present in the cell, can be determined from measurement of E and E^0, using equation *7.2.3*. In the general case it is not necessary to measure E^0, as the value can be calculated from knowledge of the standard free-energy change for the reaction.

In the present example the reaction involves the transfer of aluminium from the pure aluminium electrode (i.e. $a_{Al} = 1$) to the solid solution. Hence equation *7.2.3* becomes:

$$E - E^0 = -\frac{RT}{zF} . \ln\left(\frac{a_{Al\,(alloy)}}{a_{Al\,(pure)}}\right). \qquad 7.2.4$$

In the specific case of *both* electrodes being pure aluminium, the last term in *7.2.4* is zero, since $a_{Al} = 1$ for both electrodes. This cell would generate no e.m.f. and hence, as $E = 0$, E^0 is also zero. Therefore:

$$E = -\frac{RT}{zF} . \ln a_{Al\,(alloy)} \qquad 7.2.5$$

$$= -\left(\frac{\bar{G}_{Al} - G_{Al}^0}{zF}\right) = -\frac{\bar{G}_{Al}^M}{zF} \qquad 7.2.6$$

from *1.54*, where $\bar{G}_{Al}^M$ is the relative partial molar free energy of aluminium in the alloy.

The valency (z) of aluminium is 3, F is equal to 23,066 cal volt^{-1} g-equiv^{-1} and E is given as 0·00743 volt at 380°C (653°K). Hence, substituting in 7.2.5, at 0·38 mole fraction of aluminium in the alloy:

$$\log a_{Al} = -\frac{3 \times 23{,}066 \times 0{\cdot}00743}{4{\cdot}575 \times 653}$$

$$= -0{\cdot}172$$

or:

$$a_{Al} = 0{\cdot}673.$$

The partial molar free energy of mixing of aluminium in the alloy is obtained by use of equation 7.2.6:

$$\bar{G}_{Al}^{M} = -zFE$$

$$= -(3 \times 23{,}066 \times 0{\cdot}00743)$$

$$= -514 \text{ cal mole}^{-1}.$$

From equation 7.e applied to the present conditions:

$$\bar{H}_{Al}^{M} = -zF\left[E - T\left(\frac{\partial E}{\partial T}\right)_P\right]$$

and $(\partial E/\partial T)_P$ is given as $2{\cdot}9 \times 10^{-5}$ volt deg^{-1}. Therefore:

$$\bar{H}_{Al}^{M} = -3 \times 23{,}066[(7{\cdot}43 \times 10^{-3}) - 653(2{\cdot}9 \times 10^{-5})]$$

$$= +800 \text{ cal mole}^{-1}.$$

Experimental data from e.m.f. cells can be combined, for example, with heat capacity data to derive free-energy changes and equilibrium constants for reactions in a similar manner to that demonstrated in earlier chapters. In each case, the first step is usually to convert the e.m.f. data into one or other of the thermodynamic functions in the manner outlined in the preceding examples. However, the use of galvanic cells is not confined to the evaluation of thermodynamic quantities. As well as being used for electricity storage, etc., galvanic cells are widely applied in the extraction and refining of metals. The two following examples illustrate typical applications of thermodynamic principles to derive operating data for such cells.

7.3 *In the electrolytic refining of copper, a galvanic cell is formed in which one electrode is impure copper and the other is pure copper. Assuming that the activity of the copper is unity at both electrodes, how many kilowatt-hours of electricity are consumed per lb of copper refined if the cell is operated at 0·2 volt and the efficiency is 85 per cent?*

Because the activity of the copper is unity at both electrodes, the change in the free energy accompanying the transfer of copper from one electrode to the other is zero. It follows, therefore, from the equation:

$$\Delta G^0 = -zFE^0$$

that the e.m.f. generated by such a cell is also zero. Hence, theoretically, any imposed positive e.m.f. will cause transfer of copper from anode to cathode and 0·2 volt should be adequate to maintain the transfer reaction.

The reactions occurring in the cell are, at the anode:

$$Cu_{(s)} \rightarrow Cu^{++} + 2e^-$$

and, at the cathode:

$$Cu^{++} + 2e^- \rightarrow Cu_{(s)}.$$

Thus the transfer of 1 mole of copper from one electrode to the other requires the passage of 2 gram electron (i.e. 2 Faraday) of electricity through the cell. The gram-molecular weight of copper is 63·54 and 1 lb is equal to 453·6 gram. Therefore, the transfer of 1 lb of copper across the cell requires the passage of:

$$\frac{453 \cdot 6}{63 \cdot 54} \times 2 = 14 \cdot 272 \text{ Faraday of electricity.}$$

The answer is required in kilowatt-hours, so the units of the Faraday must be expressed in ampere-hours. Now:

$$1 \text{ Faraday} = 96{,}494 \text{ coulomb g-equiv}^{-1}$$

$$= 96{,}494 \times 2 \cdot 78 \times 10^{-4} \text{ ampere-hour g-equiv}^{-1}.$$

Therefore:

$$14 \cdot 272 \text{ Faraday} = 382 \cdot 6 \text{ ampere-hour g-equiv}^{-1}$$

and, if the cell operates at 0·2 volt at 85 per cent efficiency, the electrical energy consumed per lb of copper refined is:

$$\frac{382 \cdot 6 \times 0 \cdot 2}{1{,}000} \times \frac{100}{85} = 0 \cdot 090 \text{ kilowatt-hour.}$$

7.4   *In the commerical production of aluminium, alumina is decomposed by electrolysis in the presence of carbon, according to the reaction:*[*]

$$\tfrac{1}{2}Al_2O_{3(s)} + \tfrac{3}{4}C_{(s)} \rightleftharpoons Al_{(l)} + \tfrac{3}{4}CO_{2(g)}.$$

[*] Although this is the usual way in which the reduction of alumina is expressed, in practice carbon monoxide is formed at the high temperatures at the carbon electrode, and this is then oxidized on its path to atmosphere to give the overall reaction considered here.

Assuming that the condensed phases are pure and the CO_2 is formed at 1 atmosphere pressure, determine the theoretical minimum voltage required to effect the decomposition if the cell is operated at 950°C.

The standard free-energy change for the reduction reaction can be obtained by adding the two reactions:

$$\tfrac{3}{4}C_{(s)} + \tfrac{3}{4}O_{2(g)} \rightleftharpoons \tfrac{3}{4}CO_{2(g)} : \quad \Delta G^0 = -70,650 - 0\cdot15T \text{ cal,}$$

$$\tfrac{1}{2}Al_2O_{3(s)} \rightleftharpoons Al_{(l)} + \tfrac{3}{4}O_{2(g)} : \quad \Delta G^0 = 202,880 + 1\cdot88T\log T - 46\cdot11T \text{ cal,}$$

to obtain:

$$\tfrac{1}{2}Al_2O_{3(s)} + \tfrac{3}{4}C_{(s)} \rightleftharpoons Al_{(l)} + \tfrac{3}{4}CO_{2(g)} : \quad \Delta G^0 = 132,230 + 1\cdot88T\log T - 46\cdot26T \text{ cal.}$$

At 950°C (1,223°K) the standard free-energy change for this reaction is +82,800 cal. The positive value signifies that, in the absence of an external driving force, the reaction as written tends to go from right to left and alumina cannot be reduced spontaneously by carbon at this temperature. In the commercial process, the driving force required to make the reaction go from left to right is provided by the imposed e.m.f., the magnitude of which must be at least sufficient to provide the free energy equal to the positive value of the standard free-energy change for the reaction at the operating temperature.

The relation between the free-energy change for a reaction and the e.m.f. generated when this reaction takes place in an electrolytic cell is given by equation 7.c:

$$\Delta G^0 = -zFE^0.$$

When all the components are in their standard states the calculated free-energy change for the reaction under consideration is for the formation of 1 mole of aluminium from the oxide and, as 3 gram electron are transferred in the electrolytic cell per mole of aluminium formed (i.e. $z = 3$ for aluminium), the e.m.f. of the cell is:

$$E^0 = -\frac{82,800}{3 \times 23,066}$$

$$= -1\cdot20 \text{ volt}$$

(where $F = 23,066$ cal volt^{-1} g-equiv^{-1}).

The negative sign of the standard e.m.f. signifies that if a cell is constructed such that the reaction, as written, can occur, aluminium ions at the liquid aluminium electrode will combine continuously with oxygen to form alumina. However, an applied e.m.f. of 1·20 volt will prevent this reaction occurring, the direction of the reaction being reversed (to form liquid aluminium from the alumina) by an applied e.m.f. of greater than this value. In commercial practice, between 6·5 and 7·5 volt is applied to a cell which usually operates at a current density of about 700 amp ft^{-2} of electrode, the efficiency being 75–90 per cent.

Derivation of thermodynamic data from constitutional (phase) diagrams

It is possible to derive certain thermodynamic properties for the components of a binary system from a knowledge of the location of the liquidus and solidus lines on the constitutional diagram. (Conversely the phase diagram can be constructed from knowledge of certain thermodynamic properties of the system.) The basic principle which is used arises from the equality of the partial molar free energy of any one component in each of two or more coexisting phases at equilibrium. Thus at constant temperature the partial molar free energies of a component A in a solid solution of solidus composition and in a liquid solution of liquidus composition are equal, i.e.

$$\bar{G}_{A \,(\text{s, at solidus})} = \bar{G}_{A \,(\text{l, at liquidus})}. \qquad 7.f$$

If experimental measurements of the required thermodynamic property of the melt are not available, it is often acceptable to calculate values of this property at the liquidus from data for the solid, using the above principle. Then, assuming regular solution behaviour, these liquidus values may be extrapolated to any temperature required in the melt.

The accuracy of the calculated liquidus values of the property is dependent on the approximations necessary in the treatment adopted, and on the accuracy of both the thermodynamic data used for the pure component or compound and the location of the liquidus and solidus lines on the constitutional diagram. In certain cases, where the latter have been determined very precisely, the property values calculated for the liquid may be more reliable than the available experimental measurements. More frequently the calculated values are subject to an uncertainty of at least ± 10 per cent, in addition to any error incurred in the temperature extrapolation for the liquid when the actual solution deviates markedly from regular solution behaviour. Hence it must be realized that the values of thermodynamic properties calculated in this way for temperatures above the liquidus may be only very approximate. However, even a rough approximation on these lines is more useful than the alternative assumption that the solution behaves ideally (i.e. conforms to Raoult's law).

The standard state for a component of a solution is conventionally selected as the pure substance in the state which is stable at the temperature under consideration. Thus, at temperatures below the melting point of the pure component, the standard state to which, for example, the activity of the component in solution is referred is usually chosen as the pure solid substance. In this case the activity of a solid component A at the solidus would be given by equation *1.54* in the form:

$$\bar{G}_{A\,(s,\,at\,solidus)} - G^0_{A(s)} = RT \ln a_{A\,(s,\,at\,solidus)} \qquad 7.g$$

and the activity of A at the liquidus would be given by:

$$\bar{G}_{A\,(l,\,at\,liquidus)} - G^0_{A(s)} = RT \ln a_{A\,(l,\,at\,liquidus)}. \qquad 7.h$$

When G^0_A is defined as above (in both cases) as the free energy of pure solid A, it follows from equation *7.f* that:

$$a_{A\,(s,\,at\,solidus)} = a_{A\,(l,\,at\,liquidus)}.$$

If the solid which separates from the melt is practically pure A (i.e. the solubility of B in A is negligible), then $a_{A\,(s,\,at\,solidus)}$ can be taken as unity. It follows then that the activity of the liquid at the liquidus, referred to the same pure solid A standard state, is also unity.

As an alternative to the convention just described, it is sometimes more convenient to refer the activities of a component in a molten solution to the pure liquid as the standard state at temperatures below the melting point of the pure component. This is particularly desirable when it is required to extrapolate these activity values to temperatures above the melting point of the pure component, where the pure liquid is, of course, the normally accepted standard state.

At temperatures below the melting point the pure liquid is less stable (i.e. has a less negative free energy) than the pure solid. Thus expressing *1.54* in terms of the pure, supercooled liquid as the standard state:

$$G_{A\,(pure\,solid)} - G^0_{A(l)} = RT \ln a_{A\,(pure\,solid)}. \qquad 7.j$$

Hence the activity of the solid, relative to the pure, supercooled liquid standard state, is less than unity for all temperatures below the melting point.

Dividing *7.j* throughout by T and differentiating with respect to T at constant pressure, it is obtained that:

$$\left(\frac{\partial \ln a_{A\,(pure\,solid)}}{\partial T}\right)_P = \frac{1}{R}\left[\frac{\partial\left(\frac{G_{A(s)}}{T}\right)}{\partial T} - \frac{\partial\left(\frac{G^0_{A(l)}}{T}\right)}{\partial T}\right]_P$$

$$= \frac{H^0_{A(l)} - H_{A(s)}}{RT^2} \qquad 7.k$$

from the Gibbs–Helmholtz relation *1.34*. The quantity $H_{A(s)}$ is the molar enthalpy of pure solid A, and $(H^0_{A(l)} - H_{A(s)})$ is equal to the enthalpy change for the transformation from pure solid to pure liquid (ΔH_{tr}) at the temperature T. Therefore, at constant pressure:

$$\ln a_{A \text{ (pure solid)}} = \int \frac{\Delta H_{tr}}{RT^2} \cdot dT \qquad 7.l$$

which can be solved to obtain $a_{A \text{ (pure solid)}}$, with respect to the pure, supercooled liquid standard state, if ΔH_{tr} is known as a function of temperature. This latter can be obtained from use of the Kirchhoff equation *1.18*. Alternatively, ΔH_{tr} may be assumed to be independent of temperature over a small temperature interval, being equal to L_f, the latent heat of fusion of pure A at the melting point. These methods are illustrated in the worked examples which follow.

In alloy systems where the solubility of the solute B is negligible, the liquid at the liquidus is in equilibrium with the pure solid at the same temperature, and it follows that the activities of these two phases are equal when both activities are measured with respect to the same pure liquid standard state. In this case, equation *7.l* can be written as:

$$\ln a_{A \text{ (l, at liquidus)}} = \int \frac{\Delta H_{tr}}{RT^2} \cdot dT. \qquad 7.m$$

When the solid solubility of the second component is appreciable, the activity of pure solid A, relative to the pure liquid standard state, is obtained for the required temperature in the manner previously outlined. However, in order to derive the activities at the solidus (to be equated to the liquid activities at the liquidus) it is necessary to know the variation with composition of the activity of A in the solid solution range. This is sometimes available from experimental data. In other cases some limiting assumption, such as conformity to Raoult's or Henry's law, or regular solution behaviour of the solid solution, is made in order to estimate the required data.

7.5 *The zinc–tin system is a simple binary eutectic, the eutectic point occurring at $0·85$ atom fraction of tin and $198°C$. The solid solubility of tin in zinc is small, being less than $0·1$ weight-per cent at the eutectic temperature. The temperatures corresponding to various compositions on the zinc liquidus, read from the phase diagram given by Hansen [5], are given in the first two columns of Table 7.1 Assuming that the liquid alloys behave as regular solutions, calculate the activity of zinc as a function of composition at $430°C$.*

Because the solid solubility of tin in zinc is very restricted, the activity of zinc in liquid alloys along the zinc liquidus can be equated to the activities of pure solid zinc at corresponding temperatures, relative to the pure liquid zinc standard state. The first step, therefore, is to calculate the activities of zinc along the zinc liquidus, using equation 7.m.

The heat capacities of liquid and solid zinc are given as:

$$C_{p_{Zn(l)}} = 7{\cdot}50 \text{ cal deg}^{-1} \text{ mole}^{-1}$$

$$C_{p_{Zn(s)}} = 5{\cdot}35 + 2{\cdot}4 \times 10^{-3}T \text{ cal deg}^{-1} \text{ mole}^{-1}.$$

Because of the inaccuracies involved in the experimental measurements, the known C_p data for liquid zinc may be adequately represented by a temperature-independent constant. If the variation of C_p with temperature in the liquid state was known with greater precision, it is probable that the empirical equation would contain one or more temperature-dependent terms. However, with the presently available data, there is no significant decrease in the accuracy of the calculated activity values if $C_{p_{Zn(s)}}$ is also represented as a temperature-independent constant. For this purpose, a mean value of $C_{p_{Zn(s)}}$ ($6{\cdot}84$ cal deg^{-1} mole^{-1}) for the temperature range of interest (160–420°C) will be used.

Thus, for the fusion reaction, $Zn_{(s)} \rightleftharpoons Zn_{(l)}$:

$$\Delta C_p = C_{p_{Zn(l)}} - C_{p_{Zn(s)}}$$

$$= 0{\cdot}66 \text{ cal deg}^{-1} \text{ mole}^{-1}.$$

Combination of the Kirchhoff relation in indefinite integral form (equation 1.20), i.e.:

$$\Delta H_{tr} = \int \Delta C_p . dT$$

with equation 7.m yields:

$$R \ln a_{Zn \, (l, \, at \, liquidus)} = \int \frac{1}{T^2} \left[\Delta H_0 + \int 0{\cdot}66 . dT \right] . dT.$$

Hence:

$$R \ln a_{Zn \, (l, \, at \, liquidus)} = -\frac{\Delta H_0}{T} + 0{\cdot}66 \ln T + I \qquad 7.5.1$$

where ΔH_0 and I are integration constants which may be evaluated from a knowledge of either $\ln a_{Zn \, (l, \, at \, liquidus)}$ at two temperatures or $\ln a_{Zn \, (l, \, at \, liquidus)}$ and ΔH_{tr} at one temperature. The latter information is presently available, for at 420°C (693°K), the melting point of pure zinc:

$$a_{Zn(l)} = 1$$

$$\Delta H_{tr} = L_f = 1,740 \text{ cal mole}^{-1}$$

where L_f is the latent heat of fusion of pure zinc. Hence:

$$\Delta H_{693} = 1,740 = \Delta H_0 + \int 0 \cdot 66 . dT$$

from which:

$$\Delta H_0 = 1,280.$$

Substituting this value in *7.5.1* yields:

$$R \ln a_{\text{Zn (l, at liquidus)}} = -\frac{1,280}{T} + 0 \cdot 66 \ln T + I.$$

But:

$$\ln a_{\text{Zn (l, at liquidus)}} = 0 \text{ at } 693°K.$$

Therefore, substituting $T = 693°K$ yields:

$$I = -2 \cdot 464$$

and:

$$\log a_{\text{Zn (l, at liquidus)}} = \frac{1}{4 \cdot 575} \left(-\frac{1,280}{T} + 0 \cdot 66 \ln T - 2 \cdot 464 \right).$$

This equation may now be used to obtain values for the activity of zinc in liquid alloys along the zinc liquidus line. The values so obtained are given in the third column of Table 7.1 and the corresponding values of the activity coefficient are given in the fourth column.

Table 7.1

Liquidus		Calculated				Experimental
Temperature °K	Composition N_{Zn}	$a_{\text{Zn(l)}}$ (liquidus)	$\gamma_{\text{Zn(l)}}$ (liquidus)	$\gamma_{\text{Zn(l)}}$ 703°K	$a_{\text{Zn(l)}}$ 703°K	$a_{\text{Zn(l)}}$ 703°K
693	1·0	1	1	1	1	
673	0·95	0·967	1·018	1·017	0·966	
661	0·90	0·941	1·046	1·043	0·939	0·953
649	0·80	0·921	1·150	1·140	0·912	0·914
636	0·70	0·895	1·279	1·250	0·875	0·874
623	0·60	0·867	1·446	1·388	0·832	0·830
610	0·50	0·846	1·691	1·580	0·790	0·757
586	0·40	0·799	1·997	1·781	0·712	0·665
551	0·30	0·730	2·437	2·010	0·603	0·536
504	0·20	0·634	3·170	2·285	0·457	0·395
471	0·15	0·566	3·775	2·438	0·365	
433*	0·10*	0·488	4·88	2·657	0·266	0·210

* Extrapolated.

Extrapolation of these data to 703°K requires the assumption of regular solution behaviour for the liquid alloys. For, from this assumption it follows that the function $RT\ln\gamma_i$ is independent of temperature at constant composition (see example 5.8). Thus equating the values of this function for zinc at the liquidus temperature and the temperature required (430°C or 703°K):

$$T_{(\text{liquidus})} \cdot \ln\gamma_{\text{Zn (l, at liquidus)}} = 703 \ln\gamma_{\text{Zn (l, 703)}}$$

or:

$$\log\gamma_{\text{Zn (l, 703)}} = \log\gamma_{\text{Zn (l, at liquidus)}} \cdot \frac{T_{(\text{liquidus})}}{703}.$$

This yields the activity coefficient of zinc in liquid alloys at 703°K at the compositions for which the activity coefficient of zinc is known at the appropriate liquidus temperature, as in Table 7.1.

The extrapolated values of $\gamma_{\text{Zn(l)}}$ at 703°K, obtained by use of this equation and the data in column 4 of Table 7.1, are given in column 5. Column 6 gives the corresponding values of the activities of zinc in liquid alloys at 703°K.

Kubaschewski and Evans list values of $\bar{H}_{\text{Zn}}^M$ and $\bar{S}_{\text{Zn}}^M$ for various compositions of Zn–Sn alloys at 703°K. The values were obtained from a critical assessment of experimental measurements (mainly e.m.f.) of the thermodynamic properties of these solutions. The activities of zinc in the liquid alloys at 703°K, calculated from these data (through *1.63*, the definition of $\bar{G}_{\text{Zn}}^M$, and *1.54*) are given in the last column of Table 7.1.

Comparison of the experimental and calculated values shows that the differences are insignificant for zinc concentrations between 0·9 and 0·6 atom fraction, but the error increases and becomes quite large at low zinc concentrations. The values of $\bar{S}_{\text{Zn}}^M$ given by Kubaschewski and Evans are some 40 per cent larger than the ideal values (i.e. $\bar{S}_{\text{Zn}}^E$ is positive), so the actual solutions do not conform to regular behaviour as assumed in the calculations. In view of this, the close agreement between the calculated and measured activities of zinc at zinc concentrations as low as 0·6 atom fraction is remarkable.

7.6 *Pure cadmium melts at 321°C and the freezing point is lowered 2·4°C by the addition of 0·51 atom-per cent of bismuth. The solid solubility of bismuth in cadmium is negligibly small. Calculate the heat of fusion of cadmium at the melting point, 321°C.*

The method adopted to solve this problem depends on the fact that a solvent conforms to Raoult's law (i.e. exhibits ideal behaviour) as the atom fraction of the solvent tends to unity. Thus, at very low concentra-

11

tions of solute, the activity of the solvent is equal to its atom fraction. Because the solid solubility is negligible, the concentration of cadmium may be related to the heat of fusion through equation 7.m which, in differential form, for the present system may be written as:

$$\frac{d \ln N_{Cd\,(l,\,at\,liquidus)}}{dT} = \frac{\Delta H_{tr}}{RT^2} \qquad 7.6.1$$

where $N_{Cd\,(l,\,at\,liquidus)}$ is the composition of the liquidus at temperature T.

It is reasonable to assume that ΔH_{tr} will not change appreciably with temperature over the small range considered here. Thus, at the melting point (T_M) of pure cadmium, ΔH_{tr} will equal the latent heat of fusion of cadmium (L_f). Integration of 7.6.1 from $T\,(= 591\cdot6°K)$ to $T_M\,(= 594°K)$ yields:

$$\ln N_{Cd\,(l\,at\,T)} = \frac{L_f}{R}\left(\frac{1}{T_M} - \frac{1}{T}\right) \qquad 7.6.2$$

(since at T_M, $N_{Cd(l)} = 1$), or:

$$\log N_{Cd\,(l\,at\,T)} = \frac{L_f}{4\cdot575}\left(\frac{1}{T_M} - \frac{1}{T}\right).$$

Substitution of the given values for $N_{Cd\,(l\,at\,T)}$, T and T_M yields:*

$$L_f = 1,470 \text{ cal mole}^{-1}.$$

The value for the heat of fusion given by Kubaschewski and Evans is 1,530 (± 40) cal mole^{-1}, which is in good agreement with the calculated value. The accuracy of the computed value depends critically on the accuracy of location of the liquidus line at small concentrations of solute. Reasonable values of L_f are obtained only when the freezing point depression is known with an accuracy of better than $\pm 0\cdot1°C$. In the calculation it is assumed that the solvent obeys Raoult's law up to the solute concentration for which the freezing point depression is known. The error arising from this assumption will, in general, decrease as this concentration of solute decreases.

From knowledge of the heat of fusion of a solvent, the reverse computation can be carried out, and the initial freezing-point depression for this solvent can be calculated as a function of the concentration for *any* solute over the concentration range in which the solvent conforms to ideal behaviour. Thus the 'ideal liquidus' for a solvent with latent heat of fusion L_f follows from 7.6.2:

$$N_{(ideal\,liquidus)} = \exp\left[\frac{L_f}{R}\left(\frac{1}{T_M} - \frac{1}{T}\right)\right]$$

* The use of 4-figure log tables is necessary in this calculation.

an exponential relation between composition and temperature, applicable when the solvent obeys Raoult's law. This 'ideal' liquidus can be calculated for any solute concentration and the temperature difference between the 'ideal' and measured liquidi can then be related to the excess free energy of the solution at the composition where the temperature difference is measured.

7.7   *The free-energy change accompanying the fusion of pure iron is given as a function of temperature by the relation:*

$$\Delta G^0 = 3,130 - 0{\cdot}3T \ln T + 0{\cdot}518T.$$

At 1,477°C, *a* 12 *atom-per cent liquid solution of copper in iron is in equilibrium with solid* (δ) *iron containing* 5 *atom-per cent of copper. Calculate the activity of iron in the liquid iron–copper solution, relative to pure liquid iron as the standard state.*

Since solid iron dissolves a significant amount of copper, the activity of the iron in the iron–copper solid solution will be less than the activity of pure solid iron at the same temperature, both activities being measured relative to the same standard state. As no information is given concerning the variation of the activity of iron with composition of the solid solution, it will be assumed as an approximation that iron conforms to Raoult's law up to 0·05 atom fraction of copper. Thus in the terminal solid solution, the activity of iron, referred to the pure solid metal as unity, is assumed equal to its atom fraction. On this basis, the activity of iron at the solidus at 1,477°C, is equal to 0·95, relative to pure solid iron as the standard state. Since liquid and solid of the respective compositions are in equilibrium at this temperature, it follows that the activity of iron in the 12 atom-per cent Cu liquid solution (i.e. at the liquidus) is also equal to 0·95, relative to pure *solid* iron as the standard state.

The problem requires that the activity in the melt is referred to the pure *liquid* standard state. The necessary change of standard state can be effected by first calculating the activity of pure solid iron at 1,477°C, relative to pure (supercooled) liquid iron at the same temperature. From 7.*l*:

$$\ln a_{\text{Fe (pure solid)}} = \int \frac{\Delta H_{\text{tr}}}{RT^2} \, \mathrm{d}T \qquad\qquad 7.7.1$$

where the activity of the pure solid iron is measured with respect to the supercooled pure liquid as the standard state. The data given for the fusion reaction are in terms of the free-energy change. However, insertion in *7.7.1* of *1.35*, the Gibbs–Helmholtz relation applied to a reaction:

$$\frac{\Delta G^0_{tr}}{T} = -\int \frac{\Delta H^0_{tr}}{T^2} . dT$$

yields:

$$\ln a_{Fe \text{ (pure solid)}} = -\frac{\Delta G^0_{tr}}{RT}.$$

(Alternatively, this relation may be deduced from *1.54* applied to the activity of solid iron, relative to pure liquid as the standard state.) Substituting the relation given for ΔG^0:

$$\ln a_{Fe \text{ (pure solid)}} = -\left[\frac{3,130 - 0 \cdot 3T \ln T + 0 \cdot 518T}{RT}\right].$$

Hence, at $T = 1,477°C$ $(1,750°K)$:

$$a_{Fe \text{ (pure solid)}} = 0 \cdot 967.$$

This is the activity of pure solid iron, relative to the pure supercooled liquid at $1,750°K$ as the standard state. From this value and that previously calculated for the activity of iron in the 12 atom-per cent Cu liquid solution (relative to pure solid iron as the standard state), the required value of the activity of iron in this solution (relative to pure liquid iron as the standard state) may be calculated. This is most easily appreciated if the activities are expressed in terms of the fugacity (f) of iron in its various states. Thus:

$$a_{Fe \text{ (liquidus)}} = \frac{f_{Fe \text{ (liquidus)}}}{f_{Fe \text{ (pure solid)}}} = 0 \cdot 95, \text{ as calculated}$$

(Relative to Fe, pure solid)

$$a_{Fe \text{ (pure solid)}} = \frac{f_{Fe \text{ (pure solid)}}}{f_{Fe \text{ (pure liquid)}}} = 0 \cdot 967, \text{ as calculated.}$$

(Relative to Fe, pure liquid)

Therefore:

$$a_{Fe \text{ (liquidus)}} = \frac{f_{Fe \text{ (liquidus)}}}{f_{Fe \text{ (pure liquid)}}} = 0 \cdot 95 \times 0 \cdot 967$$

(Relative to Fe, pure liquid)

$$= 0 \cdot 92.$$

The assumption was made at the beginning of this example that iron behaves ideally in the solid solution at concentrations up to 0·05 atom fraction of copper. This assumption is, of course, justified at infinite dilution of copper since, as stated in chapter 1, the activity of the solvent tends towards Raoultian behaviour as its atom fraction tends to unity. However, liquid iron–copper solutions show pronounced positive deviations from ideality, in addition to which it is usually found that the magnitude of such deviations is greater in the solid than in the liquid state. Hence, on this basis it appears very doubtful that the iron solid solution can be regarded as behaving ideally up to the solidus composition considered here. In general, it may be anticipated that uncertainties in calculated liquidus activities may be very large when it is necessary to make the sometimes doubtful assumption of ideal behaviour of the solvent in a terminal solid solution containing appreciable solute. This error does not arise, of course, if experimental data are available relating the activity of the solvent with the composition in the solid solution at the temperature of interest.

Exercises

7.A   The e.m.f. of the cell:

$$Ag_{(s)} | AgCl_{(s)} | Pt, Cl_{2(1\ atm)}$$

is 1·13 volt at 25°C, and the temperature coefficient of the e.m.f. is $-6·0 \times 10^{-4}$ volt deg^{-1} at this temperature. Calculate the standard entropy, enthalpy and free energy of AgCl at 298°K.

7.B   The standard oxidation potential of the Pt, $Cl_{2(g)}$, Cl$^-$ electrode is $-1·358$ volt at 25°C. At the same temperature the standard oxidation potential of the $Pb_{(s)}$, $PbCl_{2(s)}$, Cl$^-$ electrode is $+0·263$ volt. Determine the partial pressure of chlorine gas in equilibrium with Pb and $PbCl_2$ (i.e. the dissociation pressure of $PbCl_2$) at this temperature.

7.C   Find the minimum potential which must be applied in order to produce pure liquid tin from pure liquid $SnCl_2$ in an electrolytic cell operated at 500°C.

7.D   An electrolytic cell is set up in which one electrode is liquid cadmium and the other a liquid cadmium–lead alloy. When the atom fraction of cadmium in the alloy is 0·45, the e.m.f. is 0·0125 volt at 480°C. Calculate the activity coefficient of cadmium in the alloy at this temperature.

7.E   The e.m.f. of the cell:

$$Cd_{(pure,\ l)}|LiCl\text{--}KCl\text{--}CdCl_2|Cd_{(in\ Pb)}$$

is 0·0225 volt at 544°C and the temperature coefficient of the e.m.f. is $6·7 \times 10^{-5}$ volt deg^{-1} when the atom fraction of cadmium in the alloy is 0·269. Find the partial molar enthalpy of mixing, the excess partial molar free energy and the excess partial molar entropy of cadmium in the alloy.

7.F   An electrolytic cell is set up with an Al–Bi alloy ($N_{Al} = 0·167$) as one electrode and pure aluminium as the other electrode. The cell e.m.f. is 0·01304 volt at 900°C and the temperature coefficient of the e.m.f. is $6·26 \times 10^{-5}$ volt deg^{-1}. Determine the activity, the activity coefficient, and the partial molar entropy, enthalpy and free energy of mixing of aluminium in the alloy. By calculating the enthalpy of pure aluminium at 900°C, find the partial molar enthalpy of aluminium in the alloy at this temperature.

7.G   The e.m.f. of an electrolytic cell comprising a liquid Pb–Zn alloy ($N_{Zn} = 0·094$) as one electrode and pure liquid zinc as the other electrode is 0·0105 volt at 600°C. Assuming zinc vapour behaves ideally, determine the vapour pressure of zinc over the alloy. The free-energy change for the vaporization of zinc is given by:

$$\Delta G^0 = 30,300 + 5·74 T \log T - 43·25T, \text{ cal mole}^{-1}.$$

7.H   The e.m.f. of an electrolytic cell comprising a zinc–tin alloy ($N_{Zn} = 0·50$) as one electrode and pure zinc as the other electrode is $10·8 \times 10^{-3}$ volt at 479°C. The e.m.f. of a similar cell comprising a zinc–tin ($N_{Zn} = 0·50$) and a zinc–tin ($N_{Zn} = 0·173$) alloy electrodes is $26·9 \times 10^{-3}$ volt at the same temperature. Find the activity coefficient of zinc in the ($N_{Zn} = 0·173$) alloy.

7.I   The standard electrode potential of the $Ag|Ag^+$ electrode (i.e. the e.m.f. of the cell comprising pure silver and hydrogen ($p_{H_2} = 1$ atmosphere) electrodes) is $-0·799$ volt at 25°C. The standard electrode potential of the $Sn|Sn^{++}$ electrode is $+0·140$ volt at the same temperature. Determine the maximum e.m.f. generated between pure silver and pure tin electrodes when they are immersed in a suitable electrolyte at 25°C. What would be the maximum value of the e.m.f. if the activity of tin in the tin electrode was 0·5 ?   *Pure Ag.*

7.J   At 25°C the activity of mercury in a thallium amalgam is 0·95 when $N_{Hg} = 0·96$ and the activity decreases to 0·50 at $N_{Hg} = 0·66$. Find the maximum e.m.f. which could be developed between electrodes of these two amalgams when immersed in a suitable electrolyte containing Hg^{++} ions at 25°C.

7.K The standard oxidation potentials at 25°C for the Fe, Fe^{++} and Cu, Cu^{++} electrodes are $+0\cdot440$ and $-0\cdot340$ volt respectively. Show that when solid iron is placed in a normal solution of copper sulphate at 25°C the copper is almost completely precipitated from solution. (Assume that the solid iron and copper are pure metals.)

7.L The following e.m.f. measurements at 900°C have been obtained with electrolytic cells comprising pure liquid aluminium as one electrode and liquid aluminium–lead alloys as the other electrode:

$N_{Al \text{ (in Al–Pb)}}$	E, millivolt
0·0017	100·8
0·0067	56·2
0·0084	48·9
0·0131	35·5
0·0165	29·4
0·0404	6·15

Find the activity of aluminium in the ($N_{Al} = 0\cdot0404$) alloy at this temperature relative to the infinitely dilute, atom fraction standard state for aluminium.

7.M Assuming that the latent heat of fusion of nickel is independent of temperature, draw a graph of the 'ideal liquidus' for dilute alloys containing nickel as the solvent.

7.N The freezing point of silver is lowered by 3·5°C by the addition of 0·5 atom-per cent barium. If the solid solubility of barium in silver is negligible, calculate the latent heat of fusion of silver at the melting point, 960·5°C.

7.O A cadmium–zinc alloy containing 7·5 atom-per cent of zinc starts to solidify on cooling at 300°C. Calculate the approximate composition of the first solid which separates from the melt. Assume that $L_{f(Cd)}$ is independent of temperature and that cadmium conforms to ideal behaviour in both liquid and solid solutions.

7.P In dilute solution the logarithm of the atom fraction solubility of nickel in solid aluminium is approximately a linear function of the reciprocal of the temperature in degrees absolute. The solubility varies from $N_{Ni} = 0.0022$ at 500°C to $N_{Ni} = 0.022$ at 650°C. Estimate the partial molar heat of mixing (i.e. the heat of solution) of nickel in these solutions.

7.Q The cobalt–lead system shows extensive liquid immiscibility, the liquidus temperature rising rapidly from the eutectic point, close to the melting point of lead (327°C), as shown by the following data for liquidus compositions:

Liquidus, °C	913	969	1,076
N_{Co} at liquidus	0.022	0.029	0.055

Assuming that the latent heat of fusion of cobalt is independent of temperature, estimate the heat of solution of solid cobalt in the alloys.

7.R A motor-car radiator is filled with an 'anti-freeze' mixture consisting of water and ethylene glycol ($HOCH_2CH_2OH$, molecular weight = 62·07), the freezing point of which is -15°C. Calculate the weight-per cent of ethylene glycol required:

(a) assuming that the latent heat of fusion of ice is independent of temperature,
(b) using the heat-capacity data for water and ice, which can be taken as 18·0 and 9·0 cal deg^{-1} mole^{-1} respectively.

7.S At 1,050°C a solid gold–copper alloy containing 6 atom-per cent of gold is in equilibrium with a liquid alloy of the composition 0·90 N_{Cu}, 0·10 N_{Au}. Assuming that the copper in the solid alloy conforms to Raoult's law, determine the activity of copper in the liquid alloy at the liquidus temperature.

The free-energy change accompanying the solidification of pure copper can be represented as a function of temperature (cf. example 3.3) by:

$$\Delta G_T = -1,650 + 2.09T\ln T - 0.75 \times 10^{-3} T^2 - 12.85T \text{ cal mole}^{-1}.$$

7.T At 1,000°C a copper–zinc alloy containing 0·160 atom fraction of zinc lies on the solidus and that containing 0·206 atom fraction lies on the liquidus. The activity coefficient of zinc in liquid Cu–Zn alloys, relative to pure liquid zinc as the standard state, can be represented by:

$$RT\ln\gamma_{Zn} = -4,600N_{Cu}^2.$$

Find the activity of copper in the alloy of the solidus composition, relative to pure solid copper as the standard state, using the free-energy data for the solidification of copper given in the previous exercise.

7.U A silicon–silver alloy containing 76·9 weight-per cent silver lies on the silicon-rich liquidus at 1,289°C and, at this composition, the activity of silicon (relative to pure liquid silicon as standard state) is 0·72 at 1,400°C. The solid solubility of silver in silicon is negligible.

Assuming that $\ln a_{Si}$ varies linearly with temperature between the liquidus and 1,400°C, determine the activity and the partial molar entropy and enthalpy of silicon in the liquid alloy at 1,289°C. As an approximation, the difference in the heat capacities of solid and liquid silicon can be taken as:

$$\Delta C_{p\,(s\rightarrow l)} = -0\cdot 5 \text{ cal deg}^{-1} \text{ mole}^{-1}.$$

7.V The following values have been determined for the liquidus and solidus compositions at various temperatures in the system Fe–Pd:

Temperature °C	Liquidus atom-per cent Pd	Solidus atom-per cent Pd
1,535	0	0
1,517	2·05	1·05
1,497	4·36	2·20
1,480	6·50	3·55

Calculate the latent heat of fusion of pure iron.

References

1. C. WAGNER, *Thermodynamics of Alloys*, Addison Wesley, 1952.
2. F. D. ROSSINI, *Experimental Thermochemistry*, Interscience, New York, 1956.
3. O. KUBASCHEWSKI and E. LL. EVANS, *Metallurgical Thermochemistry*, Pergamon, 1958.
4. G. KORTUM and J. O'M. BOCKRIS, *Textbook of Electrochemistry*, Elsevier Publishing Co., London, 1951.
5. M. HANSEN, *Constitution of Binary Alloys*, McGraw-Hill, 1958.

CHAPTER 8

The Ternary Gibbs–Duhem Equation

Graphical (iso-activity curve slope) method

8.1.   In recent years, thermodynamic data on ternary systems have become more readily available, and as with binary systems, values for one component often yield to experimental determination more readily than values for other components. It is very desirable to be able to calculate these unknown values from the measured quantities. This will be possible if the Gibbs–Duhem relation *1.43*, applied to a three-component system, can be expressed in a practically usable form. Various treatments of this problem have been made, being either graphical, analytical or a combination of both. However, all these methods may be regarded as originating from *1.43* applied to a ternary system A–B–C, i.e.

$$n_A \, d\bar{G}_A + n_B \, d\bar{G}_B + n_C \, d\bar{G}_C = 0 \qquad 8.1.1$$

where n_A, n_B and n_C are the number of moles of components, A, B, C respectively. Thus complete differentiation of *1.41*:

$$G' = n_A \, \bar{G}_A + n_B \, \bar{G}_B + n_C \, \bar{G}_C$$

applied to the same ternary system, and subtraction of *8.1.1* yields:

$$dG' = \bar{G}_A \, dn_A + \bar{G}_B \, dn_B + \bar{G}_C \, dn_C \qquad 8.1.2$$

where G' is the free energy of the whole system containing $n_A + n_B + n_C$ mole. Equation *8.1.2* is an expression for the complete differential of the free energy of the system at constant temperature and pressure. Thus, from the fundamental laws of partial differentiation* and with the restriction of $n_C =$ constant (or $dn_C = 0$):

$$\left(\frac{\partial \bar{G}_B}{\partial \bar{G}_A} \right)_{n_B, \, n_C} = - \left(\frac{\partial n_A}{\partial n_B} \right)_{\bar{G}_A, \, n_C} \qquad 8.1.3$$

which may be regarded as a further alternative form of *8.1.1*. For a single-phase field in an isothermal section of a ternary system, *8.1.3* may be integrated along a path of constant n_B and n_C which corresponds to a path of constant mole ratio n_B/n_C ($= N_B/N_C$). Such a path is a straight line passing through the corner $N_A = 1$ on the ternary chart.

* See appendix 5.

Integrating *8.1.3* between the composition limits X and x (assuming that data for component A are available and data for B are required) then:

$$\left[\bar{G}_{B(x)} = \bar{G}_{B(x)} - \int_{\bar{G}_{A(x)}}^{\bar{G}_{A(x)}} \left(\frac{\partial n_A}{\partial n_B} \right)_{\bar{G}_A, \, n_C} d\bar{G}_A \right]_{\frac{n_B}{n_C} = \text{constant}} \qquad 8.1.4$$

where X is a composition on $n_B/n_C = $ constant for which $\bar{G}_B$ is known and x is the composition for which $\bar{G}_B$ is desired. The integration may be made, therefore, if the experimental data for $\bar{G}_A$ are adequate to enable the partial derivative $(\partial n_A/\partial n_B)_{\bar{G}_A, \, n_C}$ to be evaluated, as a function of $\bar{G}_A$, along the integration path $n_B/n_C = $ constant between the limits $\bar{G}_{A(x)}$ and $\bar{G}_{A(x)}$.

This partial derivative $(\partial n_A/\partial n_B)_{\bar{G}_A, \, n_C}$ is the direction, expressed in terms of composition, of the tangent to a curve along which $\bar{G}_A$ is constant (i.e. the tangent to an 'iso-activity' curve) at a point which must also be on the integration path given by $n_B/n = $ constant. Thus, on the isothermal triangle, tangents to iso-activity curves at the points where the latter cut the integration path are extended to intersect the A–B side of the triangle. These points of intersection, expressed in terms of the mole ratio of component A to component B, yield values of $(\partial n_A/\partial n_B)$ corresponding to the values of $\bar{G}_A$ for the iso-activity curves.* The area under the curve of $(\partial n_A/\partial n_B)$ versus $\bar{G}_A$, between the limits $\bar{G}_{A(x)}$ and $\bar{G}_{A(x)}$ will then yield a value for the integral of *8.1.4*.

This technique may, of course, be applied equally readily to either activity or activity coefficient data. For by substitution of:

$$d\bar{G}_i = RT \, d\ln a_i$$

or:

$$d\bar{G}_i = RT \, d\ln \gamma_i N_i$$

into *8.1.3*, relations similar to *8.1.4* may be obtained with $\log a_i$ or $\log \gamma_i$ replacing $\bar{G}_i$. The available data are then plotted in the form of constant $\log a_A$ or $\log \gamma_A$ curves in the ternary diagram, and the procedure used to obtain the solution of the appropriate integral is identical to that just described to evaluate *8.1.4*.

The following example illustrates the use of the 'tangent intercept method' [1] for solving the Gibbs–Duhem relation for a ternary system.

* In physical terms, this point of intersection of the tangent gives the composition of a binary A–B alloy which could be added (in infinitesimal amount) to the ternary alloy on the integration path without changing the value of $\bar{G}_A$ in the latter.

Liquid aluminium–bismuth–lead alloys exhibit a miscibility gap, the Bi–Pb
rich liquid containing 5 atom-per cent Al *in* Pb-*rich melts and up to 35
atom-per cent* Al *in* Bi-*rich melts at 900°C. The* Bi–Pb-*rich liquid has been
extensively investigated at this temperature* [2] *using an e.m.f. technique
with* Al^{+++} *as the current-carrying ion. Ternary alloy compositions were
selected along various lines of constant mole ratio* N_{Bi}/N_{Pb} *in the ternary
isotherm. The e.m.f.s generated in cells containing such alloy anodes with*

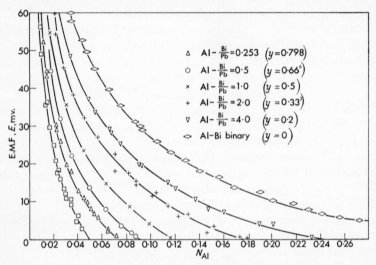

Fig. 8.1a. E.M.F.'s of composition cells in Al–Bi–Pb system at 900°C. (2).

pure liquid aluminium cathodes are given in Fig. 8.1a *as a function of the
atom fraction of aluminium. If for binary* Bi–Pb *alloys:*

$$RT\ln\gamma_{Bi} = -1{,}179N_{Pb}^2$$

calculate the activity of bismuth in an alloy of composition:

$$(N_{Bi} = 0.60, N_{Pb} = 0.20, N_{Al} = 0.20).$$

As activity data for aluminium in the Al–Bi–Pb system are available
and the activity of bismuth is required, equation *8.1.4*, expressed in
terms of activity, will be of the form:

$$\log a_{Bi(x)} = \log a_{Bi(x)}$$
$$- \int_{\log a_{Al(X)}}^{\log a_{Al(x)}} \left(\frac{\partial n_{Al}}{\partial n_{Bi}}\right)_{\log a_{Al},\, n_{Pb}} \mathrm{d}\log a_{Al} \Bigg]_{\frac{n_{Bi}}{n_{Pb}}=\frac{N_{Bi}}{N_{Pb}}=\text{constant}} \qquad 8.1.5$$

The 'unknown' composition x will be $N_{Bi} = 0.60$, $N_{Pb} = 0.20$, $N_{Al} = 0.20$, and thus the line of the integration path is $N_{Bi}/N_{Pb} = 3$, as shown on the bismuth corner of the ternary coordinate chart, Fig. 8.1b. The only point along this path at which the activity of bismuth is known is at the intersection of this path with the binary Pb–Bi side of the triangle. That is, the composition X will be given by ($N_{Bi} = 0.75$, $N_{Pb} = 0.25$, $N_{Al} = 0$).

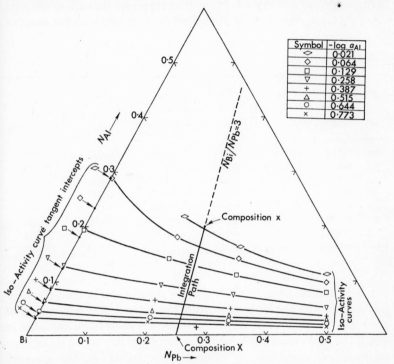

Symbol	$-\log a_{Al}$
⬦	0·021
◇	0·064
□	0·129
▽	0·258
+	0·387
△	0·515
○	0·644
×	0·773

Fig. 8.1b. Graphical solution of ternary Gibbs–Duhem equation. (Tangent intercept method (1)).

The integration of *8.1.5* is made, therefore, along the heavy continuous line shown in Fig. 8.1b.

It is required that the available data be expressed in terms of the compositions for which values of $\log a_{Al}$ are constant. For the concentration cells used to obtain the data of Fig. 8.1a, the activity of aluminium in the alloy anode will be related to the reversible e.m.f. E generated (in volts), by the relation:

$$RT\ln a_{Al} = -3FE$$

where a_{Al} is the activity of aluminium in the alloy with respect to pure aluminium as the standard state, F is the Faraday, equal to 23,066 cal volt-equiv^{-1}, and the valence of the aluminium ion Al^{+++} is taken as 3. At 900°C (1,173°K), $\log a_{Al} = -12\cdot89E$, and the compositions for which $\log a_{Al}$ is constant will be those for which the e.m.f.s of the cells are constant. Thus, from Fig. 8.1a, at values of constant e.m.f., a series of composition values are obtained, expressed in terms of N_{Al} for various values of the mole ratio N_{Bi}/N_{Pb}. These, with the corresponding values of $\log a_{Al}$, are listed in Table 8.1. Iso-activity curves for the various constant values of $\log a_{Al}$ may now be plotted on the ternary coordinate chart of

Table 8.1

E milli-volt	$-\log a_{Al}$	N_{Al} $\left(\dfrac{N_{Bi}}{N_{Pb}} = \infty\right)$	N_{Al} $\left(\dfrac{N_{Bi}}{N_{Pb}} = 4\cdot0\right)$	N_{Al} $\left(\dfrac{N_{Bi}}{N_{Pb}} = 2\cdot0\right)$	N_{Al} $\left(\dfrac{N_{Bi}}{N_{Pb}} = 1\cdot0\right)$	$\left(\dfrac{\partial n_{Al}}{\partial n_{Bi}}\right)_{a_{Al},\,n_{Pb}}$
60	0·773	0·033	0·024	0·020	0·014	0·034
50	0·644	0·045	0·032	0·026	0·019	0·045
40	0·515	0·062	0·044	0·034	0·026	0·064
30	0·387	0·088	0·064	0·049	0·035	0·094
20	0·258	0·127	0·093	0·074	0·052	0·141
10	0·129	0·195	0·140	0·110	0·078	0·220
5	0·064	0·290	0·180	0·138	0·097	0·305
1·66[7]	0·021	—	0·218	0·161	0·111	0·408

Fig. 8.1b and tangents drawn to each of these curves at their points of intersection with the integration path $N_{Bi}/N_{Pb} = 3$. The intersection of these tangents with the Bi–Al side of the ternary chart (shown arrowed in Fig. 8.1b) yield values which, when converted into the ratio of the number of mole of aluminium to bismuth, correspond to the quantity $(\partial n_{Al}/\partial n_{Bi})_{\log a_{Al},\,n_{Pb}}$. These are also listed in Table 8.1 and are plotted against $-\log a_{Al}$ in Fig. 8.1c. It will be noted that the resulting curve is asymptotic to both axes (cf. the curve of example 5.5).

The area to be integrated is between $\log a_{Al}$ at X ($N_{Bi} = 0\cdot75$, $N_{Pb} = 0\cdot25$, $N_{Al} = 0$) for which $\partial n_{Al}/\partial n_{Bi} = 0$ and $\log a_{Al}$ at x ($N_{Bi} = 0\cdot6$, $N_{Pb} = 0\cdot2$, $N_{Al} = 0\cdot2$). This latter value is found to be $\log a_{Al} = -0\cdot016$ by plotting values of this quantity versus the values of N_{Al} along the integration path and extrapolating to yield the value corresponding to $N_{Al} = 0\cdot2$. Thus the area to be integrated is as shown shaded in Fig. 8.1c where it is seen that an error will be involved, due to the necessity of area measurement under a curve going to infinity. With the present data, this error is fairly small, though in general, it will be significant.

Measurement of this area (using the trapezoidal rule* with chord width $\triangle \log a_{Al} = 0.05$) yields a value of the integral in *8.1.5* of 0·111. As for binary Pb–Bi alloys:

$$RT \ln \gamma_{Bi} = -1,179 N_{Pb}^2$$

then:

$$\log a_{Bi_{(x)}}(N_{Bi} = 0.75, N_{Pb} = 0.25) = -0.139.$$

Hence:

$$\log a_{Bi_{(x)}} = -0.139 - 0.111$$

$$= -0.250$$

and, at the required composition:

$$a_{Bi}(N_{Bi} = 0.6, N_{Al} = 0.2, N_{Pb} = 0.2) = 0.563.$$

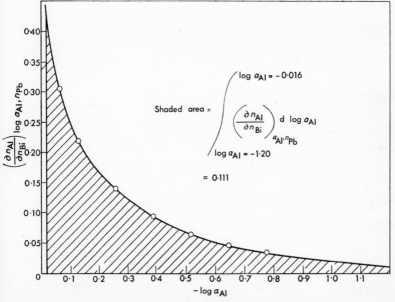

Fig. 8.1c. Graphical solution of ternary Gibbs–Duhem equation. Solution of the integral in equation (*8.1.5*).

Alternative graphical (iso-composition curve slope) method

8.2 An alternative treatment [3] of the solution of the Gibbs–Duhem equation applied to ternary systems is based on a further relation between the quantities in equation *8.1.2*, arising from the fundamental

* See appendix 5.

laws of partial differentiation. For, it may readily be shown that, with the restriction n_C = constant (or $dn_C = 0$) applied to *8.1.2*, then:

$$\left(\frac{\partial \bar{G}_B}{\partial n_A}\right)_{n_B, n_C} = \left(\frac{\partial \bar{G}_A}{\partial n_B}\right)_{n_A, n_C} \qquad 8.2.1$$

which is an alternative expression of the Gibbs–Duhem relation with the restriction n_C = constant applied. In this form, the relation is inconvenient to apply in practice and can be improved by substituting the variables:

$$x = \frac{n_C}{n_A + n_C}\left[= \frac{N_C}{N_A + N_C}\right]^*$$

$$y = \frac{n_C}{n_B + n_C}\left[= \frac{N_C}{N_B + N_C}\right]$$

where N_A, N_B and N_C are the atom or mole fractions of components A, B and C respectively. As:

$$\left(\frac{\partial x}{\partial n_A}\right)_{n_B, n_C} = \frac{-n_C}{(n_A + n_C)^2}$$

then:

$$\left[\partial n_A = \frac{-n_C}{x^2}\partial x\right]_{n_B, n_C}.$$

Similarly:

$$\left[\partial n_B = \frac{-n_C}{y^2}\partial y\right]_{n_A, n_C}.$$

Substituting these into *8.2.1* and noting that the constancy subscripts can be replaced by x and y:

$$\left.\begin{array}{l} n_A, n_C \equiv x \\ n_B, n_C \equiv y \end{array}\right\}$$

then:

$$\left(\frac{\partial \bar{G}_B}{\partial x}\right)_y = \frac{y^2}{x^2}\left(\frac{\partial \bar{G}_A}{\partial y}\right)_x. \qquad 8.2.2$$

If, for purposes of example, it is assumed that data for component A are available, the relation *8.2.2* may be integrated between the composition

* These variables x and y are particularly convenient to use, for they are always finite, having values between zero and one, and become constant when the restrictions on the right- and left-hand sides (respectively) of *8.2.1* are applied, as in deriving *8.2.2*.

at which data for component B are desired and any composition for which data for the latter component are known. Such an integration must, of course, be along a path of constant y passing through the 'unknown' composition. That is:

$$\left[\bar{G}_{B(x)} = \bar{G}_{B(X)} + \int_{X}^{x} \frac{y^2}{x^2} \left(\frac{\partial \bar{G}_A}{\partial y} \right)_x dx \right]_{y=\text{constant}} \qquad 8.2.3$$

where X is a composition at which $\bar{G}_B$ is known, this composition and the whole integration being on a path corresponding to $y = \text{constant}$. Such paths are shown as the shorter-dashed lines in the ternary coordinate chart of Fig. 8.2a.

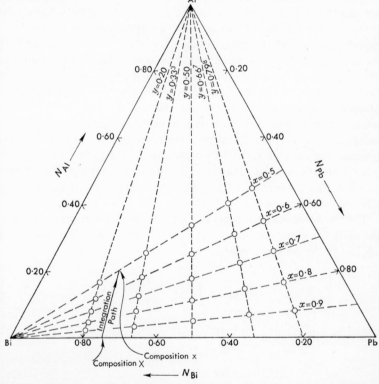

Fig. 8.2a. Ternary co-ordinate chart showing details of solution of equation (8.2.5).

The integrated ternary Gibbs–Duhem relation expressed in 8.2.3 is not particularly convenient to use from a practical standpoint, and it is

12

preferable to express 8.2.3 in terms of activities rather than partial molar free energies. The substitutions:

$$\bar{G}_A = G_A^0 + RT \ln a_A \quad \text{from } 1.54$$

and the equivalent for component B are made into 8.2.1 and yield a relation corresponding to 8.2.3:

$$\left[\log a_{B(x)} = \log a_{B(X)} + \int_X^x \frac{y^2}{x^2} \left(\frac{\partial \log a_A}{\partial y} \right)_x dx \right]_{y=\text{constant}} \quad 8.2.4$$

where X is the composition at which a_B is known.

The solution of 8.2.4 for a ternary alloy of a particular composition x is obtained through the following procedure. The data for component A are assembled in the form of values of $\log a_A$ for constant values of the composition variable x. This may entail interpolation between available experimental values, though in an original study of a system, the necessity for the data to be in this form would be kept in mind. The assembled data are plotted in the form of $\log a_A$ versus the composition variable y for the constant values of x. The slopes of tangents to the resulting family of curves, at the particular constant value of y corresponding to the integration path, yield values of the quantity $(\partial \log a_A / \partial y)_x$ for the various values of x. These, multiplied by (y^2/x^2), are then plotted against this composition variable x, the area under the resulting graph between the composition X and the 'unknown' composition x yielding the integral in 8.2.4. The application of this method to the data of example 8.1 will illustrate the necessary procedure.

The ternary coordinate chart of Fig. 8.2a shows the composition x of the alloy for which the activity of bismuth is required. Equation 8.2.4 applied to the present problem:

$$\left[\log a_{Bi(x)} = \log a_{Bi(X)} + \int_X^x \frac{y^2}{x^2} \left(\frac{\partial \log a_{Al}}{\partial y} \right)_x dx \right]_{y=\text{constant}} \quad 8.2.5$$

has to be solved along the path:

$$y = \frac{N_{Pb}}{N_{Pb} + N_{Bi}} = \text{constant}$$

which must pass through the 'unknown' composition x. Paths of constant y are straight lines passing through the corner Al = 1 of the Al–Bi–Pb ternary isotherm as shown by short-dashed lines in Fig. 8.2a. The heavy continuous line of Fig. 8.2a is that for $y = 0.25$, which passes through the composition x, and the integration in *8.2.5* must be made along this line from a composition X for which a_{Bi} is known. From the data for the binary Pb–Bi system, a_{Bi} may be calculated at $N_{Bi} = 0.75$ or $y = 0.25$, and the integration is made between this composition on the Pb–Bi binary side of the isotherm and the composition x (i.e. along the heavy line of Fig. 8.2a).

The available data for the ternary Al–Bi–Pb alloys are for compositions along lines of constant mole ratio N_{Bi}/N_{Pb}, which correspond to lines of constant y as shown in Table 8.2. These lines are those shown in Fig. 8.2a. The quantity $(\partial \log a_{Al}/\partial y)$ is required for the condition:

$$x = \frac{N_{Pb}}{N_{Pb} + N_{Al}} = \text{constant.}$$

Lines for which ($x = $ constant) pass through the Bi $= 1$ corner of the Al–Bi–Pb ternary isotherm, those for increments of 0.10 between $x = 0.9$ and $x = 0.5$ being shown as long-dashed lines in Fig. 8.2a. It will be noted that the line $x = 0.5$ passes through the 'unknown' composition x.

In accordance with the outline given earlier, values are first required for $\log a_{Al}$ at constant values of the composition variable x. With the presently available data, these values of $\log a_{Al}$ will be obtained for alloy compositions in the ternary chart of Fig. 8.2a at the intersections (shown circled) of the short-dashed lines $y = $ constant (for which data are available) with the long-dashed lines $x = $ constant (for which the data are required). The points of intersection may be deduced graphically from an enlarged version of Fig. 8.2a, or, more accurately, may be calculated individually from the three simultaneous equations which describe the constancies of x and y and the condition that the sum of the mole fractions is unity. For example, the composition of the intersection of the line $y = 0.333$ and the line $x = 0.7$ is calculated as $N_{Al} = 0.1249$, $N_{Bi} = 0.5834$, $N_{Pb} = 0.2917$ (to four-figure accuracy) from the equations:

$$\frac{N_{Pb}}{N_{Pb} + N_{Bi}} = 0.333 \quad \text{or} \quad N_{Bi} - 2N_{Pb} = 0$$

$$\frac{N_{Pb}}{N_{Pb} + N_{Al}} = 0.7 \quad \text{or} \quad N_{Al} - 0.428 N_{Pb} = 0$$

$$N_{Al} + N_{Bi} + N_{Pb} = 0.$$

In practice, only the value of N_{Al} for each point of intersection is required and values calculated in the foregoing manner are listed in Table 8.2. (p. 170) These compositions (i.e. values of N_{Al}) are then used to deduce values of the e.m.f.s of cells containing such alloys from the appropriate

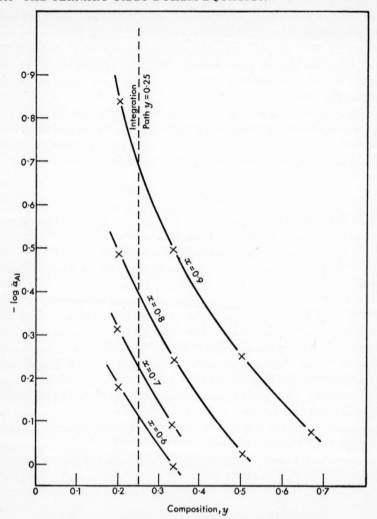

Fig. 8.2b. Plots of $(-\log a_{Al})_x$ versus the composition variable y.

$y = $ constant curve of Fig. 8.1a. The e.m.f.s so deduced are also given in the table.*

* It will be noted that the available data for the Al–Bi–Pb system are not readily amenable to solution by this method, for only a small number of the calculated points of intersection of the $x = $ constant and $y = $ constant lines are inside the composition field for which data are available. Hence the scarcity of points in Fig. 8.2c. However, this must not be regarded as a shortcoming of the method (compared, for instance, to the tangent-intercept method) but rather that the experimental data were not obtained with the use of this method in mind (see example 8.3).

The relation between the reversible e.m.f. generated (in volts) and activity of aluminium in the alloy anode:

$$RT \ln a_{Al} = -3FE$$

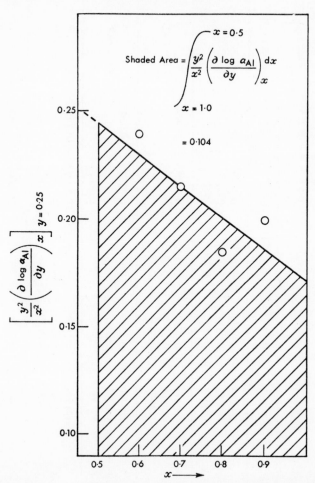

Fig. 8.2c. Graphical solution of ternary Gibbs–Duhem equation. Solution of integral in equation (8.2.5).

is again applicable, and values of $\log a_{Al}$ may be calculated directly from the e.m.f. values of the table. These are also listed. The data are plotted as $\log a_{Al}$ versus y for constant values of x as in Fig. 8.2b, the slopes of these curves at $y = 0.25$ yielding values of $(\partial \log a_A/\partial y)_x$ for the various values of x. These latter quantities are also listed in Table 8.2, as is the

Table 8.2

Mole ratio, $\dfrac{N_{Bi}}{N_{Pb}}$		4.0	2.0	1.0	0.5	0.253	$\left(\dfrac{\partial \log a_{Al}}{\partial y}\right)$ at $y = 0.25$	$\dfrac{y^2}{x^2}$ at $y = 0.25$
Composition variable, y		0.2	0.33	0.5	0.667	0.798		
$x = 0.9$	N_{Al}	0.0215	0.0358	0.0526	0.0689	0.1169	(+)2.585	0.0772
	E, volt	0.065	0.0387	0.0194	0.0057	–		
	$\log a_{Al}$	−0.838	−0.499	−0.250	−.074	–		
$x = 0.8$	N_{Al}	0.0475	0.0769	0.1112	0.1429	0.1664	(+)1.892	0.0977
	E, volt	0.0380	0.0190	0.0016	–	–		
	$\log a_{Al}$	−0.490	−0.245	−0.0206	–	–		
$x = 0.7$	N_{Al}	0.0790	0.1249	0.1764	0.2222	0.2548	(+)1.688	0.1276
	E, volt	0.0241	0.0071	–	–	–		
	$\log a_{Al}$	−0.311	−0.0915	–	–	–		
$x = 0.6$	N_{Al}	0.1175	0.1819	0.2500	0.3077	0.3473	(+)1.380	0.1736
	E, volt	0.0142	−0.0003	–	–	–		
	$\log a_{Al}$	−0.183	+0.0039	–	–	–		
$x = 0.5$	N_{Al}	0.1667	0.2500	0.333^3	0.4000	0.4438	–	0.2500
	E, volt	−0.0063	–	–	–	–		
	$\log a_{Al}$	−0.0811	–	–	–	–		

value of y^2/x^2 for the various values of x. The product of this and the partial differential is then plotted against x as in Fig. 8.2c. The scarcity of the derived points does not merit curve-fitting and a straight line has been drawn in this figure.

The integral in 8.2.5 is evaluated as the area under this graph between $x = 1\cdot0$ and $x = 0\cdot5$, along the integration path of Fig. 8.2a. The value of the integral is given by this area as:

$$\left[\int_{x=1}^{x=0\cdot5} \frac{y^2}{x^2}\left(\frac{\partial \log a_{Al}}{\partial y}\right)_x \, dx \right]_{y=0\cdot25} = -0\cdot104.$$

Thus, from 8.2.5:

$$\log a_{Bi_{(x)}} = \log a_{Bi_{(x)}} - 0\cdot104$$

which, using the value of $\log a_{Bi_{(x)}}$ calculated in 8.1 (p. 163), gives:

$$\log a_{Bi_{(x)}} = -0\cdot139 - 0\cdot104$$

$$= \bar{1}\cdot757$$

or:

$$a_{Bi_{(x)}} = 0\cdot572$$

which value compares very well with that calculated in example 8.1.

Analytical (data curve-fitting) method

8.3 With all graphical techniques, errors arise from the difficulties involved in drawing tangents and measuring areas under curves. In the previous two examples these errors would appear to be small, but this is not necessarily true in all cases. Hence it is desirable to be able to apply analytically the ternary Gibbs–Duhem relation to a set of experimental data. The practicability of this application will depend on the data available, for if the latter yield readily to expression in the form of empirical equations relating to composition, the analytical solution of the ternary Gibbs–Duhem relation is straightforward. On the other hand, if considerable time must be spent in trying to fit composition relations to the experimental data, the use of a graphical technique is probably preferable.

It is obvious that the probability of finding relations to describe the experimental data for a newly investigated system will be improved if the latter are expressed as functions which, in other systems, have been found to be simply related to composition. Such a function is the quantity α, previously noted as arising in the Wagner solution for the binary Gibbs–

Duhem relation (see chapter 1, p. 15 and equation 5.6.1, p. 103). The use of functions of this type is found to facilitate greatly the analytical solution of the Gibbs–Duhem relation applied to ternary systems [4].

As in the previous examples, the general relation *8.1.1* is the starting point for the analytical method. The composition variable:

$$y = \frac{n_C}{n_A + n_C} \qquad\qquad 8.3.1$$

is used, where n_A, (n_B) and n_C are the number of moles of components A, (B) and C respectively. Thus:

$$n_A = (n_A + n_C)(1 - y) \qquad\qquad 8.3.2$$

and:

$$n_C = (n_A + n_C)y. \qquad\qquad 8.3.3$$

Also as:

$$N_B = \frac{n_B}{n_A + n_B + n_C}$$

where N_B is the mole fraction of component B, then:

$$n_B = \frac{N_B(n_A + n_C)}{(1 - N_B)}. \qquad\qquad 8.3.4$$

Dividing *8.1.1*, the general Gibbs–Duhem relation for a ternary system A–B–C, by dy, substituting *8.3.2*, *8.3.3* and *8.3.4* and then dividing throughout by $(n_A + n_C)$ yields:

$$(1 - y)\left(\frac{\partial \bar{G}_A}{\partial y}\right)_{N_B} + \left(\frac{N_B}{1 - N_B}\right)\left(\frac{\partial \bar{G}_B}{\partial y}\right)_{N_B} + y\left(\frac{\partial \bar{G}_C}{\partial y}\right)_{N_B} = 0. \qquad 8.3.5$$

Similarly, dividing *8.1.1* by dN_B, substituting *8.3.2*, *8.3.3* and *8.3.4* and dividing by $(n_A + n_C)$ yields:

$$(1 - y)\left(\frac{\partial \bar{G}_A}{\partial N_B}\right)_y + \left(\frac{N_B}{1 - N_B}\right)\left(\frac{\partial \bar{G}_B}{\partial N_B}\right)_y + y\left(\frac{\partial \bar{G}_C}{\partial N_B}\right)_y = 0. \qquad 8.3.6$$

Differentiating *8.3.5* with respect to N_B and *8.3.6* with respect to y, and subtracting, yields:

$$\left[\left(\frac{\partial \bar{G}_A}{\partial N_B}\right)_y - \left(\frac{\partial \bar{G}_A}{\partial y}\right)_{N_B} \cdot \left(\frac{\partial y}{\partial N_B}\right)_{\bar{G}_A}\right] + \frac{1}{(1 - N_B)^2}\left[\left(\frac{\partial \bar{G}_B}{\partial y}\right)_{N_B} - \left(\frac{\partial \bar{G}_B}{\partial N_B}\right)_y \cdot \left(\frac{\partial N_B}{\partial y}\right)_{\bar{G}_B}\right]$$

$$+ \left[\left(\frac{\partial \bar{G}_C}{\partial y}\right)_{N_B} \cdot \left(\frac{\partial y}{\partial N_B}\right)_{\bar{G}_C} - \left(\frac{\partial \bar{G}_C}{\partial N_B}\right)_y\right] = 0. \qquad 8.3.7$$

But, from the fundamental laws of partial differentiation:

$$\left(\frac{\partial M}{\partial x}\right)_y \cdot \left(\frac{\partial x}{\partial y}\right)_M = -\left(\frac{\partial M}{\partial y}\right)_x$$

where M is a function of x and y. Hence 8.3.7 reduces to:

$$\left(\frac{\partial \bar{G}_A}{\partial N_B}\right)_y + \frac{1}{(1-N_B)^2}\left(\frac{\partial \bar{G}_B}{\partial y}\right)_{N_B} - \left(\frac{\partial \bar{G}_C}{\partial N_B}\right)_y = 0. \qquad 8.3.8$$

Multiplying 8.3.8 by y and adding to 8.3.6 yields:

$$\left(\frac{\partial \bar{G}_A}{\partial N_B}\right)_y = -\frac{y}{(1-N_B)^2}\cdot\left(\frac{\partial \bar{G}_B}{\partial y}\right)_{N_B} - \left(\frac{N_B}{1-N_B}\right)\left(\frac{\partial \bar{G}_B}{\partial N_B}\right)_y. \qquad 8.3.9$$

Alternatively, multiplying 8.3.8 by $(1-y)$ and subtracting from 8.3.6 yields:

$$\left(\frac{\partial \bar{G}_C}{\partial N_B}\right)_y = \frac{1-y}{(1-N_B)^2}\cdot\left(\frac{\partial \bar{G}_B}{\partial y}\right)_{N_B} - \frac{N_B}{1-N_B}\left(\frac{\partial \bar{G}_B}{\partial N_B}\right)_y. \qquad 8.3.10$$

Relations 8.3.9 and 8.3.10 are useful forms of the Gibbs–Duhem equation, for they may be integrated to yield $\bar{G}_A$ or $\bar{G}_C$ if $\bar{G}_B$ is known such that its variation with the composition variables y and N_B can be evaluated.

By expressing 8.3.9 and 8.3.10 in terms of activity coefficients or excess partial molar free energies (see equation 1.79), the practicability of solving the integrals by analytical means is improved. Thus 8.3.9 in terms of excess partial molar free energies is:

$$\left(\frac{\partial \bar{G}_A^E}{\partial N_B}\right)_y = -\frac{y}{(1-N_B)^2}\left(\frac{\partial \bar{G}_B^E}{\partial y}\right)_{N_B} - \left(\frac{N_B}{1-N_B}\right)\left(\frac{\partial \bar{G}_B^E}{\partial N_B}\right)_y \qquad 8.3.11$$

which may be integrated between $N_B = 0$ (i.e. the binary system A–C) and $N_B = N_B$, along the pseudo-binary path $y = $ constant in the ternary isotherm. Integrating by parts:

$$\left\{ \bar{G}_{A\,(N_B)}^E = \bar{G}_{A\,(N_B=0)}^E + \int_0^{N_B}\left[\frac{\bar{G}_B^E}{(1-N_B)^2} - y\cdot\frac{\partial}{\partial y}\left(\frac{\bar{G}_B^E}{(1-N_B)^2}\right)\right]dN_B \right.$$

$$\left. -\frac{N_B\,\bar{G}_B^E}{(1-N_B)}\right\}_{y=\text{constant}} . \qquad 8.3.12$$

If a function α is defined such that:

$$\alpha_i = \frac{RT\ln\gamma_i}{(1-N_i)^2} \qquad 8.3.13$$

$$= \frac{\bar{G}_i^E}{(1-N_i)^2} \quad \text{from } 1.79,$$

then 8.3.12 becomes:

$$\left\{\bar{G}_{A\,(N_B)}^E = \bar{G}_{A\,(N_B=0)}^E + \int_0^{N_B}\left[\alpha_B - y\frac{\partial\alpha_B}{\partial y}\right]dN_B \\ - \alpha_B N_B(1-N_B)\right\}_{y\,=\,\text{constant}} \qquad 8.3.14$$

Similarly, for component C, from 8.3.10:

$$\left\{\bar{G}_{C\,(N_B)}^E = \bar{G}_{C\,(N_B=0)}^E + \int_0^{N_B}\left[\alpha_B - (1-y)\frac{\partial\alpha_B}{\partial y}\right]dN_B \\ - \alpha_B N_B(1-N_B)\right\}_{y\,=\,\text{constant}} \qquad 8.3.15$$

Thus, if the quantity α can be expressed as a function of composition, 8.3.14 or 8.3.15 may be solved analytically to yield $\bar{G}_A^E$ or $\bar{G}_C^E$ respectively at any composition N_B along the pseudo-binary path, $y = \text{constant}$. As expressions of the form $\ln\gamma_i/(1-N_i)^2$ are generally found to be well behaved functions of composition (e.g. $\ln\gamma_i/(1-N_i)^2$ is independent of composition in a regular solution), the expression of α_i as a function of composition is usually an easy matter.

If data for the binary system A–C are not available, a somewhat less accurate solution of 8.3.11 may be obtained by integrating between the composition $N_B \to 1$ and the composition desired. Thus:

$$\left\{\bar{G}_{A\,(N_B)}^E = \bar{G}_{A\,(N_B\to1)}^E + \int_1^{N_B}\left[\frac{\bar{G}_B^E}{(1-N_B)^2} - y\cdot\frac{\partial}{\partial y}\left(\frac{\bar{G}_B^E}{(1-N_B)^2}\right)\right]dN_B \\ - \frac{N_B\bar{G}_B^E}{1-N_B}\right\}_{y\,=\,\text{constant}} \qquad 8.3.16$$

However, as an approximation, the quantity $\bar{G}^E_{A\,(N_B\to1)}$, the excess partial molar free energy of component A in infinitely dilute solution in B, may be taken to be equal to the same quantity in the binary system A–B. That is:

$$\bar{G}^E_{A\,(N_B\to1)} = [\bar{G}^E_{A\,(N_B\to1)}]_{N_C=0 \text{ or } y=0}.$$

Integrating 8.3.11 by parts between the limits $N_B = 0$ and $N_B = 1$, with the condition $y = 0$, yields:

$$\bar{G}^E_{A\,(N_B\to1)} = -\left\{\int_0^1 \left(\frac{N_B}{1-N_B}\right)\cdot\frac{\partial\bar{G}^E_B}{\partial N_B}\cdot dN_B\right\}_{y=0}$$

$$= \left\{\left[\frac{N_B\,\bar{G}^E_B}{1-N_B}\right]^{N_B=1}_{N_B=0} - \int_0^1 \frac{\bar{G}^E_B}{(1-N_B)^2}\,dN_B\right\}_{y=0}$$

$$= \left\{\int_0^1 \frac{\bar{G}^E_B}{(1-N_B)^2}\,dN_B\right\}_{y=0} \qquad 8.3.17$$

where the assumption is made that:

$$\frac{\bar{G}^E_B}{1-N_B} \to 0 \text{ as } N_B \to 1.$$

Inserting 8.3.17 into 8.3.16 and substituting the α functions as defined by 8.3.13:

$$\bar{G}^E_{A(N_B,y)} = \left\{\int_0^1 \alpha_B\,dN_B\right\}_{y=0} + \left\{\int_1^{N_B}\left[\alpha_B - y\frac{\partial\alpha_B}{\partial y}\right]dN_B - N_B(1-N_B)\,\alpha_B\right\}_y \quad . \;\; 8.3.18$$

Similarly for component C:

$$\bar{G}^E_{C(N_B,y)} = \left\{\int_0^1 \alpha_B d\,N_B\right\}_{y=0} + \left\{\int_1^{N_B}\left[\alpha_B + (1-y)\cdot\frac{\partial\alpha_B}{\partial y}\right]dN_B - N_B(1-N_B)\,\alpha_B\right\}_y \quad .$$

$$8.3.19$$

As before, 8.3.18 or 8.3.19 may be solved analytically to yield $\bar{G}^E_A$ or $\bar{G}^E_C$ (respectively), and their associated functions, at any composition along the pseudo-binary path, $y = $ constant, if the quantity α is known as a function of composition.

The data for the Al–Bi–Pb system shown in Fig. 8.1a will again be used to derive the activity of bismuth in the alloy ($N_{Al} = 0\cdot20$, $N_{Bi} = 0\cdot60$, $N_{Pb} = 0\cdot20$). These data are amenable to the analytical treatment just outlined, as the α_{Al} function is found to be related very simply to composition. In fact, this analytical method was used by the original workers [2] to assess their data.

To treat this problem by the method just outlined, the data of Fig. 8.1a must be transformed into the function α_{Al} as defined by *8.3.13*.

As:

$$RT\ln a_{Al} = -3FE$$

therefore:

$$\alpha_{Al} = \frac{-3FE - RT\ln N_{Al}}{(1-N_{Al})^2}$$

where E is the e.m.f. of the concentration cell (in volts) containing the alloy of the composition given by N_{Al} and the mole ratio N_{Bi}/N_{Pb}, the latter corresponding to a constant value of the composition variable:

$$y = \frac{N_{Bi}}{N_{Bi} + N_{Pb}}.$$

Thus the data of Fig. 8.1a may readily be made to yield the quantity α as functions of N_{Al} along the various pseudo-binary lines $y = \text{constant}$ (which correspond to the various mole ratios of Fig. 8.1a). On plotting the derived values of α as a function of N_{Al} for each value of y, it is found that a linear relation adequately expresses this function. These relations are shown in Table 8.3, with the ranges of N_{Al} over which they apply.

In the present problem, data are available for the binary Bi–Pb system. Hence equation *8.3.15* can be used to obtain the desired value for the activity of bismuth in the alloy ($N_{Al} = 0·20$, $N_{Bi} = 0·60$, $N_{Pb} = 0·20$). As this alloy lies on the path $y = 0·75$, *8.3.15* must be applied with y constant at this value. Thus:

$$\left\{ \bar{G}^E_{Bi\,(N_{Al})} = \bar{G}^E_{Bi\,(N_{Al}=0)} + \int_0^{N_{Al}} \left[\alpha_{Al} - (1-y)\frac{\partial\alpha_{Al}}{\partial y} \right] dN_{Al} \right.$$

$$\left. -\alpha_{Al} N_{Al}(1-N_{Al}) \right\}_{y=0·75}. \qquad 8.3.20$$

The solution of this relation requires that the quantity α_{Al} be expressed as a function of the composition variable y for constant values of N_{Al} between $N_{Al} = 0$ and $N_{Al} = 0·20$. To this end, values of α_{Al} at various values of N_{Al} (at 0·025 intervals) are calculated from the α_{Al}/N_{Al} equations of the table. These values of α_{Al} are shown also in Table 8.3. On plotting these α_{Al} values versus y, for the various constant values of N_{Al}, essentially linear relations are found to apply. The equations for the

Table 8.3

$y = \dfrac{N_{Bi}}{N_{Bi} + N_{Pb}}$	$\alpha_{Al} = f_1(N_{Al})$	Values of function α_{Al} at N_{Al} equal to:								
		0.0	0·025	0·050	0·075	0·100	0·125	0·150	0·175	0·200
0·0	$f_1 = 7·83 - 1·69\,N_{Al}$ $(0 < N_{Al} < 0·049)$	7·83	7·79							
0·202	$f_1 = 7·19 - 1·27\,N_{Al}$ $(0 < N_{Al} < 0·071)$	7·19	7·16	7·13						
0·333	$f_1 = 6·61 + 1·83\,N_{Al}$ $(0 < N_{Al} < 0·088)$	6·61	6·66	6·70	6·75					
0·50	$f_1 = 5·93 + 3·33\,N_{Al}$ $(0 < N_{Al} < 0·118)$	5·93	6·01	6·10	6·18	6·26				
0·667	$f_1 = 5·28 + 3·40\,N_{Al}$ $(0 < N_{Al} < 0·179)$	5·28	5·37	5·45	5·53	5·62	5·71	5·79	5·87	
0·80	$f_1 = 4·75 + 3·73\,N_{Al}$ $(0 < N_{Al} < 0·245)$	4·75	4·84	4·94	5·03	5·12	5·22	5·31	5·40	5·50
1·00	$f_1 = 4·02 + 3·72\,N_{Al}$ $(0 < N_{Al} < 0·20)$	4·02	4·11	4·21	4·30	4·39	4·49	4·58	4·67	4·76
	$\alpha_{Al} = f_2(y)$	$f_2 = 7·83 - 3·82\,y$ $(0·50 < y < 1·0)$	$f_2 = 7·93 - 3·83\,y$ $(0·20 < y < 1·0)$	$f_2 = 7·96 - 3·77\,y$ $(0·333 < y < 1·0)$	$f_2 = 8·01 - 3·71\,y$ $(0·333 < y < 1·0)$	$f_2 = 8·11 - 3·74\,y$ $(0·50 < y < 1·0)$	$f_2 = 8·14 - 3·65\,y$ $(0·667 < y < 1·0)$	$f_2 = 8·20 - 3·61\,y$ $(0·667 < y < 1·0)$	$f_2 = 8·26 - 3·59\,y$ $(0·667 < y < 1·0)$	$f_2 = 8·48 - 3·72\,y$ $(0·80 < y < 1·0)$
$\alpha_{Al} + (1-y)\dfrac{\partial \alpha_{Al}}{\partial y}$		4·02	4·11	4·21	4·30	4·39	4·49	4·58	4·67	4·76

latter are also shown in the table, with the limiting values of y between which they are valid. From these equations, the integrand of 8.3.20:

$$\alpha_{A1} + (1-y)\frac{\partial \alpha_{A1}}{\partial y} (\equiv A)$$

may be calculated for the various values of N_{A1}. As a consequence of the linear α_{A1}/y relations, the values of the integrand are independent of y, and are listed in the bottom row of Table 8.3. They are equal to the values of α_{A1} at $y = 1$.

On plotting the values of the integrand versus N_{A1}, a linear relation is found to apply, being adequately expressed by:

$$A = 4 \cdot 01 + 3 \cdot 80 N_{A1}.$$

Substituting this relation into 8.3.20:

$$\left\{ \bar{G}^E_{Bi(N_{A1})} = \bar{G}^E_{Bi(N_{A1}=0)} + \int_0^{N_{A1}} (4 \cdot 01 + 3 \cdot 8 N_{A1}) \, dN_{A1} - N_{A1}(1-N_{A1})\alpha_{A1} \right\}_{y=0 \cdot 75}.$$

This equation may now be used to yield $\bar{G}^E_{Bi}$ at any value of N_{A1} ($\leqslant 0 \cdot 20$) along the path $y = 0 \cdot 75$, the value of α_{A1} in the last term being that corresponding to the value of N_{A1} with $y = 0 \cdot 75$. Thus, at $N_{A1} = 0 \cdot 20$:

$$\left\{ \bar{G}^E_{Bi(N_{A1}=0 \cdot 20)} = \bar{G}^E_{Bi(N_{A1}=0)} + \int_0^{N_{A1}=0 \cdot 20} (4 \cdot 01 + 3 \cdot 8 N_{A1}) \, dN_{A1} \right.$$

$$\left. - N_{A1}(1-N_{A1})(8 \cdot 48 - 3 \cdot 72 y) \right\}_{y=0 \cdot 75}$$

or:

$$\bar{G}^E_{Bi \left\{ {y=0 \cdot 75 \atop N_{A1}=0 \cdot 20} \right\}} = \bar{G}^E_{Bi \left\{ {y=0 \cdot 75 \atop N_{A1}=0} \right\}}$$

$$+ [4 \cdot 01 N_{A1} + 1 \cdot 9 N_{A1}^2 - 5 \cdot 69 N_{A1}(1-N_{A1})]_{N_{A1}=0 \cdot 20}$$

$$= \bar{G}^E_{Bi \left\{ {y=0 \cdot 75 \atop N_{A1}=0} \right\}} - 0 \cdot 04.$$

However:

$$\bar{G}^E_{Bi \left\{ {y=0 \cdot 75 \atop N_{A1}=0} \right\}} = RT \ln \gamma_{Bi} \quad \text{in Pb–Bi binary at } N_{Pb} = 0 \cdot 25.$$

The data for the Pb–Bi binary system are adequately represented by:

$$RT \ln \gamma_{Bi} = -1,179 N_{Pb}^2$$

and hence:

$$RT \ln \gamma_{Bi} = -73 \cdot 6 \quad \text{at } N_{Pb} = 0 \cdot 25.$$

Thus:

$$\bar{G}^E_{Bi \left\{ \substack{y=0.75 \\ N_{A1}=0.20} \right\}} = -73 \cdot 6 - 0 \cdot 04*$$

$$= -73 \cdot 6.$$

Hence:

$$\gamma_{Bi \left\{ \substack{N_{A1}=0.20 \\ y=0.75} \right\}} = 0 \cdot 969$$

or:

$$a_{Bi \left(\substack{N_{A1}=0.20 \\ N_{B1}=0.60 \\ N_{Pb}=0.20} \right)} = 0 \cdot 581.$$

This value compares well with those previously calculated, and is probably equally accurate. It will be appreciated that the method just demonstrated is not much less tedious than the graphical techniques for working out a single unknown value and could be much more so if the α function is not simply related to composition. However, in such cases as presently considered, the analytical technique is well suited for the calculation of thermodynamic data for the unknown components over the whole range of composition investigated. For once the composition relations for α have been derived, they will yield the required data for any alloy within the composition range to which they are applicable much more easily than a graphical technique, where almost the whole operation must be repeated to gain each value.

---

* The value of $\bar{G}^E_{Bi \left\{ \substack{y=0.75 \\ N_{A1}=0.20} \right\}}$ is insignificantly different from the value of $\bar{G}^E_{Bi \left\{ \substack{y=0.75 \\ N_{A1}=0} \right\}}$. This is because, in the present example, the integration path ($y = 0.75$) corresponds quite closely to the line in the isothermal triangle along which the activity coefficient of bismuth is constant. In the general case, the change in the value of the excess partial molar free energy along the integration path will be significant, and could be of similar magnitude to that for the binary composition.

References

1. R. SCHUHMANN, JR., *Acta Met.*, **3**, 1955, p. 219.
2. T. C. WILDER and J. F. ELLIOTT, *J. Electrochem. Soc.*, **111**, No. 3, 1964, p. 352.
3. N. A. GOKCEN, *J. Phys. Chem.*, **64**, 1960, p. 401.
4. C. WAGNER, *Thermodynamics of Alloys*, Addison Wesley, 1952.

Answers to Exercises

2.A Specific heat of ice $= 0.40$ cal deg^{-1} g^{-1}.

2.B Weight of steam required $= 6,100$ lb.

2.C Heat required $= 15.6$ kcal.

2.D Temperature of water $= 45°C$.

2.E Time for isothermal solidification $= 71.4$ min
Cooling rate after solidification $= 4.55°C$ min^{-1}.

2.F Maximum depth of groove $= 0.0188$ mm

From deceleration rate, the deceleration force (F) is calculated from $F = m.a$ as 2.97×10^6 dyne. Thus work done on ice for each cm of movement is 2.97×10^6 erg, or 0.0710 cal. From data for ice, volume just melted in each cm with this heat is 9.42×10^{-4} cc.

2.G Instantaneous acceleration of aircraft $= 0.325$ g. (Acceleration due to gravity.)

Volume of incoming air at 400 m.p.h. is 35,764 litre sec^{-1}. The theoretical thrust of ramjet will be given by this volume of air at 273°K and 0.8 atm pressure becoming CO_2, H_2O and N_2 at T_M °K and X atm pressure, assuming ideal gas behaviour of combustion products. Rate of heat supply in burning fuel is 27,400 kcal sec^{-1} which can be equated to

$$\int_{273}^{T_M} \Sigma \, C_{p\,(\text{products})} . \, dT$$

if adiabatic conditions are assumed. Thus T_M calculated as 2,410°K. From fuel data and volume of incoming air, volume of exhaust gases at 273°K and 0.8 atm is 38,280 litre sec^{-1}, which is at 7.06 atm at 2,410°K. Thus maximum theoretical thrust $= 6.48$ kg cm^{-2}. Hence thrust on aircraft with 5 per cent efficiency $= 648$ kg.

2.H Difference in molar heat capacities $= 0.106$ cal deg^{-1} mole^{-1}.

In the relation $C_p - C_v = \alpha^2 VT/\beta$, V is the atomic volume, which is given by the atomic weight divided by the density. The units of $C_p - C_v$ thus calculated will be cc$-$atm deg^{-1} mole^{-1}, which is converted to cal deg^{-1} mole^{-1} by the factor in appendix 2.

2.I Vapour pressure at 850°C $= 0.555$ atm, (420 mm Hg).

The relation:

$$\log p_2 - \log p_1 = \frac{\Delta H_v}{4 \cdot 575}\left(\frac{1}{T_1} - \frac{1}{T_2}\right)$$

is used to yield p_2 at 850°C (1,123°K) as it is known that $p_1 = 1$ atm at the boiling point 1,180°K.

2.J Approximate pressure required = 0·3 mm Hg.

2.K Correction = 0·0119 deg mm^{-1}.

The exercise is concerned with the elevation of the boiling temperature of nitrogen by the pressure over atmospheric necessary to operate the flow-meter. The values of integrated heat capacity will need correction by this temperature increment. The pressure variation of the temperature of a transformation is given by the Clapeyron equation

$$\frac{dT}{dP} = \frac{T\Delta V}{\Delta H}.$$

2.L Heat of reaction = $-110 \cdot 1$ kcal.

2.M Standard heat of formation of $Fe_2O_3 = (-)196 \cdot 3$ kcal mole^{-1}.

2.N Standard heat of formation of $Al_4C_3 = (-)45 \cdot 30 \pm 15 \cdot 15$ kcal mole^{-1}.

2.O Heat of formation of FeO at 1,390°C = $-55,200$ cal mole^{-1}.

2.P Heat of formation of CaO at 1,000°C = $-153,300$ cal mole^{-1}.

Calcium undergoes an allotropic change at 440°C and melts at 850°C The heats of these transformations and the relevant heat capacity data in appendix 3 enable the operations illustrated in example 2.6 to be applied to the oxidation reaction for calcium.

2.Q Optimum ratio $p_{CO}/p_{H_2} = 1 \cdot 24$.

Heat of reaction for decomposition of ferrous oxide at 1,273°K (calculated, or from example 2.6) is 63,156 cal mole^{-1}. Heat of reaction for oxidation of carbon monoxide at 1,273°K (calculated, or from example 2.7) is $-67,423$ cal mole^{-1} (of CO). Heat of reaction of oxidation of hydrogen at 1,273°K is calculated as $-59,640$ cal mole^{-1} (of H_2). Heat loss from charge is 793 cal mole^{-1} of FeO. Thus proportion (X) of H_2 in gas for process to be just autogenous is given by:

$$59,640X + 67,423(1-X) = (63,156 + 793).$$

2.R Minimum volume of air = 2,713 cu ft.

Heat of reactions for burning of CO and H_2 at 973°K calculated as $-67,800$ and $-59,170$ cal (per mole of these gases) respectively. Exhaust gas composition calculated from producer gas analysis and required air

13

(calculate on basis of 25 mole of CO). Additional air (say N mole) must be fed in to keep adiabatic temperature of exhaust gases to 1,873°K. Thus

$$\int_{973}^{1,873} \left[\Sigma\, C_{p\,(\text{Products})} + \Sigma\, C_{p\binom{\text{N mole of}}{\text{diluting air}}} \right] dT = (67{,}800 \times 25) + (59{,}170 \times 14).$$

Total air required (for 100 mole of producer gas burnt) is N + air providing oxygen for combustion.

2.s Maximum temperature attainable = 3,300°C.

The assumption is made that the Cp data for the reaction products are valid up to this temperature. Part of the heat of reaction at 1,600°C is used to heat the oxygen and diluting nitrogen in air from 25°C to this temperature. The remainder heats the reaction products.

2.t Approximate weight of steel = 87 lb.

From heat given out by charge, the apparent heat capacity of charge plus crucible is calculated as 92·5 kcal deg^{-1}. The integrated heat capacity of iron 25→2,400°C is calculated as 26·34 kcal mole^{-1}. Thus mass of steel given by:

$$\frac{92\cdot5 \times 200}{26\cdot34}\,\text{mole.}$$

3.A Enthalpy change at 1,000°K = +32·5 kcal.

Entropy change at 1,000°K = 34·23 cal deg^{-1}.

Free-energy change at 1,000°K = −1·7 kcal.

3.B Free-energy change at 1,000°K = −1·8 kcal.

This value is calculated using the Gibbs–Helmholtz relation and differs from that calculated in 3.A due to the rounding off of the values of the free energy and enthalpy. The uncertainty in free-energy values is usually much greater than this difference, being as large as ± 10 kcal but more commonly about ± 2–3 kcal.

3.C $\Delta G_T = -404{,}370 - 6\cdot76 T \ln T + 2\cdot17 \times 10^{-3}\, T^2 + 3\cdot80 \times 10^5\, T^{-1}$

$\qquad\qquad + 123\cdot1 T\, (T < 932°\text{K}).$

$\quad\ \ \Delta G_T = -408{,}100 - 2\cdot64 T \ln T - 0\cdot79 \times 10^{-3}\, T^2 + 3\cdot80 \times 10^5\, T^{-1}$

$\qquad\qquad + 101\cdot8 T\, (T > 932°\text{K}).$

The Gibbs–Helmholtz equation is used to deduce the free-energy–temperature relation for the oxidation of solid aluminium, applying the appropriate standard heat of formation, entropy and heat capacity data of appendix 3. Applying Hess's law at the melting point of aluminium to enthalpy and free-energy changes in the oxidation and fusion reactions (the free-energy change in the latter being zero) gives the basis for the repeat calculation for the oxidation of liquid aluminium.

3.D Calculated standard heat of formation of $NH_3 = -10 \cdot 5$ kcal mole^{-1}.

From the heat capacity data of appendix 3, the free energy of the formation reaction for ammonia may be calculated as a function of temperature, the calculation involving the two integration constants (ΔH_0 and I) which may be deduced by substitution of the two known values of the free energy. The heat of formation is then given by the integrated Kirchhoff equation with the constant ΔH_0 inserted. The calculated value of ΔH_{298} is some $0 \cdot 5$ kcal mole^{-1} lower than the generally accepted value. This discrepancy arises primarily from the uncertainty in the free-energy values given.

3.E Graph of the variation of the entropy of Zn, 25 → 920°C.

3.F The free-energy change, $Fe_\gamma \rightleftharpoons Fe_\alpha$, is given by:

$$\Delta G_T = -4{,}290 - 2 \cdot 34 T \ln T - 0 \cdot 63 \times 10^{-3} T^2 + 20 \cdot 85 T \ (T < 1{,}033°K).$$

The variation of free energy with temperature ($T > 1{,}033°K$) is calculated using the Gibbs–Helmholtz relation with the relevant enthalpy and heat capacity data from appendix 3, the integration constants being deduced by substitution of the known values of ΔH and $\Delta G\ (=0)$ for the transformation. The calculation is repeated after application of Hess's law at the Curie temperature, $1{,}033°K$, to yield the above relation. It should be noted that this latter deviates markedly from the relation calculable for pure iron from experimental data for the γ/α equilibrium in iron–nickel alloys. These deviations indicate the doubtful validity of the present extrapolation of the C_p data for the γ phase to low temperatures (cf. example 3.5).

3.G (a) Theoretical transformation temperature $\gamma \rightarrow \alpha = 1{,}165°K$.

(b) Theoretical transformation temperature $\gamma \rightarrow \alpha = 1{,}075 \pm 3°K$.

The calculations of the values are made by the methods shown in example 3.5. It is essential that five-figure log tables are used for the latter calculation, as a slide rule is not nearly accurate enough because of the relatively slow change of free energy with temperature. This gives rise to values of ΔG less than 200 cal mole^{-1} as the difference between terms of magnitude of tens of kilocalories.

3.H 'Entropy of ordering' of $Cu_3Au = 2 \cdot 191$ cal deg^{-1} mole^{-1}.

The data are plotted as C_p/T versus T (T in °K) and the area between the estimated background curve and the data curve is measured using the trapezoidal rule formula as elaborated in appendix 5 (2).

3.I   Entropy of fusion of hexagonal thallium at $297°C = 1.99$ cal deg^{-1} mole^{-1}.

The hypothetical melting point of $Tl_{(\alpha)}$ is calculated (using five-figure log tables) by the method shown in example 3.5. By application of Hess's law to the heats of the transformation $Tl_{(\alpha)} \rightleftharpoons Tl_{(\beta)}$ and the fusion $Tl_{(\beta)} \rightleftharpoons Tl_{(l)}$ at this temperature, the heat, and hence the entropy, of fusion of $Tl_{(\alpha)}$ is deduced.

4.A $p_{CO}/p_{CO_2} = 2.26$ at $1,027°C$.

The standard free-energy change for the reaction:

$$Fe_{(s)} + CO_{2(g)} \rightleftharpoons FeO_{(s)} + CO_{(g)}$$

is calculated through Hess's law, from the free-energy changes for the reactions:

$$C_{(s)} + \tfrac{1}{2}O_{2(g)} \rightleftharpoons CO_{(g)}$$

$$C_{(s)} + O_{2(g)} \rightleftharpoons CO_{2(g)}$$

$$Fe_{(s)} + \tfrac{1}{2}O_{2(g)} \rightleftharpoons FeO_{(s)}$$

which are available in appendix 3. Thus from equation *1.58* the equilibrium constant is deduced and, assuming the solid components are pure ($a = 1$), the ratio of the gas partial pressures is calculated.

4.B   Equilibrium is not attained in the reaction chamber.

The standard free-energy change for the reaction:

$$NiCl_{2(s)} + H_{2(s)} \rightleftharpoons Ni_{(s)} + 2HCl_{(g)}$$

available in appendix 3, is used to calculate the equilibrium constant and thus the ratio of the gas partial pressures, assuming the solid components are pure. This ratio is compared with that given by the gas analysis.

4.C   Vapour pressure of magnesium = 0.40 mm Hg.

The standard free-energy change for the reaction given is calculated from the data of appendix 3 for the reactions:

$$Si_{(s)} + O_{2(g)} \rightleftharpoons SiO_{2(s)}$$

$$Mg_{(g)} + \tfrac{1}{2}O_{2(g)} \rightleftharpoons MgO_{(s)}$$

$$2MgO_{(s)} + SiO_{2(s)} \rightleftharpoons 2MgO \cdot SiO_{2(s)}$$

yielding the equilibrium constant for the reaction through equation *1.58*. The solid components are assumed to be pure and thus the pressure of magnesium is calculated.

4.D End products of separation process are ZrO_2, $HfCl_4$.

The standard free-energy changes for the reactions:

$$ZrCl_{4(g)} + O_{2(g)} \rightleftharpoons ZrO_{2(s)} + 2Cl_{2(g)}$$

$$HfCl_{4(g)} + O_{2(g)} \rightleftharpoons HfO_{2(g)} + 2Cl_{2(g)}$$

are given at $800°C$ and are used to calculate the equilibrium constants. From these values and the known gas composition, the partial pressures of the tetrafluorides are calculated and the reaction end products deduced.

4.E Activity of iron = 0·827.

The standard free-energy change for the reaction:

$$Fe_{(s)} + H_2O_{(g)} \rightleftharpoons FeO_{(s)} + H_{2(g)}$$

is calculated at $1,113°K$ from the data in appendix 3 for the formation reactions for FeO and H_2O. The calculated equilibrium constant, with the known equilibrium gas composition, yields the activity of iron in the alloy, as the activity of FeO will be unity.

4.F Minimum value of ratio $p_{CO}/p_{CO_2} = 3·50 \times 10^{-3}$.

From the data for the reactions for formation of NiO, CO and CO_2 in appendix 3, the standard free-energy change for the reaction:

$$Ni_{(s)} + CO_{2(g)} \rightleftharpoons NiO_{(s)} + CO_{(g)}$$

is calculated, yielding the equilibrium constant and thus the gas ratio required when the known activity of nickel in the alloy is substituted with $a_{NiO} = 1$.

4.G Standard free energy of formation of KCl at $1,000°K = -80·9$ kcal mole^{-1}.

From the ratio p_{HCl}/p_{H_2} given, the standard free-energy change for the reaction:

$$KCl_{(l)} + \tfrac{1}{2}H_{2(g)} \rightleftharpoons K_{(l)} + HCl_{(g)}$$

may be calculated for $1,000°K$. From the data of appendix 3 the same quantity for the formation reaction for HCl is calculated at the same temperature. By application of Hess's law to the two reactions, the required free energy of formation of KCl from K and Cl at $1,000°K$ is obtained.

4.H Ratio p_{H_2S}/p_{H_2} in equilibrium with pure Cu and $Cu_2S = 1·66 \times 10^{-4}$.

Activity coefficient of copper in alloy $(\gamma_{Cu}) = 0·895$.

From the data for the formation reactions for Cu_2S and H_2S given in appendix 3, the standard free-energy change for the reaction:

$$H_2S_{(g)} + 2Cu_{(s)} \rightleftharpoons Cu_2S_{(s)} + H_{2(g)}$$

is calculated at 500°C, from which, as the solid components are pure, the ratio p_{H_2S}/p_{H_2} over pure copper is deduced. The activity of copper in the alloy is given by this value divided by the equilibrium ratio over the alloy. The activity coefficient follows from equation *1.74*.

4.I   Ratio p_{H_2S}/p_{H_2} in equilibrium with Ag and Ag_2S at 600°C = 0·150.

From the data given, the standard free-energy change for the reaction:

$$2H_{2(g)} + S_{2(g)} \rightleftharpoons 2H_2S_{(g)} \qquad\qquad A$$

is calculated at 298°K. Thus the equilibrium constant:

$$K_A = \frac{p_{H_2S}^2}{p_{H_2}^2 \cdot p_{S_2}}$$

is deduced. By application of the van't Hoff equation *1.59* (and assuming ΔH independent of temperature), the value of K_A at 873°K may be calculated. In addition, the data given for the reaction:

$$4Ag_{(s)} + S_{2(g)} \rightleftharpoons 2Ag_2S_{(s)} \qquad\qquad B$$

yields the equilibrium constant:

$$K_B = \frac{a_{Ag_2S}^2}{a_{Ag}^4 \cdot p_{S_2}} = \frac{1}{p_{S_2}}$$

if the solids are assumed pure. Subtraction of equations *A* and *B* gives the equilibrium between silver, hydrogen sulphide, hydrogen and silver sulphide, the equilibrium constant being:

$$K_C = \frac{K_A}{K_B}.$$

Hence the gas ratio in this equilibrium is calculated, assuming the solid components are pure.

4.J   The copper cannot be bright annealed under these conditions.

The data for the equilibrium:

$$Cu_2O_{(s)} \rightleftharpoons Cu_{(s)} + \tfrac{1}{2}O_{2(g)}$$

in appendix 3 enables the equilibrium value of p_{O_2} to be calculated as $2·7 \times 10^{-10}$ atm. Thus 10^{-6} vol-per cent O_2 in nitrogen (10^{-8} atm) will oxidize copper at 750°C.

4.K   Minimum dissociation temperature of $CaCO_3 = 579$°C.

From the standard free-energy change for the reaction:

$$CaCO_{3(s)} \rightleftharpoons CaO_{(s)} + CO_{2(g)}$$

in appendix 3, the equilibrium constant is obtained as a function of temperature. The minimum dissociation temperature under the conditions specified is given by the solution of this relation with:

$$K = p_{CO_2} = 0 \cdot 0015$$

the solid components being assumed to be pure.

4.L The oxide in equilibrium with pure iron at room temperature is magnetite, Fe_3O_4. Maximum temperature of this equilibrium $= 567°C$.

The standard free-energy changes for the formation reactions of solid FeO and Fe_3O_4 are given in appendix 3. The 'low temperature' oxide is stable up to the temperature at which both oxides and iron are in equilibrium. Thus the free-energy change for the reaction:

$$2FeO_{(s)} \rightleftharpoons \tfrac{1}{2}Fe_3O_{4(s)} + \tfrac{1}{2}Fe_{(s)}$$

is given by subtraction of those for the two formation reactions. This free-energy change is equated to zero to yield the three-phase equilibrium temperature. At lower temperatures ΔG^0 becomes negative and hence the reaction goes from left-to-right to form Fe_3O_4.

4.M Maximum temperature of Fe_3O_4–Fe equilibrium $= 771°C$.

The free-energy equations used in the previous example were derived partly on the basis of the known equilibrium temperature at which the two oxides and the metal coexist. Thus they are consistent with this temperature. The calculation in this exercise is, of course, subject to errors in the assumption of temperature independent enthalpy and entropy values in addition to the errors in the values themselves.

4.N Maximum temperature without formation of $MoO_2 = 920°C$.

The free-energy changes for the formation reactions for molybdenum oxide and steam in appendix 3 are combined to yield the value for the required equilibrium. The procedure is identical to 4.K.

4.O (a) Minimum reduction temperature with 0·3 mm Hg pressure of CO $= 1,363°C$.

(b) Minimum reduction temperature with 0·001 mm Hg pressure of CO $= 1,092°C$.

4.P Activity of FeO at $1,361°C = 0·473$.

From the data given and the standard free-energy change for the reaction:

$$CO_{2(g)} + H_{2(g)} \rightleftharpoons CO_{(g)} + H_2O_{(g)}$$

calculable from the data of appendix 3, the equilibrium constant for the reaction between the steam–hydrogen mixture and the iron–iron oxide slag is obtained. Thus with the known gas mixture, the activity of FeO is calculated.

4.Q   Activity of carbon in the metal sample = 0·43.

The standard free-energy change for the equilibrium:

$$CO_{(g)} + 3H_{(g)} \rightleftharpoons CH_{4(g)} + H_2O_{(g)} \qquad\qquad A$$

is calculated from the data in appendix 3. Assuming the partial pressure of water vapour is small, then from the graphite equilibrium data:

$$p_{H_2} = 1 - (p_{CH_4} + p_{CO}) = 0·981.$$

Further, from the data of appendix 3 for the reaction:

$$C_{(s)} + 2H_{2(g)} \rightleftharpoons CH_{4(g)} \qquad\qquad B$$

applied to the same graphite equilibrium, the equilibrium constant:

$$K_B = \frac{p_{CH_4}}{p_{H_2}^2} (= 0·0069)$$

is calculated, from which $p_{CH_4} = 0·0066$, and hence $p_{CO} = 0·0124$. Thus from:

$$K_A = \frac{p_{CH_4} \cdot p_{H_2O}}{p_{CO} \cdot p_{H_2}^3} (= 5·13 \times 10^{-5})$$

the value of $p_{H_2O} = 8·9 \times 10^{-5}$ is calculated, a constant for both experiments (and, as originally assumed, a small value). Therefore, for the gas equilibrium with the iron,

$$p_{CH_4} + p_{CO} = 0·0081$$
$$p_{H_2O} = 8·9 \times 10^{-5}$$

and hence:

$$p_{H_2} = 0·9909.$$

Thus from the value of K_A, the ratio:

$$\frac{p_{CH_4}}{p_{CO}} = 0·561$$

and therefore $p_{CH_4} = 0·00291$. Hence:

$$a_C = \frac{p_{H_2}^2}{K_B \, p_{CH_4}}$$

4.R   Range of values of $p_{SO_3} = 6 \times 10^{-4}$ to 0·3 atm.

From the data given and that for the equilibria between iron, its various oxides and oxygen in appendix 3, the standard free-energy change for the reaction:

$$Fe_2O_{3(s)} + 3SO_{3(g)} \rightleftharpoons Fe_2(SO_4)_{3(s)}$$

is calculated, which, assuming the solid components are pure, yields the value of p_{SO_3} at equilibrium. Similarly, the data for the reaction:

$$CuO + SO_3 \rightleftharpoons CuSO_4$$

is deduced and yields the value of p_{SO_3} in this equilibrium. The range of p_{SO_3} for sulphating of the copper only is between these two values.

4.s Approximate equilibrium partial pressures of AlCl at 1,000 and 2,000°K $= 5 \times 10^{-3}$ and 1 atm respectively.

Combination of the free-energy data for the formation reactions for AlCl and AlCl$_3$ in appendix 3 yields the data for the equilibrium:

$$2Al_{(l)} + AlCl_{3(g)} \rightleftharpoons 3AlCl_{(g)}$$

from which the values of the ratio p^3_{AlCl}/p_{AlCl_3} are calculated for the two temperatures.

It cannot be immediately assumed that $(p_{AlCl} + p_{AlCl_3}) = 1$, for chlorine gas will be present in the system. However, consideration of either of the formation reaction equilibria shows that p_{Cl_2} will be very small at both 1,000 and 2,000°K, and the sum of the chloride partial pressures may be taken as 1 atmosphere. The individual values of these partial pressures are calculated by combination of this fact with the gas ratio values. The solution of the resultant cubic equation in p_{AlCl} involves use of the formula method given in appendix 5.

The operation of a refining process by the method of this exercise is therefore feasible by cycling the gas mixture between two chambers, one containing impure aluminium at about 750°C, the other at about 1,700°C yielding pure aluminium if none of the impurities have volatile chlorides.

4.t Value of constant $\alpha = 1,750$.

From the weights of zinc condensed from nitrogen passed over pure zinc and the alloy ($N_{Zn} = 0.706$), the activity of zinc in the latter is calculated. In the equilibrium experiment, the activities of zinc in all the alloys will be the same, and hence this value applies to all the alloys: that is, the composition/temperature data of the table represent an iso-activity curve for this system. By plotting the temperature versus:

$$\frac{(1 - N_{Zn})^2}{4.575 \log \gamma_{Zn}},$$

the linear relation demonstrates the conformity of the data with the relation given, the slope of the line giving the constant α.

4.u Pressures of molecular species S_2, S_4, S_6, S_8, are 0.166, 0.168, 0.822 and 0.892 atm respectively at 800°K. The pressure of monatomic sulphur is negligibly small.

From the standard free-energy change data of appendix 3, the ratios of the pressures of the various species are calculated. After the appropriate substitution of these into the relation expressing the sum of the pressures ($= 2 \cdot 04$ atm), the resulting quartic equation in S_2 is solved graphically.

4.V   Gas composition at regenerator outlet: $3 \cdot 4$ per cent CO_2, $27 \cdot 1$ per cent CO, $3 \cdot 1$ per cent H_2O, $11 \cdot 9$ per cent H_2, $54 \cdot 5$ per cent N_2.

From the data of appendix 3, the equilibrium constant for the reaction:

$$H_2O_{(g)} + CO_{(g)} \rightleftharpoons CO_{2(g)} + H_{2(g)}$$

is calculated at $1{,}373°K$. Consideration of the conservation of the number of atoms of each element in the final gas analysis, in relation to the initial analysis, leads to expression of this equilibrium constant in terms of one component only. Thus, from the initial analysis, the number of atoms of carbon, hydrogen and oxygen are $30 \cdot 5$, 30 and 37 per 100 mole of gas respectively. Then, if the final gas mixture contains X mole of CO_2, the number of mole of CO, H_2O and H_2 are deduced to be $(30 \cdot 5 - X)$, $(6 \cdot 5 - X)$ and $(8 \cdot 5 + X)$ respectively. Substitution of these quantities in the expression for the equilibrium constant gives X.

5.A   Latent heat of vaporization of alloy $= 44 \cdot 60$ kcal mole^{-1}.

As the alloys are ideal, the vapour pressure of a component i is given by $p_i = N_i p_i^0$. The latent heat of the alloy will be the weighted mean (in terms of the partial pressures) of the latent heats of the components.

5.B   Heat evolved by $1{,}000$ litre of gas blown through ideal Fe–Mn alloy $= 4{,}920$ cal.
        Heat evolved by $1{,}000$ litre of gas blown through regular Fe–Mn alloy $= 4{,}960$ cal.

The answers are given by the methods elaborated in examples 5.2 and 5.3.

5.C   Vapour pressure of manganese at $1{,}600°C = 0 \cdot 0491$ atm.

Manganese will be lost from the steel exposed to a vacuum of $0 \cdot 1$ mm Hg.

5.D   Density of resulting alloy $= 6 \cdot 86$ g cc^{-1}.

5.E   Partial molar heat of mixing of bismuth $= 207$ cal mole^{-1}.

The method of example 5.4 is applied to the data given.

5.F   Activity of iron $= 0 \cdot 695$.

The method of example 5.7 is applied to the data given.

5.G   Activity of mercury $= 0 \cdot 874$.

5.H   Excess integral molar free energy of solution $= -1{,}746$ cal mole^{-1}.

The value of $\bar{G}_{Pb}^{M}$ is calculated, from the data given, by either the method of example 5.4, involving the free energies of mixing, or alternatively, the method of example 5.5, involving activity coefficients. The latter are given by:

$$\log \gamma_{Mg} = \log a_{Mg} - \log N_{Mg} = \frac{\bar{G}_{Mg}^M}{4 \cdot 575T} - \log N_{Mg}.$$

Either method yields the same value of $\bar{G}_{Pb}^M$ for the equi-atomic solution. Values of $\bar{G}_{Pb}^E$ and $\bar{G}_{Mg}^E$ follow, for:

$$\bar{G}_i^E = \bar{G}_i - \bar{G}_i^{\text{ideal}} = \bar{G}_i^M - \bar{G}_i^{M \text{ ideal}}$$

and:

$$\bar{G}_i^{M \text{ ideal}} = RT \ln N_i.$$

The integral excess molar free energy follows from equation *1.42*.

5.I   Partial molar volume of mixing of tin $= 0 \cdot 06 \pm 0 \cdot 005$ cc mole^{-1}.

This quantity is obtained by application of equation *1.47* to the volumes of mixing, as in Fig. 1a.

5.J   Integral molar entropy of mixing of solution $= 1 \cdot 39$ cal mole^{-1} deg^{-1}.

5.K   Integral free energy of mixing of solution $= -554$ cal mole^{-1}.

As the solution is regular, $\log \gamma_i /(1-N_i)^2 = \text{constant}$, independent of the component. Thus the constant is determined from the data given for Hg, then γ_{Sn} is calculated at the required composition. Values of $\bar{G}_{Hg}^M$ and $\bar{G}_{Sn}^M$ follow through equation *1.54*.

5.L   Vapour pressure of iron $= 0 \cdot 083$ mm Hg.

The data for $\bar{G}_{Al}^E$ is used to calculate $\bar{G}_{Fe}^E$ in the alloy and hence γ_{Fe} from equation *1.79*. The value of a_{Fe} then gives the vapour pressure of iron over the alloy from the value over pure iron.

5.M   Vapour pressure of copper $= 1 \cdot 41 \times 10^{-3}$ mm Hg.

The relation for γ_{Zn} enables γ_{Cu} to be calculated directly (p. 107).

5.N $\log \gamma_{Ag} = 0 \cdot 491 N_{Cu}^2$.

The regular behaviour allows use of equation *1.82*.

5.O   Excess integral molar free energy given by:

$$G^E = 3,339 N_{Cu} \ln N_{Cu} - 5,350 N_{Cu}(1-N_{Cu})$$
$$+ 509(1-N_{Cu}) \ln (1-N_{Cu})$$

The data given yield $\bar{G}_{Zn}^M$ which, through the Gibbs–Duhem relation, gives $\bar{G}_{Cu}^M$ as a function of composition. The expressions for $\bar{G}_{Zn}^E$ and $\bar{G}_{Cu}^E$ follow from:

$$\bar{G}_i^E = \bar{G}_i^M - \bar{G}_i^{M \text{ ideal}}.$$

5.P   Excess partial molar free energy $= -117$ cal mole^{-1}.

From H^M data given, $\bar{H}_{Fe}^M$ calculated through equation *1.46*. As the solution is regular, equation *1.83* yields $\bar{G}_{Fe}^E$.

5.Q   Extent of lead purification is $N_{Cu} = 4 \cdot 26 \times 10^{-2}$.

The activities of the liquid metals are calculated in terms of N_{Cu} from the data given, and substituted in the expression for the reaction equilibrium constant.

5.R   Excess partial molar free energy of iron $= -68$ cal.

The activity coefficient of iron is calculated from the equilibrium constant for the reaction:

$$Fe_{(s)} + H_2O_{(g)} \rightleftharpoons FeO_{(s)} + H_{2(g)}.$$

The value of $\bar{G}_{Fe}^{E}$ follows from equation 1.79.

5.S   Activity coefficient of cadmium $= 1 \cdot 156$.

Partial molar free energy of cadmium $= -16 \cdot 36$ kcal mole^{-1}.

5.T $H_{T_2}^{M}$ is given by $\dfrac{X_A}{1 - X_A} \cdot RT_1 \ln \dfrac{(a_A)_1}{X_A}$.

From data, γ_A at T_1 calculated and, as the solution is regular:

$$\frac{RT \ln \gamma_i}{(1 - N_i)^2} = \text{constant, independent of component.}$$

Thus γ_A and γ_B may be calculated at T_2 and $\bar{H}_A^M$ and $\bar{H}_B^M$ deduced from equation 1.82 for regular solution. The quantity H^M, independent of temperature, follows.

5.U   Indication of non-regular solution behaviour.

Method of obtaining G^E from data given.

The vapour pressure measurements will yield $a_B = f_1(N_B)$ from which the non-conformity of $\gamma_B = f_2(N_B)$ with relation:

$$\ln \gamma_B = \alpha(1 - N_B)^2$$

indicates the non-regular behaviour of the solutions.

From $\gamma_B = f_2(N_B)$, $\gamma_A = f_3(N_B)$ may be calculated through the Gibbs–Duhem relation. Thus $\bar{G}_A^E$ and $\bar{G}_B^E$ are deduced from equation 1.79 and G^E obtained as a function of composition.

6.A   Oxygen concentration in nickel at equilibrium $= 8 \cdot 2 \times 10^{-31}$ weight-per cent.

From the data for the formation reactions for ZrO_2 and NiO, the equilibrium partial pressures of oxygen over the metals and oxides are calculated as $1 \cdot 3 \times 10^{-43}$ and $3 \cdot 0 \times 10^{-14}$ respectively. Thus at any pressure of oxygen less than that at equilibrium:

$$\frac{p_{O_2}}{p_{O_2 \, (satn.)}} = \frac{a_{O \, (in \, Ni)}}{a_{O \, (in \, Ni \, at \, satn.)}} = \frac{\%O}{0 \cdot 019}$$

as oxygen dissolved in nickel conforms to Henry's law.

6.B Concentration of copper in equilibrium with Pb, PbS and $Cu_2S = 99.76$ atom-per cent.

From data for Cu_2S and PbS formation reactions in appendix 3, the equilibrium constant for the reaction:

$$2Cu_{(s)} + PbS_{(l)} \rightleftharpoons Pb_{(l)} + Cu_2S_{(s)}$$

is calculated as $4.0 \times 10^{-8} = a_{Pb}/a_{Cu}^2$. As Henry's law applies for $Cu(N_{Cu} < 0.004)$ then Pb is ideal over this composition range (p. 17) Further, as $a_{Cu} = 1$ when $N_{Cu} = 0.004$ (as activity of Cu at solubility limit $\simeq$ activity of pure solid copper) then $\gamma_{Cu}^0 = 250$. Substituting in equilibrium constant equation, then:

$$\frac{(1 - N_{Cu})}{(250 N_{Cu})^2} = 4.0 \times 10^{-8},$$

a quadratic in N_{Cu}, solved by the formula method.

6.C Change in free energy for transfer of standard state $= 9.11T$ cal.

For the transfer of standard state:

$$Mn_{(l)} \rightleftharpoons Mn_{(l, wt\% dilute)},$$

$$\Delta G^0 = G^0_{(Mn, l, wt\% dilute)} - G^0_{(Mn, l, pure)}$$

$$= 4.575T \log \frac{0.5585}{54.94}.$$

6.D Change in free energy for transfer of standard state

$$= -5,500 - 11.08T \text{ cal.}$$

For the transfer of standard state:

$$V_{(l)} \rightleftharpoons V_{(l, wt\% dilute)}$$

$$\Delta G_1^0 = 4.575 \times 1,873 \times \log \gamma^0 + 4.575T \log \frac{0.5585}{50.95}$$

$$= 10,000 - 8.97T.$$

But vanadium is solid at 1,600°C, melting at 1,860°C with a latent heat of 4.5 kcal mole^{-1} (appendix 3). Thus:

$$\Delta G_f = 4,500 - 2.11T.$$

Hence:

$$\Delta G^0 = G^0_{(V, l, wt\% dilute)} - G^0_{(V, s, pure)}$$

$$= \Delta G_1^0 + \Delta G_f.$$

6.E   Equilibrium constant $K_p = 2 \cdot 4 \times 10^{14}$.

The free-energy change for the transfer of standard state:

$$B_{(F.C.C.\ pure)} \rightleftharpoons B_{(F.C.C.\ dilute,\ 2\ atom\ \%\ in\ A)}$$

is given by:

$$\Delta G^0 = RT \ln 2\gamma^0$$

where γ^0, the Henrian activity coefficient relative to pure B as standard state, is given as $0 \cdot 24$. Further, for the transformation:

$$B_{(B.C.C.\ pure)} \rightleftharpoons B_{(F.C.C.\ pure)},$$

$$\Delta G_t = 220 - \frac{220}{1,180}T.$$

The standard free-energy change for the reaction given is obtained by application of Hess's law to these reactions and that for the oxidation of pure B. The equilibrium constant follows.

6.F   Standard free-energy change $= -47,152$ cal mole^{-1}.

The method is similar to the previous example, the free-energy change for the transfer in standard state:

$$B_{(pure,\ l)} \rightleftharpoons B_{(dilute,\ 1\cdot5\ wt\ \%\ in\ A)}$$

being given by:

$$\Delta G^0 = RT \ln 1 \cdot 5 . \gamma^0 . \frac{M_A}{100 M_B},$$

and for the fusion:

$$B_{(pure,\ solid)} \rightleftharpoons B_{(pure,\ liquid)},$$

$$\Delta G_f^0 = 2,600 - \frac{2,600}{1,025}T.$$

Combination of these with the oxidation reaction for pure B yields the standard free-energy change required.

6.G   Free-energy change $\Delta G^0 = -27,200 - 1\cdot54T$ cal.

The data given are for the reaction:

$$H_{2(g)} + O_{(dilute,\ wt\ \%\ in\ iron)} \rightleftharpoons H_2O_{(g)}$$

for which:

$$K_p = \frac{p_{H_2O}}{p_{H_2} . a_O} = \frac{p_{H_2O}}{p_{H_2} . f_O . \%O}.$$

This equilibrium constant can be calculated for the three temperatures and found to conform to the relation:

$$\log K_p = \frac{6,930}{T} - 3 \cdot 20.$$

Hence:

$$\Delta G^0 = -31,700 + 14 \cdot 64T \text{ cal.}$$

The quantity required is obtained by subtraction of this from the expression for the free energy of formation of steam from hydrogen and oxygen gas.

6.H   Activity of carbon relative to wt % standard state = 0·57.

The logarithm of the activity coefficient of carbon ($\log \gamma_C$) is plotted versus N_C and extrapolated to $N_C = 0$ to yield γ_C^0. Thus, from equation *1.94*:

$$\gamma_C^0 = 1 \cdot 243 = \frac{a_{C\,(\text{pure})}}{a_{C\,(\text{dilute})}} \cdot \frac{\text{wt} \% \,C}{N_C}.$$

As at wt % C = 0·5, $N_C = 0 \cdot 0256$, substitution of the appropriate value of $a_{C\,(\text{pure})}$ from the table yields $a_{C\,(\text{dilute})}$ as required.

6.I   Interaction coefficient $f_O^V = 0 \cdot 57$. Interaction parameter $e_O^V = -0 \cdot 24$.

From the free-energy change for the standard state transfer given, and that for the steam formation reaction, the equilibrium constant for the reaction:

$$H_{2(g)} + O_{(\text{wt} \% \text{ in Fe})} \rightleftharpoons H_2O_{(g)}$$

may be calculated. Thus:

$$a_O = \frac{p_{H_2O}}{p_{H_2} \cdot K_p} = 0 \cdot 0188.$$

Since this dissolved oxygen obeys Henry's law, then in the binary Fe–O alloy, wt % O = 0·0188 at $a_O = 0 \cdot 0188$. Hence:

$$f_O^V = \frac{0 \cdot 0188}{0 \cdot 033}$$

and:

$$e_O^V = \frac{\log f_O^V}{\text{wt} \% \,V}.$$

6.J   Interaction parameter $e_S^C = 0 \cdot 11$.

Combination of the standard state transfer given and the formation reaction for H_2S yields the reaction:

$$H_{2(g)} + S_{(\text{wt} \% \text{ in Fe})} \rightleftharpoons H_2S_{(g)}$$

for which the equilibrium constant:

$$K_p = \frac{p_{H_2S}}{p_{H_2} \cdot f_S \cdot \% S}$$

is calculated as $2 \cdot 58 \times 10^{-3}$ at $1,873°K$. Thus f_S is calculated by insertion of the data given, and the required quantity e_S^C obtained by application of equation 1.105:

$$\log f_S = \%S.e_S^S + \%C.e_S^C.$$

6.K (a) Oxygen content $= 0 \cdot 003$ weight-per cent.
    (b) Oxygen content $= 0 \cdot 024$ weight-per cent.

From the data for the standard state transfer reaction and the formation reaction for MgO, the equilibrium constant for the reaction:

$$Mg_{(g)} + O_{(wt\% \text{ in Fe})} \rightleftharpoons MgO_{(s)}$$

is calculated. Thus as:

$$K_p = \frac{1}{p_{Mg}.f_O.\text{wt}\% \text{ O}}$$

and f_O is given, the wt$\%$ O can be calculated for the two values of p_{Mg}.

6.L Carbon and phosphorus are not in equilibrium.

The values of a_O in equilibrium with phosphorus and carbon are calculated and compared. Thus in equilibrium with carbon:

$$K_p = \frac{p_{CO}}{a_C.a_{O(C)}} = \frac{p_{CO}}{f_C.\text{wt}\% \text{C}.a_{O(C)}}.$$

However, by insertion of the composition and interaction parameter data given into equation 1.105, f_C is calculated and thus $a_{O(C)}$ is obtained. A similar calculation yields $a_{O(P)}$. As this latter value is much larger than $a_{O(C)}$, the phosphorus and carbon cannot be in equilibrium.

7.A Standard entropy of AgCl $= 23 \cdot 0$ cal deg^{-1} mole^{-1}.
    Standard enthalpy of AgCl $= -30,300$ cal mole^{-1}.
    Standard free energy of AgCl $= -37,150$ cal mole^{-1}.

The values are calculated by the method of example 7.1 using the standard entropies of the components in appendix 3.

7.B Partial pressure of chlorine $= 1 \cdot 4 \times 10^{-55}$.

The standard free-energy change for the cell reaction:

$$Pb_{(s)} + Cl_{2(g)} \rightleftharpoons PbCl_{2(s)}$$

is calculated from the potential of the cell, the latter being given by the difference between the oxygen potentials of the two electrodes. From this, the equilibrium constant yields the required partial pressure.

7.C Minimum potential at $500°C = 0 \cdot 626$ volt.

From the standard free-energy change for the formation reaction for SnCl$_2$, the potential of the cell is calculated as $-0 \cdot 626$ volt.

7.D Activity coefficient of cadmium in the alloy = 1·51.

The potential of the composition cell is used to calculate the partial molar free energy of mixing of cadmium in the alloy by the method shown in example 7.2.   The activity of cadmium follows from equation *1.54*.

7.E Partial molar enthalpy of mixing of cadmium = 1,486 cal mole^{-1}.

Excess partial molar free energy of cadmium = 1,092 cal mole^{-1}.

Excess partial molar entropy of cadmium = 0·4 cal deg^{-1} mole^{-1}.

The values of $\bar{H}_{Cd}^M$ and $\bar{S}_{Cd}^M$ are calculated from the e.m.f. data of the composition cell using equations *7.e* and *7.d* respectively. Calculation of $\bar{G}_{Cd}^M$ in the alloy yields a_{Cd}. The activity coefficient of cadmium enables $\bar{G}_{Cd}^E$ to be calculated through equation *1.79*. The value of $\bar{S}_{Cd}^E$ is given by the difference between $\bar{S}_{Cd}^M$ and $\bar{S}_{Cd}^M$ for an ideal solution ($= -R\ln N_{Cd}$).

7.F Activity of aluminium = 0·678.

Activity coefficient of aluminium = 4·07.

Partial molar entropy of mixing of aluminium = 4·33 cal deg^{-1} mole^{-1}.

Partial molar enthalpy of mixing of aluminium = 4,176 cal mole^{-1}.

Partial molar free energy of mixing of aluminium = 902 cal mole^{-1}.

Partial molar enthalpy of aluminium = 12,649 cal mole^{-1}.

7.G Vapour pressure of zinc over alloy = 10·64 mm Hg.

For the vaporization of pure zinc at 873°K:

$$\Delta G^0 = +7,270 \text{ cal} = -RT\ln\left[\frac{p_{Zn(g)}^0}{a_{Zn(l)}}\right].$$

However, as $a_{Zn(l)} = 1$ for pure zinc, then p_{Zn}^0 is calculable. From the e.m.f. data, the activity of zinc in the alloy is calculated and thus the partial pressure of zinc over the alloy is given by:

$$p_{Zn} = p_{Zn}^0 a_{Zn}.$$

7.H Activity coefficient of zinc in ($N_{Zn} = 0·173$) alloy = 1·80.

For the first composition cell: $\bar{G}_{Zn}^I - G_{Zn}^0 = -zFE^I$. For the second composition cell: $\bar{G}_{Zn}^{II} - \bar{G}_{Zn}^I = -zFE^{II}$. As free energy is a state variable, these values are additive and so:

$$\bar{G}_{Zn}^{II} - G_{Zn}^0 = [\bar{G}_{Zn}^M]^{II} = -zF(E^I + E^{II}).$$

Hence $a_{Zn}(N_{Zn} = 0·173)$ is calculated.

7.I E.m.f. generated by Ag$_{(pure)}$/Sn$_{(pure)}$ cell = 0·869 volt.

E.m.f. generated by Ag$_{(pure)}$/Sn$_{(alloy)}$ cell = 0·851 volt.

As the hydrogen electrode at $p_{H_2} = 1$ atm is the arbitrary zero potential, the cell reaction:

$$\tfrac{1}{2}Sn + Ag^+ \rightleftharpoons \tfrac{1}{2}Sn^{++} + Ag$$

will generate a voltage:

$$E = \tfrac{1}{2}E_{Sn} - E_{Ag}.$$

This will be the standard potential (E^0) for the cell when all the components are in their standard states. When a_{Sn} in the Sn electrode is 0·5, the relation *7.2.4* is applicable. Thus:

$$E_{(Sn\ alloy)} = E^0 - \frac{RT}{zF}\ln\frac{1}{a_{Sn}^{1/2}}.$$

7.J   Maximum e.m.f. generated = 8·26 millivolt.

7.K   Value of $\log a_{Fe^{++}}/a_{Cu^{++}} = 26\cdot9$. Thus as $a_{Fe^{++}} < 1$, then $a_{Cu^{++}}$ must be very small, and the concentration must be correspondingly low.

By consideration of the two half cells (both written as reduction reactions):

$$Fe^{++} + 2e \rightleftharpoons Fe : E_{Fe} = -E_{Fe}^0 - \frac{RT}{zF}\ln\left[\frac{a_{Fe}}{a_{Fe^{++}}}\right]$$

$$Cu^{++} + 2e \rightleftharpoons Cu : E_{Cu} = -E_{Cu}^0 - \frac{RT}{zF}\ln\left[\frac{a_{Cu}}{a_{Cu^{++}}}\right]$$

and as $a_{Cu} = a_{Fe} = 1$ and $E_{Fe} = E_{Cu}$ at equilibrium, then:

$$\log\left[\frac{a_{Fe^{++}}}{a_{Cu^{++}}}\right] = \frac{zF}{RT}(E_{Fe}^0 - E_{Cu}^0).$$

7.L   Activity of aluminium in $(N_{Al} = 0\cdot0404)$ alloy, relative to infinitely dilute atom fraction standard state = 0·0278.

From the data given, the quantity $\log\gamma_{Al}$ can be calculated and plotted versus N_{Al} to yield γ_{Al}^0 by extrapolation to $N_{Al} = 0$. Then from equation *1.88*:

$$a_{Al\,(inf.\ dilute)} = \frac{a_{Al\,(pure)}}{\gamma_{Al}^0}.$$

7.M   Graph of 'ideal liquidus' of nickel.

The ideal liquidus for any solvent is given by equation *7.6.2* where the latent heat of fusion of the solvent (in this case nickel) is assumed independent of temperature.

7.N   Latent heat of fusion of Ag = 2,620 cal mole^{-1}.

The data are applied to equation *7.6.2* with silver as the solvent.

7.O   First solid separating at 300°C contains 3 atom-per cent Zn.

Equation *7.6.2* is applied to the present system showing solid solubility. Thus:

$$\log\left[\frac{N_{Cd(l)}}{N_{Cd(s)}}\right] = \frac{L_f}{4\cdot575}\left(\frac{1}{T_f} - \frac{1}{T}\right).$$

7.P Partial molar heat of mixing of nickel $= -21{,}760$ cal mole^{-1}.

For a solute in the composition range where Henry's law holds, equation 7.k becomes (in the present context):

$$\frac{\partial \ln N_{Ni}}{\partial T} = -\frac{[\bar{H}_{Ni} - H^{\circ}_{Ni}]}{RT^2} = \frac{\bar{H}^M_{Ni}}{RT^2}.$$

Hence, when the log of the atom fraction is a reciprocal function of the absolute temperature:

$$\log\left[\frac{N_{Ni(923)}}{N_{Ni(773)}}\right] = \frac{\bar{H}^M_{Ni}}{4\cdot575}\left(\frac{1}{923} - \frac{1}{773}\right).$$

7.Q Heat of solution of solid cobalt $= 11{,}950$ cal mole^{-1}.

The heat of solution of liquid cobalt is calculated, as in 7.P, from equation 7.k, using the liquidus temperatures and compositions as given in the table. The heat of solution of solid cobalt is given by this value subtracted from the heat of fusion of pure cobalt, assumed to apply at these temperatures.

7.R (a) Weight-per cent of ethylene glycol $= 36\cdot5$.

  (b) Weight-per cent of ethylene glycol $= 34\cdot2$.

As no activity or liquidus/solidus data are given, it must be assumed that the mixture is an ideal solution. Thus equation 7.6.2 is applicable, with L_f assumed (a) constant and (b) calculated as a function of temperature using the Kirchhoff equation 1.20.

7.S Activity of copper at liquidus temperature $= 0\cdot91$.

The answer is obtained by the method of example 7.7.

7.T Activity of copper in alloy of solidus composition $= 0\cdot797$.

From the activity coefficient data, the activity of (liquid) copper in an alloy of liquidus composition at 1,273°K may be calculated as $0\cdot735$ with respect to pure liquid copper as the standard state. This is equal to the activity of solid copper at the solidus with respect to the same standard state. From the free-energy data, the activity of pure solid copper with respect to a standard state of pure liquid copper may also be calculated for the same temperature. The required activity of copper at the solidus, with respect to the pure solid copper standard state, is given by the ratio of these two quantities.

7.U Activity of silicon in liquid alloy at 1,289°C $= 0\cdot75$.

  Partial molar entropy of silicon in same alloy $= 1\cdot17$ cal deg^{-1} mole^{-1}.

  Partial molar enthalpy of silicon in same alloy $= 940$ cal mole^{-1}.

7.V Latent heat of fusion of iron $= 3{,}600$ cal mole^{-1}.

Table of Constants and Useful Conversion Factors

Constants

Avogadro's number	N =	$6 \cdot 02 \times 10^{23}$ mole^{-1}
Boltzmann's constant	k =	$1 \cdot 38 \times 10^{-23}$ joule deg^{-1}
Electronic charge	e =	$1 \cdot 60 \times 10^{-19}$ coulomb
Gas constant	$R = Nk$ =	$8 \cdot 314$ joule deg^{-1} mole^{-1}
	=	$1 \cdot 987$ cal deg^{-1} mole^{-1}
Faraday's constant	$F = Ne$ =	96,494 coulomb g-equiv^{-1}
	=	23,066 cal volt^{-1} g-equiv^{-1}
Gravitational constant	g =	$980 \cdot 7$ cm sec^{-2}

Conversion Factors

1 atmosphere	= $1,033 \cdot 2$ g cm^{-2}
	= $14 \cdot 7$ lb in^{-2}
1 calorie	= $4 \cdot 184$ joule
	= $4 \cdot 184 \times 10^7$ erg
	= $0 \cdot 00397$ B.Th.U
	= $41 \cdot 293$ cc-atm
1 coulomb	= $2 \cdot 78 \times 10^{-4}$ ampere-hr
1 electron-volt	= $1 \cdot 60 \times 10^{-19}$ joule
1 electron-volt molecule^{-1}	= $23 \cdot 05$ kcal mole^{-1}
1 gram-molecular volume	= $22 \cdot 4$ litre at N.T.P.
1 cubic foot	= $28 \cdot 3$ litre
1 pound	= $453 \cdot 6$ g
1 mile	= $1 \cdot 609$ kilometre
60 m.p.h.	= 88 ft sec^{-1}
$\log_e$ (ln)	= $2 \cdot 303 \log_{10}$
$R \log_e$ (ln)	= $4 \cdot 575 \log_{10}$

Thermochemical Data

Heats of formation, transformation and fusion, and standard entropies

⟨⟩ Solid, () Liquid, [ ] Gas.

Element or compound	Heat of formation $-\Delta H_{298}$ kcal mole^{-1}	Entropy of formation S_{298} cal deg^{-1} mole^{-1}	Transformation or fusion		L_t or L_f kcal mole^{-1}
			Reaction	°C	
⟨Ag⟩	0	10·2			
⟨AgCl⟩	30·3	23·0			
⟨Al⟩	0	6·77	S→L	659	2·5
⟨Al$_2$O$_3$⟩	400·0	12·2			
⟨Au⟩	0	11·32	S→L	1,063	3·05
⟨C⟩	0	1·361			
[CH$_4$]	17·89	44·5			
[CO]	26·40	47·3			
[CO$_2$]	94·05	51·1			
⟨Ca⟩	0	9·95	S$_\alpha$→S$_\beta$	440	0·24
			S$_\beta$→L	850	2·1
⟨CaO⟩	151·5	9·5			
⟨Cd⟩	0	12·3	S→L	321	1·53
[Cl]	0	53·3			
⟨Co⟩	0	7·18	S→L	1,495	3·75
⟨Cr⟩	0	5·68	S→L	1,850	4·6
⟨Cr$_2$O$_3$⟩	270·0	19·4			
⟨Cu⟩	0	7·97	S→L	1,083	3·1
⟨Cu$_2$O⟩	40·0	22·45			
⟨Fe⟩	0	6·49	S$_\alpha$→S$_\alpha$ mag. non-mag.	760	0·66
			S$_\alpha$→S$_\gamma$ non-mag.	910	0·22
			S$_\gamma$→S$_\delta$	1,401	0·21
			S$_\delta$→L	1,539	3·7
⟨FeO⟩	63·2	14·05	S→L	1,378	7·4
⟨Fe$_3$O$_4$⟩	266·9	36·2			
[H$_2$]	0	31·2			
[HCl]	22·0	44·65			

⟨⟩ Solid, () Liquid, [] Gas.

Element or compound	Heat of formation $-\Delta H_{298}$ kcal mole^{-1}	Entropy of formation S_{298} cal deg^{-1} mole^{-1}	Transformation or fusion		
			Reaction	°C	L_t or L_f kcal mole^{-1}
⟨H$_2$O⟩			S→L	0	1·436
(H$_2$O)	68·32	16·75			
[H$_2$O]	57·80	45·1			
⟨Mn⟩	0	7·6	S$_\alpha$→S$_\beta$	720	0·48
			S$_\beta$→S$_\gamma$	1,100	0·55
			S$_\gamma$→S$_\delta$	1,136	0·43
⟨Na⟩	0	12·3	S→L	97·8	0·63
⟨NaCl⟩	98·6	17·4			
⟨Na$_2$O⟩	100·7	17·0			
⟨Ni⟩	0	7·12	S→L	1,455	4·22
[O$_2$]	0	49·02			
⟨Pb⟩	0	15·5	S→L	327	1·15
⟨PbO⟩	52·4	16·2			
⟨Si⟩	0	4·5	S→L	1,420	12·1
⟨Ti⟩	0	7·3	S$_\alpha$→S$_\beta$	882	0·83
			S$_\beta$→L	1,660	4·5
⟨Tl⟩	0	15·4	S$_\alpha$→S$_\alpha$	234	0·09
			S$_\beta$→L	304	1·03
⟨V⟩	0	7·0	S→L	1,860	4·5
⟨Zn⟩	0	9·95	S→L	419·5	1·74
⟨ZnCl$_2$⟩	99·5	25·9			

Heat capacities

$C_p = a + bT + cT^{-2}$, cal deg^{-1} mole^{-1}

Element or compound	a	b × 10^3	c × 10^{-5}	Temperature range, °K
⟨Al⟩	4·94	2·96	–	298–932
(Al)	7·00	–	–	932–1,273
⟨Al$_2$O$_3$⟩	27·38	3·08	− 8·20	298–1,800
⟨Au⟩	5·66	1·24	–	298–1,336
(Au)	7·00	–	–	1,336–1,600
⟨C⟩	4·10	1·02	− 2·10	298–2,300
[CO]	6·79	0·98	− 0·11	298–2,500
[CO$_2$]	10·55	2·16	− 2·04	298–2,500
⟨Ca⟩$_\alpha$	5·31	3·33	–	273–713

Element or compound	a	$b \times 10^3$	$c \times 10^{-5}$	Temperature range, °K
$\langle Ca \rangle_\beta$	1·50	7·74	2·5	713–1,123
(Ca)	7·4	–	–	1,123–1,220
$\langle CaO \rangle$	11·86	1·08	−1·66	298–1,177
$\langle Cr \rangle$	5·84	2·36	−0·88	298–2,123
(Cr)	9·40	–	–	2,123–
$\langle Cr_2O_3 \rangle$	28·53	2·20	−3·74	350–1,800
$\langle Cu \rangle$	5·41	1·50	–	298–1,356
(Cu)	7·50	–	–	1,356–1,600
$\langle Cu_2O \rangle$	14·90	5·70	–	298–1,200
$\langle Fe \rangle_{\alpha, mag.}$	4·18	5·92	–	273–1,033
$\langle Fe \rangle_{\alpha, non-mag.}$	9·0	–	–	1,033–1,183
$\langle Fe \rangle_\gamma$	1·84	4·66	–	1,183–1,674
$\langle Fe \rangle_\delta$	10·5	–	–	1,674–1,812
(Fe)	10·0	–	–	1,812–1,873
$\langle FeO \rangle$	11·66	2·00	−0·67	298–1,651
(FeO)	16·30	–	–	1,651–1,800
$\langle Fe_3O_4 \rangle_\alpha$	21·88	48·2	–	298–900
$\langle Fe_3O_4 \rangle_\beta$	48·0	–	–	900–1,800
$[H_2]$	6·52	0·78	0·12	298–3,000
$[H_2O]$	7·17	2·56	0·08	298–2,500
$\langle Mn \rangle_\alpha$	5·16	3·81	–	298–993
$\langle Mn \rangle_\beta$	8·33	0·66	–	993–1,373
$\langle Mn \rangle_\gamma$	10·70	–	–	1,373–1,410
$\langle Mn \rangle_\delta$	11·30	–	–	1,410–1,517
$[N_2]$	6·66	1·02	–	298–2,500
$[NH_3]$	7·11	6·00	−0·37	298–1,800
$[O_2]$	7·16	1·00	−0·40	298–3,000
$\langle Pb \rangle$	5·63	2·33	–	298–600
$\langle Ti \rangle_\alpha$	5·28	2·4	–	298–1,155
$\langle Ti \rangle_\beta$	6·91	–	–	1,155– 1933
(Ti)	8·00	–	–	1,933–
$\langle Tl \rangle_\alpha$	5·26	3·40	–	298–505
$\langle Tl \rangle_\beta$	7·30	–	–	505–577
(Tl)	7·50	–	–	577–800
$\langle Zn \rangle$	5·35	2·40	–	298–693
(Zn)	7·50	–	–	693–1,200
$[Zn]$	4·97	–	–	298–1,200

Standard free energies of reaction

$$\Delta G^0 = A + BT \log T + CT, \text{cal}$$

Reaction		A	B	C	Temperature range, °K
$2\langle Al\rangle + 1\frac{1}{2}[O_2]$	$\rightleftharpoons \langle Al_2O_3\rangle$	−405,760	−3·75	+92·22	923–1,800
$2\langle Al\rangle + [Cl_2]$	$\rightleftharpoons 2[AlCl]$	−25,860	+11·8	−71·9	933–2,000
$\langle Al\rangle + 1\frac{1}{2}[Cl_2]$	$\rightleftharpoons [AlCl_3]$	−140,400	+2·5	+7·05	> 933
$\langle C\rangle + 2[H_2]$	$\rightleftharpoons [CH_4]$	−21,600	–	+26·2	1,073–1,373
$\langle C\rangle + \frac{1}{2}[O_2]$	$\rightleftharpoons [CO]$	−26,700	–	−20·95	298–2,500
$\langle C\rangle + [O_2]$	$\rightleftharpoons [CO_2]$	−94,200	–	−0·2	298–2,000
$\langle CaO\rangle + [CO_2]$	$\rightleftharpoons \langle CaCO_3\rangle$	−40,250	–	+34·4	298–1,150
$2\langle CaO\rangle + \langle SiO_2\rangle$	$\rightleftharpoons \langle 2CaO.SiO_2\rangle$	−30,200	–	−1·2	298–1,700
$2\langle Cr\rangle + 1\frac{1}{2}[O_2]$	$\rightleftharpoons \langle Cr_2O_3\rangle$	−267,750	–	+62·1	298–2,100
$\frac{2}{3}\langle Cr\rangle + \langle C\rangle$	$\rightleftharpoons \frac{1}{6}\langle Cr_{23}C_6\rangle$	−16,380	–	−1·54	298–1,673
$2\langle Cu\rangle + \frac{1}{2}[O_2]$	$\rightleftharpoons \langle Cu_2O\rangle$	−40,500	−3·92	+29·5	298–1,356
$2\langle Cu\rangle + \frac{1}{2}[S_2]$	$\rightleftharpoons \langle Cu_2S\rangle$	−34,150	−6·22	+28·74	623–1,360
$\langle Cu_2O\rangle + \frac{1}{2}[O_2]$	$\rightleftharpoons 2\langle CuO\rangle$	−34,950	−6·1	+44·3	298–1,300
$\langle Fe\rangle + \frac{1}{2}[O_2]$	$\rightleftharpoons \langle FeO\rangle$	−62,050	–	+14·95	298–1,642
$(Fe) + \frac{1}{2}[O_2]$	$\rightleftharpoons (FeO)$	−55,620	–	+10·83	1,808–2,000
$3\langle Fe\rangle + 2[O_2]$	$\rightleftharpoons \langle Fe_3O_4\rangle$	−260,770	–	+74·75	298–1,600
$2\langle Fe_3O_4\rangle + \frac{1}{2}[O_2]$	$\rightleftharpoons 3\langle Fe_2O_3\rangle$	−59,620	–	+33·62	298–1,460
$\frac{1}{2}[H_2] + \frac{1}{2}[Cl_2]$	$\rightleftharpoons [HCl]$	−21,770	0·99	−5·22	298–2,100

Reaction	A	B	C	Temperature range, °K
$[H_2]+\frac{1}{2}[O_2]$ ⇌ $[H_2O]$	-58,900	—	+13·1	298-2,500
$2[H_2]+[S_2]$ ⇌ $2[H_2S]$	-43,160	—	+23·61	298-1,800
$[Mg]+\frac{1}{2}[O_2]$ ⇌ ⟨MgO⟩	-181,600	-7·37	+75·7	1,380-2,500
$2\langle MgO\rangle+\langle SiO_2\rangle$ ⇌ ⟨2MgO.SiO₂⟩	-15,120	—	0·0	298-1,700
⟨Mn⟩$+\frac{1}{2}[O_2]$ ⇌ ⟨MnO⟩	-91,950	—	+17·4	298-1,500
(Mn)$+\frac{1}{2}[O_2]$ ⇌ (MnO)	-84,700	—	+14·5	1,800-2,500
⟨Mo⟩$+[O_2]$ ⇌ ⟨MoO₂⟩	-140,100	-4·6	+55·85	298-1,300
$\frac{1}{2}[N_2]+1\frac{1}{2}[H_2]$ ⇌ $[NH_3]$	-10,400	+7·1	+3·79	298-2,000
⟨Ni⟩$+\frac{1}{2}[O_2]$ ⇌ ⟨NiO⟩	-58,450	—	+23·55	298-1,725
⟨NiCl₂⟩$+[H_2]$ ⇌ ⟨Ni⟩$+2[HCl]$	+29,075	+6·15	-58·53	298-1,260
(Pb)$+\frac{1}{2}[S_2]$ ⇌ ⟨PbS⟩	-75,160	—	+38·25	600-1,380
$[S_2]$ ⇌ $\frac{1}{2}[S_4]$	-14,200	—	+15·94	298-1,300
$[S_2]$ ⇌ $\frac{1}{3}[S_6]$	-21,240	—	+23·1	298-1,300
$[S_2]$ ⇌ $\frac{1}{4}[S_8]$	-23,040	—	+25·3	298-2,000
$[S_2]$ ⇌ $2[S]$	+77,250	—	-29·7	298-2,000
⟨Si⟩$+[O_2]$ ⇌ ⟨SiO₂⟩	-210,600	-3·0	+52·22	298-1,700
(Si)$+[O_2]$ ⇌ (SiO₂)	-226,500	—	+47·50	1,986-2,100
(Sn)$+[Cl_2]$ ⇌ (SnCl₂)	-79,600	—	+28·3	520-925
⟨Zr⟩$+[O_2]$ ⇌ ⟨ZrO₂⟩	-259,940	-4·33	+59·12	298-1,143

Atomic Weights of Stable Elements

Element	Symbol	Weight	Element	Symbol	Weight
Actinium	Ac	227	Neodymium	Nd	144·27
Aluminium	Al	26·98	Neon	Ne	20·18
Antimony	Sb	121·76	Nickel	Ni	58·71
Argon	A	39·94	Niobium	Nb	92·91
Arsenic	As	74·91	Nitrogen	N	14·01
Barium	Ba	137·36	Osmium	Os	190·2
Beryllium	Be	9·01	Oxygen	O	16·000
Bismuth	Bi	209·00	Palladium	Pd	106·7
Boron	B	10·82	Phosphorus	P	30·98
Bromine	Br	79·92	Platinum	Pt	195·09
Cadmium	Cd	112·41	Polonium	Po	210
Calcium	Ca	40·08	Potassium	K	39·10
Carbon	C	12·01	Praseodymium	Pr	140·92
Cerium	Ce	140·13	Protactinium	Pa	231
Caesium	Cs	132·91	Radium	Ra	226·05
Chlorine	Cl	35·46	Radon	Rn	222
Chromium	Cr	52·01	Rhenium	Re	186·22
Cobalt	Co	58·94	Rhodium	Rh	102·91
Copper	Cu	63·54	Rubidium	Rb	85·48
Dysprosium	Dy	162·51	Ruthenium	Ru	101·1
Erbium	Er	167·27	Samarium	Sm	150·35
Europium	Eu	152·0	Scandium	Sc	44·96
Fluorine	F	19·00	Selenium	Se	78·96
Gadolinium	Gd	157·26	Silicon	Si	28·09
Gallium	Ga	69·72	Silver	Ag	107·88
Germanium	Ge	72·60	Sodium	Na	22·99
Gold	Au	197·0	Strontium	Sr	87·63
Hafnium	Hf	178·58	Sulphur	S	32·07
Helium	He	4·00	Tantalum	Ta	180·95
Holmium	Ho	164·94	Tellurium	Te	127·61
Hydrogen	H	1·008	Terbium	Tb	158·93
Indium	In	114·82	Thallium	Tl	204·39
Iodine	I	126·91	Thorium	Th	232·05
Iridium	Ir	192·2	Thulium	Tm	168·94
Iron	Fe	55·85	Tin	Sn	118·70
Krypton	Kr	83·8	Titanium	Ti	47·90
Lanthanum	La	138·92	Tungsten	W	183·86
Lead	Pb	207·21	Uranium	U	238·07
Lithium	Li	6·94	Vanadium	V	50·95
Lutetium	Lu	174·99	Xenon	Xe	131·30
Magnesium	Mg	24·32	Ytterbium	Yb	173·04
Manganese	Mn	54·94	Yttrium	Y	88·92
Mercury	Hg	200·61	Zinc	Zn	65·38
Molybdenum	Mo	95·95	Zirconium	Zr	91·22

Mathematical Operations

There are various mathematical operations used in this book with which some students may not be familiar, or which they find not immediately obvious in the context of the examples and exercises. To clarify their use and for the sake of completeness, these operations are here elaborated as they are used in the book.

1. Some fundamental laws of partial differentiation

If the quantity $z = f(x, y, u \ldots)$ then:

$$dz = \left(\frac{\partial z}{\partial x}\right)_{y, u \ldots} \cdot dx + \left(\frac{\partial z}{\partial y}\right)_{x, u \ldots} \cdot dy + \left(\frac{\partial z}{\partial u}\right)_{x, y \ldots} \cdot du \ldots$$

where $(\partial z/\partial x)_{y, u \ldots}$ is the first partial derivative of z with respect to x, while $y, u \ldots$ remain constant. This relation is widely used for expression of the incremental changes in the thermodynamic state variables of a system, which are, of course, functions of the other state variables (e.g. chapter 1, page 7, derivation of *1.43*).

Further if:

$$z = f_1(x, y)$$

and:

$$v = f_2(x, y)$$

then, of course:

$$z = f_3(v, x)$$

$$z = f_4(v, y)$$

and the identities:

$$\left(\frac{\partial z}{\partial x}\right)_y = \left(\frac{\partial z}{\partial v}\right)_y \cdot \left(\frac{\partial v}{\partial x}\right)_y$$

$$\left(\frac{\partial z}{\partial y}\right)_x = \left(\frac{\partial z}{\partial v}\right)_x \cdot \left(\frac{\partial v}{\partial y}\right)_x$$

are valid. In addition, as:

$$dz = \left(\frac{\partial z}{\partial x}\right)_y dx + \left(\frac{\partial z}{\partial y}\right)_x dy,$$

then dividing throughout by dy yields:

$$\frac{dz}{dy} = \left(\frac{\partial z}{\partial x}\right)_y \frac{dx}{dy} + \left(\frac{\partial z}{\partial y}\right)_x$$

which will be applicable for all values of dz/dy and hence when $dz/dy = 0$. Thus:

$$\left(\frac{\partial z}{\partial y}\right)_x = -\left(\frac{\partial z}{\partial x}\right)_y \cdot \left(\frac{\partial x}{\partial y}\right)_z.$$

Such identities between the partial differentials of the state variables are repeatedly applied in the development of the relations used in thermo-dynamics (e.g. in examples 8.1, 8.2 and 8.3).

2. Trapezoidal rule for measurement of areas under graphs

If $y_0, y_1, y_2, \ldots, y_n$ are the lengths of a series of equally spaced ordinates to a curve and h is their distance apart, the area enclosed by the curve between the ordinates y_0 and y_n is given by:

$$A = h[\tfrac{1}{2}(y_0 + y_n) + y_1 + y_2 + \ldots + y_{n-1}].$$

This is the trapezoidal rule which, in effect, subdivides the area under a curve into a series of adjacent trapezia, of constant width, the latter being chosen such that the curve approximates to a straight line over the length that forms the end of any trapezium. The sum of the areas of these trapezia is then given by the formula or, equivalently, by the sum of the mean heights of the trapezia multiplied by their width.

3. Application of determinants to the solution of simultaneous linear equations

A determinant of order n:

$$D = \begin{vmatrix} a_{11}\, a_{12} \ldots a_{1n} \\ a_{21}\, a_{22} \ldots a_{2n} \\ \cdot \quad \cdot \quad \ldots \quad \cdot \\ \cdot \quad \cdot \quad \ldots \quad \cdot \\ \cdot \quad \cdot \quad \ldots \quad \cdot \\ \cdot \quad \cdot \quad \ldots \quad \cdot \\ \cdot \quad \cdot \quad \ldots \quad \cdot \\ a_{n1}\, a_{n2} \ldots a_{nn} \end{vmatrix}$$

is defined as the sum:

$$\sum (\pm)\, a_{1i}\, a_{2j}\, a_{3k} \ldots a_{nl}$$

of $n!$ terms, the sign of any given term being plus or minus as the number of inversions from the natural order* of the numbers $1, 2, 3, \ldots, n$ in the sequence i, j, k, ..., 1 is even or odd respectively.

For example, the third-order determinant:

$$\begin{vmatrix} a_{11} & a_{12} & a_{13} \\ a_{21} & a_{22} & a_{23} \\ a_{31} & a_{32} & a_{33} \end{vmatrix}$$

is given by:

$$a_{11}\begin{vmatrix} a_{22} & a_{23} \\ a_{32} & a_{33} \end{vmatrix} - a_{12}\begin{vmatrix} a_{21} & a_{23} \\ a_{31} & a_{33} \end{vmatrix} + a_{13}\begin{vmatrix} a_{21} & a_{22} \\ a_{31} & a_{32} \end{vmatrix}$$

$$= a_{11}(a_{22}a_{33} - a_{23}a_{32}) - a_{12}(a_{21}a_{33} - a_{23}a_{31}) + a_{13}(a_{21}a_{32} - a_{22}a_{31}).$$

Further, the solutions of a series of linear equations:

$$a_{i1}x_1 + a_{i2}x_2 + \ldots + a_{in}x_n = c_i, \quad i = 1, 2, \ldots, n,$$

are given by:

$$x_1 = \frac{C_1}{D}, x_2 = \frac{C_2}{D}, \text{ etc.}$$

where C_1, C_2, etc., are the determinant D when the elements of the first, second, etc., column are replaced by c_1, c_2, etc., respectively.

For example, the solutions to the relations:

$$2x_1 + x_2 - 2x_3 = -6$$

$$x_1 + x_2 + x_3 = 2$$

$$-x_1 - 2x_2 + 3x_3 = 12$$

are given by:

$$x_1 = \frac{\begin{vmatrix} -6 & 1 & -2 \\ 2 & 1 & 1 \\ 12 & -2 & 3 \end{vmatrix}}{\begin{vmatrix} 2 & 1 & -2 \\ 1 & 1 & 1 \\ -1 & -2 & 3 \end{vmatrix}} = \frac{8}{8} = 1,$$

* The number of inversions in a term is the total number of pairs of numbers in the sequence which are inverted from their natural order. For example, for the fifth-order term (43521), the inversions are 43, 42, 41, 32, 31, 52, 51 and 21 – that is, eight inversions which, being an even number, would make this term positive. On the other hand, the third-order term (321) will be negative, as the number of inversions is three.

$$x_2 = \frac{\begin{vmatrix} 2 & -6 & -2 \\ 1 & 2 & 1 \\ -1 & 12 & 3 \end{vmatrix}}{\begin{vmatrix} 2 & 1 & -2 \\ 1 & 1 & 1 \\ -1 & -2 & 3 \end{vmatrix}} = \frac{-16}{8} = -2,$$

$$x_3 = \frac{\begin{vmatrix} 2 & 1 & -6 \\ 1 & 1 & 2 \\ -1 & -2 & 12 \end{vmatrix}}{\begin{vmatrix} 2 & 1 & -2 \\ 1 & 1 & 1 \\ -1 & -2 & 3 \end{vmatrix}} = 3.$$

4. Solution of quadratic, cubic and quartic algebraic equations

The solutions of the quadratic:

$$ax^2 + bx + c = 0$$

are given by:

$$x = \frac{-b \pm \sqrt{(b^2 - 4ac)}}{2a}.$$

If:

$b^2 - 4ac > 0$, the solutions are real and unequal,

$b^2 - 4ac = 0$, the solutions are real and equal,

$b^2 - 4ac < 0$, the solutions are imaginary.

The solutions of the cubic:

$$x^3 + ax + b = 0$$

are given by:

$$x_1 = A + B$$

$$x_2, x_3 = -\tfrac{1}{2}(A+B) \pm \frac{i\sqrt{(3)}}{2}(A-B)$$

where:

$$i^2 = -1, A = \sqrt[3]{\left[\frac{-b}{2} + \sqrt{\left(\frac{b^2}{4} + \frac{a^3}{27}\right)}\right]}, \quad B = \sqrt[3]{\left[\frac{-b}{2} - \sqrt{\left(\frac{b^2}{4} + \frac{a^3}{27}\right)}\right]}.$$

If:

$$\frac{b^2}{4} + \frac{a^3}{27} > 0, \text{ one solution is real and the others imaginary,}$$

$$\frac{b^2}{4} + \frac{a^3}{27} = 0, \text{ all solutions are real and at least two are equal,}$$

$$\frac{b^2}{4} + \frac{a^3}{27} < 0, \text{ all solutions are real and unequal.}$$

The solutions of the quartic equation:

$$x^4 + ax^2 + bx + c = 0$$

may be obtained by a formula method, but, as the latter is tedious, a simpler method is the graphical one which, of course, may be used to deduce the solutions for any equation. Thus, by plotting the expression on the left-hand side of the equation as a function of x, the intersections of the curve with the x-axis gives the solutions of the equation. By increasing the scale of the graph in the region of a solution, the latter may be obtained with any desired accuracy.